John Dustin Kemper

THE ENGINEER
AND HIS PROFESSION

University of California, Davis

HOLT, RINEHART AND WINSTON, INC.

New York • *Chicago* • *San Francisco* • *Toronto* • *London*

ACKNOWLEDGMENTS

The author is deeply indebted to the following associates, all of whom took their valuable time to read portions of the manuscript and to make suggestions for improvement. They may not all be in complete agreement with everything I have said; but if the book is better than it might otherwise have been, the credit is theirs.

At Anadex Instruments, Inc.: A. J. Winter, Vice-president of Research.

At the College of Engineering, University of California, Davis: D. O. Brush, Chairman, Dept. of Civil Engrg.; J. A. Cheney, Assoc. Prof. of Engrg.; W. H. Giedt, Chairman, Dept. of Mech. Engrg.; J. M. Henderson, Asst. Prof. of Engrg.; S. M. Henderson, Prof. of Agricultural Engrg.; J. W. LaPatra, Assoc. Prof. of Electrical Engrg.; Coby Lorenzen, Chairman, Dept. of Agricultural Engrg.; R. B. Krone, Assoc. Prof. of Engrg.; H. H. Loomis, Jr., Asst. Prof. of Electrical Engrg.; A. T. McDonald, Asst. Prof. of Engrg.; E. W. Owens, Asst. Prof. of Electrical Engrg.; W. K. Talley, Asst. Prof. of Applied Science; A. T. Yang, Asst. Prof. of Engrg.

At SCM Corp.: A. G. Guibert, Patent Mngr.; Data Processing Sys. Div.; H. R. Kattelmann, Mngr., Engrg. Services, Data Processing Sys. Div.; R. B. LeVino, Vice-president of Research & Engrg.; C. W. Martin, Asst. to Patent Counsel.

At Zehntel, Inc.; W. L. Martin, President.

To my wife, Barbara

Preface

This book is primarily intended for students who are preparing themselves to become engineers and for those who have recently entered the profession. However, even engineers with many years of experience should find the book rewarding. It is surprising how little information most engineers possess concerning their own profession. But this probably reflects, not lack of interest on their part, but a lack of pertinent and readily available information.

We have nearly 1 million engineers in the United States at the present writing; this means that engineers constitute an important part of our adult population. In addition, we have about 350,000 scientists, who tend to possess many of the same attitudes and behavioral characteristics as engineers. The shared points of view of this immense group make it something of a monolith, in terms of its social effects. The group's basic devotion is to *technical advancement*, and to a large degree, this has also become the devotion of the general public. Some might even say that technical advancement has become engineering's religion, in the broad meaning of the word: namely, a set of principles and beliefs to which a man devotes his life.

Technical advancement may be the guiding devotion of the engineering profession, but the members of this group should be fully aware that *human welfare* is the ultimate justification for technology's existence. Regardless of whatever views the reader may hold concerning the workings of society, history shows that no society will long tolerate any group within itself whose aims are regarded as antagonistic to those of the majority.

To my knowledge, no attempt has been made until now to bring together the kind of material contained in this book. Other books have been written about the engineering profession, of course, but these books have dealt primarily with engineering ethics, with descriptions of the various branches of engineering, or with the organization of the profession. This book is different, in that it attempts to capture some of the feel and vitality of what it is like to be *in* engineering. Ethics *are* considered here, as is the organization of the engineering profession—for both ethics and organizational structure form a part of the environment within which the engineer works. But my primary concern is with the engineer as a creator and as a decision-maker.

The basic objective of the book is to present information; nevertheless, I have not been hesitant to present my own value judgments. Wherever statements do not necessarily represent the consensus, a special effort has been made to identify the source—especially if the statement is mostly the author's personal opinion.

If many of the subjects herein are controversial, this is merely a reflection of the state of affairs: I have made no attempt to avoid controversy, but rather have sought it. Engineering is a dynamic, changing profession; and concentrated debate in an atmosphere of controversy should result only in improvement.

Because management is likely to be one of the areas of greatest mystery and misinformation for young engineers, this book dwells at some length upon the subject: Many engineering students want to go into management, and indeed, a large percentage of them do wind up in some kind of management activity. However, many other young men are uncertain, and even confused, regarding careers in management. It is hoped that this book will resolve some of their doubts.

Engineering is an enormous field and a highly diversified one. It may be that not every engineer will find his particular kind of engineering included in this book. The aspects of engineering that are treated in most detail are those of research, design, and development as carried out in an industrial environment, together with related management activities. In my opinion, it is these functions that represent the very heart of the engineering profession and distinguish it from all other callings.

I should like to express my indebtedness and gratitude toward six men who have had a profound impact upon the development of my own ideas concerning engineering and engineering education. All these men either have been, or currently are, deans of engineering at the different campuses of the University of California. They are Roy Bainer, University of California, Davis; the late Llewellyn M. K. Boelter, University of California, Los Angeles; Clyne F. Garland, formerly at Berkeley and now at the University of California, Davis; Morrough P. O'Brien, University of California, Berkeley; John B. Powers, University of California, Davis; and John R. Whinnery, University of California, Berkeley.

Davis, Calif.   *John Dustin Kemper*
January 1967

Contents

1 ▸ | Is engineering really a profession?

The self-consciousness conveyed by the above heading is a quality that is typical of engineering: the profession is exceedingly introspective. It is continually asking itself what it is, where it is going, and why it is going there. During the twentieth century, there have been no less than eight major studies in the United States concerning the education of engineers.

Most engineers want very deeply to be regarded as professionals (although there may be some who are indifferent). Just why this should be so—both the caring and the notcaring—is of interest to us.

1.1 Who is an engineer?

Science and engineering

The following saying received so much circulation during the late 1950s and early 1960s that it eventually almost assumed the status of a cliché:

> Every rocket-firing that is successful is hailed as a *scientific achievement;* every one that isn't is regarded as an *engineering failure.*

Some engineers became so sensitized to the foregoing statement that they winced every time it was made, because of the image it evokes of an engineering profession standing petulantly aside while the scientists accept all the glory.

If this were the statement's only significance, it could have been placed in the "file-it-and-forget-it" department, while we pass on to more important things; but, basically, the little epigram cited here dramatizes the confusion in which we have been foundering, concerning what is "science" and what is "engineering." Ignoring the issue of who gets the credit for rocket firings, it is important that we clarify our thoughts about these two words, because the distinction is central to a man's self-image of what

1

he is doing, why he is doing it, and for whom he is doing it.[1] If a man is working in an environment that demands an engineering result and if he instead produces a scientific one, it is probable that disturbances will occur. On a national scale, the effects could be important.

Most of the current definitions of these two words, "science" and "engineering," shed little light on the matter. In attempting to invent definitions that are acceptable to everyone, one is frequently driven toward the use of more and more general language, with the result that the definitions become increasingly vague. Soon everybody is satisfied, because anyone can read into the definition whatever he wants to. Thus, the definition is useless. Let us, therefore, use simple definitions and focus our attention upon the concepts behind them. For instance:

> Scientists primarily produce *knowledge*.
> Engineers primarily produce *things*.[2]

Note, however, that a given individual may at one time be producing knowledge and, at another, be producing things. This is because engineering and science are so intimately related. In fact, as our society grows technologically more sophisticated, engineering projects tend to become a mixture of these two: in order to achieve the final engineering objective of a project (the creation of a working device, system, or structure), it may be necessary to uncover much scientific knowledge which was previously unknown.

The basic task of the scientist is to perform *research* (create new knowledge), while the basic task of the engineer is to perform *design and development* (create new things). A number of specialized words have been used in this context: for example, it is said that scientists characteristically employ induction, while engineers employ deduction. (Induction

---

[1] J. A. Stratton, president of the Massachusetts Institute of Technology, commented thus: "It matters not a whit whether a man doing a particular piece of work calls himself a physicist or an electrical engineer. But comprehension of the fact that physics and engineering are indeed different, with different professional missions, is essential,"—from "Physics and Engineering in a Free Society," *Physics Today,* vol. 14, March 1961, p. 23.

[2] Eric Walker, president of The Pennsylvania State University, has essentially stated the definitions set forth here, in his article "Engineers and/or Scientists"; he says: "Science aims at the discovery, verification, and organization of fact and information . . . engineering is fundamentally committed to the translation of scientific facts and information to create machines, structures, materials, processes, and the like that can be used by men."—from *J. Engrg. Educ.,* vol. 51, February 1961, pp. 419–421. (For some dictionary definitions, see Appendix.)

is the process by which generalities are drawn from specifics, and deduction is the reverse.) Although there is nothing wrong with these terms, they have little concrete meaning for most people. Consequently, they are not so starkly graphic or useful as the simple terms with which we started. M. P. O'Brien has suggested that much of our confusion about engineering has resulted from the tendency toward "inflation" of terms; he writes: ". . . drafting is called design; design is called development; development is called research; and true research must be modified for clarity and called 'basic research.' "[3]

A scientist may be primarily a theoretician (that is, he may specialize in creating new theoretical explanations for previously unexplained phenomena), or he may be primarily an experimentalist. In either event, his final output is a report or paper published in a scholarly journal. As soon as a given bit of work is published, the scientist's job is complete with respect to that particular piece of information. In the ensuing discussion, the words "science" and "research" will be treated essentially as synonyms.

Engineers, on the other hand, are concerned with the creation of devices, systems, and structures for human use. However, it should be noted that the output of an engineer may not always be tangible. For example, many engineers are engaged in the design of intangibles, such as processes and systems, but in this discussion, such intangibles will be considered "things." Engineers also are frequently employed in liaison or consulting capacities in construction, testing, manufacturing, and as agents for governmental bodies. Such men are not directly engaged in design, but design is still at the core of their activities. Their role is to interpret the design and to see that it is carried out correctly.

It is true that, in many instances, persons originally trained as physicists or chemists have had to step in and handle important engineering tasks, probably because engineering education in the past generally did not carry the student deeply enough into science and mathematics.[4] Still, a person whose entire educational experience has been structured around a core consisting of research is likely to consider it a misdirection of his interests if he is expected to produce working devices or physical structures—hard-

---

[3] *Technological Planning on the Corporate Level.* Cambridge, Mass.: Grad. School of Business Admin., Harvard Univ., 1962, p. 73. See "Technological Planning and Misplanning," by M. P. O'Brien.

[4] An excellent example is the development of radar at MIT., during World War II. The participants readily admit that this was an engineering development task; yet over half of the 1000 top-level participants were basic scientists, mostly physicists. See "Longhairs and Short Waves," *Fortune,* November 1945, p. 163 ff.

ware, as it is called. He is likely to believe that his proper mark of achievement is publication in a scholarly journal where his research contribution can be judged by acknowledged authorities in the field.

This discussion now leads to a consideration of the term "engineering scientist." Many persons in engineering believe that the term should not be used at all and that the words "engineering" and "science" are mutually exclusive. This is one of the deeply controversial subjects in engineering. The following fact must be borne in mind, however: many science fields that were once considered the property of physicists or chemists have, in the last thirty years, become primarily the domain of engineers. These fields, designated as the *engineering sciences*, by a committee of the American Society for Engineering Education (ASEE), are: 1) mechanics of solids, 2) mechanics of fluids, 3) transfer and rate processes, 4) thermodynamics, 5) electrical sciences, and 6) nature and properties of materials.[5] The difference between engineering science and any other kind of science is that engineering science seeks new knowledge for the specific purpose of facilitating the design and development process, while *science* in general seeks knowledge without regard to its application. The latter is sometimes called "basic" science.

Many American engineering educational institutions, including some of the best, have made the preparation of men for research in the engineering sciences their principal objective. One controversial issue of current importance in engineering is based upon the belief of many engineering educators that too much effort is being centered upon graduate education to prepare men for research and that more attention should be given to graduate education to prepare men for creative design.

In 1962, the President's Science Advisory Committee published a report that will probably have a permanent impact on engineering: the report called for a massive build-up in the number of graduate degrees in engineering, mathematics, and the phsyical sciences, to meet the future needs of the nation. The Committee recommended that some of these men prepare themselves for research and others, for creative design.[6]

Engineering activities mostly consist of some combination of engineering research and engineering design or development. Those principally engaged in the former activity will be referred to as "engineering scientists"; those principally engaged in the latter activity will be called simply

---

[5] *Report on the Engineering Sciences.* Washington, D.C.: ASEE, 1956–1958.
[6] *Meeting Manpower Needs in Science and Technology, Report No. 1: Graduate Training in Engineering, Mathematics, and Physical Sciences.* Washington, D.C.: The White House, Dec. 12, 1962.

"engineers." Some writers have defined the word "research" so broadly that it would include all technological creative activity, while others have used the word "design" to include all of engineering. In this book, the word "design" is employed to define creative engineering activity that is focused upon actual determination of the configuration and characteristics of a device, system, or structure, once the general function to be satisfied has been established. The word "development" is essentially used as a synonym for this same activity, but is more descriptive of that phase of creative design which lies beyond the current state of the art. (An entire chapter has been devoted to engineering design and development later in this book.)

Everybody wants to be an engineer

One of the difficulties in establishing who is, and who is not, an engineer is that there are no clear-cut guide lines. For example, it has been estimated that 45 percent of the nine hundred thirty-five thousand engineers in the United States in 1963 did not have college degrees; that only about two-hundred-thirteen thousand (or less than one quarter of the total) were legally registered; and that only a third (three hundred thirty thousand) were members of one or more of the five major professional societies known as the Founder Societies.[7,8] Thus, a large portion of the nation's nine hundred thirty thousand engineers were not 1) college graduates, 2) legally registered engineers, or 3) members of one of the principal engineering societies. With such a heterogeneous engineering population, it is easy to see why many people honestly ask the question, "Is engineering really a profession?"

There is a great attractiveness to the title of "engineer." Many groups (and individuals) have sought the right to use the title, and those who have historically possessed this right have strived hard to keep it. For example, locomotive engineers and stationary engineers (power plant operators) wish to preserve their traditional names, and it must be granted that they probably have as much historically established right as anyone, to use these titles.

Many "subprofessional" and semiprofessional people have sought the title of engineer and generally mark it a red-letter day in their lives when (and if) that goal is achieved. As an interesting sidelight on human be-

---

[7] *Professional Income of Engineers, 1964.* New York: Engrg. Manpower Comm., Engrs. Joint Council, December 1964, p. 8.
[8] For full description of Founder Societies, see chap. 11.

havior, it can be mentioned that previously sport-shirted technicians have been observed to pop up in white shirt, tie, and dark suit the day following a promotion to *engineer*.

Management men who have been basically educated as engineers frequently continue to think of themselves as the latter. Engineering societies are heavily populated by managers who are not currently functioning as engineers, but who continue to be active in engineering affairs. Charles Wilson, Secretary of Defense under President Eisenhower, and prior to that, chairman of the board of General Motors, was regarded by much of the public as an engineer, although he worked as an engineer for a relatively short time before starting the climb up the ladder of general management. Herbert Hoover, known throughout his long life as "The Great Engineer," actually was graduated from college as a geologist, having switched to geology from mechanical engineering in his sophomore year at Stanford University. He worked for a time as a field geologist, but was quickly swept into world-wide mining activities; first as a mine manager, and then as an international businessman and financier with his operations based in London.[9] Even though only a small part of Mr. Hoover's career included direct engineering activities, apparently he was very willing to be known to the public as an engineer.

Public image

There are at least four classic sources of confusion concerning the question, "Who is an engineer?":   1) the matter of science versus engineering; 2) men who perform as engineers, but possess none of the usual hallmarks of the engineer such as college degree, registration, or professional society membership: 3) men who were originally educated as engineers, but who have actually done engineering for only a short time (or not at all) before making their careers in some other field such as sales, manufacturing, or management; and 4) the situation illustrated by the little girl who thinks an engineer is a man who drives a train. Even after these classic sources are removed from the picture, however, the public remains in a state of considerable confusion regarding what an engineer is and does. The technician was in no doubt: the engineer was a clean-cut fellow in a white shirt and a dark suit. But to some of the public, the engineer is a man in a dirty shirt and a hard hat.

---

[9] H. G. Warren, *Herbert Hoover and the Great Depression* (New York: Oxford Univ. Press, 1959), pp. 20–22.

The mass entertainment media—television, for example—presents one picture of how engineers appear to the other fellow. On one musical variety show, the script called for one of the group to exclaim, "Here come the engineers!" And onto the scene they came, complete with hard hats and dirty shirts. Apparently, this particular scriptwriter's image of an engineer called for him to have both feet firmly planted in the mud, peering down the Burma Road through his transit.

Yet, the ubiquitous hard hat is appropriate for only about 5 percent of all engineers (mostly those in construction or mining); of these, only a portion have a need for wearing them, and, then, only a fraction of the time. Hard hats are also worn by architects, lawyers, and members of boards of directors when visiting on the job—without becoming identified with those occupations. The hard hat image gives the impression that an engineer is a construction superintendent. Engineers frequently do become construction superintendents, but this kind of activity is not the engineer's *characteristic* one, which is the creation of new devices, systems, structures, or processes.

What kind of an image would engineers prefer? A reasonably accurate one, of course. The technician was closest to being right. The engineer generally *is* a clean-cut young man in a white shirt, tie, and business suit. He is young, these days, because of the tremendous rate at which engineering has been growing. Furthermore, the image of youth will probably continue through the 1960s and the 1970s, because, during this time, the U.S. Department of Labor estimates that five-hundred thousand engineers will be added to the eight-hundred thousand practicing in 1960.[10] Of these 1,300,000 engineers, 60 percent are predicted to be in manufacturing; less than 8 percent, in construction, and 2 percent, in mining. Yet construction and mining, which *were* engineering fifty years ago, still condition the public's thinking to a large extent—hence, the hard hat.

Today's typical engineer is a college graduate (and there is increasing likelihood that he has an advanced degree) and is at home with science and mathematics. He is a resident of Suburbia, and is a commuter. He is absent from home on business trips more often than one might expect, is alert to his environment, and is often more competent at self-expression than he is usually given credit for being. He is ambitious (though not feverishly so), generally believes he can advance only by "going into management," and may vaguely resent the alleged "fact."

---

[10] U.S. Dept. of Labor, Bureau of Labor Statistics, *Scientists and Engineers, 1960–70: Supply and Demand.* Washington, D.C.: November 1963.

His salary and standard of living frequently make him the envy of other white-collar workers.[11] His orientation, which is usually toward technical achievement as a criterion of excellence and often studiously away from the usual status and success symbols, may mark him as a "queer duck" in the eyes of these same white-collar workers.

In a detailed analysis of a group of 100 mechanical engineers, a team of psychologists found the following traits to be those most frequently mentioned: easy-going, little friction in personal relations; emotionally stable; active, energetic; direct, straightforward; conscientious. At the bottom of the list, or missing altogether, were traits such as snobbishness, conceit, and arrogance. Although the psychological team deplored that the scope of engineers' cultural interests did not measure up to their intellectual potential, they stated, "While they are not smooth, they nevertheless usually make a favorable impression because of their transparent integrity and sincerity."[12]

The engineer's customary habitat is an office (perhaps shared with one or two colleagues) or the conference room. He may occasionally be found using the tools that are characteristic of the subprofessionals he supervises, and this partially accounts for some of the erroneous notions the public has about him. For example: if he is an electronic engineer, he may occasionally be found in the lab, twisting dials on instruments or making connections with a soldering-iron as he de-bugs a circuit; if his sphere is mechanical, he may occasionally be found at a drafting board, performing a particularly difficult bit of layout work; and, yes, if he is a civil engineer, he may occasionally be found peering through a transit, with his feet in the mud. None of these situations is really characteristic of the engineer in his professional capacity. Being an eminently practical person, he employs these tools upon occasion when he believes he will get the job done faster or better that way. The *characteristic* activity of the engineer is one of intellectual effort, basically directed toward creative design.

---

[11] The average salary was $10,500 per year in 1963 for the first level below that of supervisor. (This level is generally called "senior engineer" and requires from six to twelve years of experience.) Accountants at the same responsibility level had an average salary of $9000 per year—These data are from the *National Survey of Professional, Administration, Technical and Clerical Pay*, U.S. Dept. of Labor, Bureau of Labor Statistics, Bulletin No. 1387, October 1963. (The survey included 270,000 engineers.)

[12] R. Harrison, D. Tomblen, and T. Jackson, "Profile of the Mechanical Engineer III: Personality," *Personnel Psychology*, vol. 8 (1955), Cleveland: Personnel Research Inst., Western Reserve Univ., pp. 480-481.

Self-image

One of the most regrettable things the author ever heard was a remark made by an engineer that he had described himself to his son as a sort of white-collar plumber. Such remarks have a self-fulfilling quality: if a man believes himself to be a white-collar plumber, then that is probably what he will become.

Similarly, in surveys of engineering professionalism in industry, the interrogators will occasionally encounter an engineer who refers to himself as "just a peon" or as a "factory hand."[13] Unquestionably, some companies do tend to treat their engineers as a commodity, a practice that encourages the "peon" frame of mind. However, it is also certain that the man who thinks like a peon will be one.

A related finding in the survey just cited is of great interest: the interviewees were shown cards containing lists of various things engineers can do to build professionalism. The engineers chose the following as the most important:

> Becoming better communicators.
> Advancing in technical competence.
> Becoming better aware of how engineers fit in with the company as a whole.

When asked what engineers actually do to build professionalism, between 60 and 80 percent of the engineers said that they do the three things listed. To answer to the same question, only 20 to 40 percent of the *managers* agreed that engineers do these things.[13]

It is often said that engineers do a poor job of expressing themselves, by either the written or the spoken word, and engineers humbly accept this judgment. It is indisputable that they frequently cannot spell (in one engineering survey, the statement was made that ". . . for certain individuals the spelling was suggestive of the orthography of the fifth grade").[14] In the case of the spoken word, however, they may do a better job than is generally attributed to them.

Engineers tend to have a poor opinion of their status in the eyes of society. In one survey, two thirds of the engineers interviewed said they

---

[13] *Engineering Professionalism in Industry*, Washington, D.C.: Professional Engrs. Conf. Board for Industry, 1960, p. 23. In cooperation with The Nat'l Soc. of Professional Engrs. (The survey findings were based on personal interviews with 350 engineers who worked for well-known large companies.)

[14] R. Harrison, W. Hunt, and T. Jackson, "Profile of the Mechanical Engineer, II: Interests," *Personnel Psychology*, vol. 8 (1955), Cleveland: Personnel Research Inst., Western Reserve Univ., p. 315 ff.

believed that engineering is not yet fully recognized by the public as a profession.[15] Yet, the results of a survey of 3880 Chicago households taken by the *Chicago Tribune* in 1956 (and subsequently published in Vance Packard's *The Status Seekers*) seem to indicate that engineers are far harder on themselves than is the general public. Among seven status groups, engineers wound up in Group 2, along with top executives of local firms, newspaper editors, doctors, lawyers, local judges, and college professors at prestige schools. In Group 1 were top executives of national firms, architects, medical specialists, federal judges, and stock brokers. Group 3 contained bank cashiers, junior executives, high-school teachers, and office supervisors, among others.[16]

A somewhat gay sidelight on engineers has emerged from a recent study of forty-five research scientists and engineers which tends to refute at least one of the drab things that engineers are sometimes led to believe about themselves. In this case, the characteristic in question is that they have narrow interests and tend to confine themselves to technical things. The results of the survey showed quite the reverse. It had to do with non-bookish things like rules of poker, football, jazz, baseball, movies, and wildlife. The scientists and engineers were the most knowledgeable of all the groups, far outscoring adult males in general (test scores: scientists and engineers—46.1; adult males—36.5).[17] It is questionable that possession of data in these fields will improve an engineer's competence, but it is reassuring to have a group of psychologists decide he is not narrow.

1.2 What is a profession?

A definition

In cases where a definition of the word "profession" has been prepared by the same body that is seeking professional recognition, the process may be considered somewhat suspect; as it has been said, "To choose a definition is to plead a cause. . . ."[18] It would therefore be best to turn to Web-

---

[15] *Career Satisfactions of Professional Engineers in Industry.* Washington, D.C.: Professional Engrs. Conf. Board for Industry, p. 33. In cooperation with the Nat'l Soc. of Professional Engrs.

[16] Vance Packard, *The Status Seekers* (Giant Cardinal ed.; New York: Pocketbooks, Inc., 1961), pp. 98–99. Orig. publ. 1959, by McKay, New York.

[17] *Proc.*, The Creative Person Conference, sponsored by the Inst. of Personality Assessment and Research, Lake Tahoe, Calif., Oct. 13–17, 1961, p. III–3.

[18] *The Annals of the American Academy of Political Science*, vol. 297, January 1955. Attributed to C. L. Stevenson by M. L. Cogan, in "The Problem of Defining a Profession," p. 105.

ster's Unabridged for a reasonably general meaning of the word as it is interpreted by nonengineers.

> **profession:** A calling requiring *specialized knowledge* and often long and *intensive preparation* including instruction in skills and methods as well as in the scientific, historical, or scholarly principles underlying such skills and methods, maintaining by force of *organization* or concerted opinion *high standards of achievement and conduct,* and committing its members to *continued study* and to a kind of work which has for its prime purpose the rendering of a *public service.* By permission, from *Webster's Third New International Dictionary,* copyright 1966 by G. & C. Merriam Co., Publishers of the Merriam-Webster Dictionaries.

The italics have been supplied by the author in order to make those items stand out that constitute the essence of the definition. The italicized items might be examined, one by one, to see how well engineering fits the definition of a profession. Engineering certainly requires *specialized knowledge* and *intensive preparation,* but the degree of preparation is not so great as that in medicine or law, two favorite professions with which engineers frequently compare their own. For many decades, engineering has required four years of preparation beyond high school, for entrance into the profession, while medicine and law have required from seven to nine years. However, in 1965, major segments of the engineering profession declared it was time to require a master's degree for entrance into the profession. In addition, each year, an increasing number of students go on to doctor's degrees in engineering.

There is no doubt that the engineering profession has a very strong *organizational structure.* (In this book, an entire chapter, entitled "Engineering Societies," has been given over to the subject.)

There may be some question whether engineering meets the tests of *high standards, continued study,* and *public service.* However, it should be noted that these three points relate more to the behavior of the individual professional than to his group. The following paragraphs will examine these issues in detail.

High standards of achievement and conduct. To the author's knowledge, the most earnest effort conducted to date to learn something about the actual degree of professionalism in engineering is a survey made by The Professional Engineers Conference Board for Industry. When engineers were asked what engineering professionalism meant to them, the three most frequent responses were:

1) Technical competence and skill: high standards of learning and ability
2) Prestige for the profession: stature; dignity; respect

3) Become more like lawyers and doctors: raise standards as in medicine and law; have something like the AMA or Bar Association[19]

It should be gratifying that technical competence is number one, but on the other hand, it ought to be embarrassing to engineers that the second and third responses relate to the *fruits* of professionalism, and not at all to what we do to merit the status. In this survey, personal qualities such as creativity, responsibility, and ethical standards were far down on the list.

In response to the same question, the engineers' *managers* designated the following points as the most important:

1) Technical competence
2) A high standard of ethics
3) An attitude of individual responsibility

The aspects of prestige, and of becoming more like lawyers and doctors, were well toward the bottom of the managers' ranking.

Continued study. This is a difficult matter, for just exactly what does "continued study" mean? The man who scans the articles in the magazines that cross his desk will probably state that he engages in continued study and so will the man who is pursuing a crushing load of evening studies at a university. As a practical matter, it probably does not mean the latter. This may be acceptable for a man who is trying to upgrade himself (by getting a master's degree, for example), but it simply is not reasonable to expect a man to be away from home three or four evenings a week (plus whatever evenings his job may require) on a permanent basis, during a period when he presumably is also trying to raise a family. Some companies have adopted "released time" policies to make it possible for qualified employees to attend daytime university classes (early morning hours, for example) partly at company expense. This is a highly satisfactory plan, but it requires cooperation from the university in scheduling classes, as well as from industry.

For a minimum fulfillment of the criterion for continued study, a man must keep up on the current literature in his field. It is true that some of the literature in engineering is difficult to read. No doubt, many men excuse themselves from reading it on exactly these grounds, but, often, this does not prevent them from energetically asserting their claims to professionalism.

Some engineers have discovered that they can coast for a long time on

---

[19] *Engineering Professionalism in Industry.*

what they learned in college and during the first few years of their professional life. But coasting, by definition, means going down-hill. Many men remark upon their feelings of surprise when they pick up some of their own college work and examine it after a few years lapse of time. They cannot believe they really wrote it, or that they once understood all that material. Through the years, the mind is relentlessly busy at forgetting things; meanwhile, knowledge increases and diversifies. Hence, continued study takes on a double importance: not only must a man pursue the expansion of knowledge, but he also must take action against the erosion of his own knowledge. It takes a considerable amount of running, just to stay in the same place.

Public service. Some young engineers misunderstand what is meant by "public service" and assume it means they should offer their services to the public at no charge. However, this would be an unrealistically severe interpretation. The engineer's public service role is a real one, but is not so evident as a doctor's or lawyer's. Moreover, the fact that most engineers are employees of corporations, renders their public service even less apparent. The effect of engineering upon the public's well-being is a vital one, nevertheless. We are more fully aware of this when we reflect that there is hardly anything we touch, use, or eat that has not been subjected to an engineer's influence at some stage in its development.

Admittedly, a corporation engineer might be hard pressed to identify a connection between his activities on any given day and a specific human benefit. To convince himself of his service role, however, he should imagine a situation where his activities, and those of all others in similar capacities throughout all society, suddenly vanish. It takes only a minimum of imagination to realize that such a disappearance would have a profound and deleterious effect upon the nation's productivity, together with all which that implies: fewer jobs, lowered national income, and general economic decline.

Of course, if all blue-collar (or white-collar) workers were suddenly wiped out, the economy would also suffer an abrupt decline. They render a public service, too; every productive worker does. The difference is that an engineer is engaged in the creation of things *that didn't exist before.* He should be conscious that his creative efforts—however small they may seem—have an immense influence upon the future, when added to those of all other engineers.

The preceding paragraphs should establish that engineering meets all the criteria set forth in Webster's definition of a profession. However, just because engineering is a profession, it does not necessarily follow that every engineer is automatically a professional. Every individual remains charged with the responsibility to meet the criteria on a personal basis. In the final summing up, the professional status of a group depends upon the individual behavior of its members.

Professionalism by legislation

It should be noted that the federal government, in the Taft-Hartley Act, defines "professionals" in a way that includes engineers. Furthermore, the title "Professional Engineer" is protected by law in all states but three. The definition of a professional employee given by the Taft-Hartley law is reproduced in this section. Engineers should read it carefully because, being the law, it governs the relationship of every engineer with his employer.

The term "professional employee" means—(a) any employee engaged in work (i) predominantly intellectual and varied in character as opposed to routine mental, manual, mechanical, or physical work; (ii) involving the consistent exercise of discretion and judgment in its performance; (iii) of such a character that the output produced or the result accomplished cannot be standardized in relation to a given period of time; (iv) requiring a knowledge of an advanced type in a field of science or learning customarily acquired by a prolonged course of specialized intellectual instruction and study in an institution of higher learning or a hospital, as distinguished from a general academic education or from an apprenticeship or from training in the performance of routine mental, manual, or physical processes; or

(b) any employee, who (i) has completed the courses of specialized intellectual instruction and study described in clause (iv) of paragraph (a), and (ii) is performing related work under the supervision of a professional person to qualify himself to become a professional employee as defined in paragraph (a).[20]

One result of this definition is that professional employees may not be included against their wishes in a union with nonprofessional employees. Another result is that professional employees are "exempt" from the provision of the law which makes it obligatory that employers pay time-and-a-half for overtime.[21] An "exempt" employee's work "cannot be standardized"; he is paid his salary, not by the hour, but for accomplishing a

---

[20] *Labor-Management Relations Act, 1947.* (Taft-Hartley Act), U.S. code, title 29, chap. 7, par. 152(12).

[21] *Fair Labor Standards Act of 1938,* U.S. code, title 29, chap. 8. [See par. 207(a) for overtime clause and par. 213(a) for exemption of executive, administrative, and professional employees.]

responsible task. In fact, he frequently receives no pay at all for overtime; he is expected to fulfill his responsibilities, however long this may take. The law also makes it possible for engineers to keep their own time records, instead of being required to punch a time clock. (The law requires, for nonexempt employees, that accurate daily records be kept of their times in and times out.)

In addition, the National Labor Relations Board has used certain general criteria as a guide in determining whether a particular group consists of professionals. If state registration is typically associated with the group's classification (as for engineers), this has been considered strong evidence that the work is of professional level. Also, a college degree has been increasingly emphasized as a criterion. The Board has refused to accord professional status to work being performed by some groups on the basis that most of the occupants of positions in the groups did not possess college degrees.[22]

Taking the opposite stand, articles appearing in some union periodicals have striven to convince engineers that they are *not* professionals. An officer of one of the AFL-CIO unions has given his opinion that "engineers are *workers*,"[23] and that engineering and production employees have common interests.[24] He issued a call to all engineers to join the American Federation of Technical Engineers (AFTE), under the protection of AFL-CIO. (A chapter dealing with engineers' unions is included later in this book.)

1.3 Ethics and public responsibility

The nature of ethics

There has seldom been a more semantically loaded word than "ethics." Ethics is concerned with concepts of right and wrong. A large number of people (especially young people) believe any act or event can be measured against some absolute standard, with a complete determination of its intrinsic rightness or wrongness. More experienced people often are not so sure. With only a little effort, they can recall far too many episodes in which socially desirable aims have been in conflict, with the consequence

---

[22] *The Engineer in Industry in the 1960's.* Washington, D.C.: Nat'l Soc. of Professional Engrs., 1961, pp. 55–58.

[23] R. M. Stephens, "Engineers are *Workers*," AFL-CIO American Federationist, November 1958.

[24] R. M. Stephens, "Helluva Engineer," The I.U.D. Digest (Industrial Union Dept., AFL-CIO), Winter 1957.

that Solomon-like judgment was required to select a rational course of action.

Some ethical questions have religious connotations; however, it is not necessary to include religious aspects in order to accept the social desirability of ethical rules. Ethics constitute the basic code of civilized behavior, without which our environment, as we know it, would be impossible. Such rules constitute the basic constraints each of us agrees to practice in his relationships with others. We consent to these constraints so that our *own* existence may be more pleasurable. We mutually agree to refrain from robbing one another, from killing one another, or from practicing any of those unpleasantries upon others that we would find distressing if practiced upon ourselves.

The basic point is that life would be much less congenial than it is, if there were a universal abandonment of ethical behavior. As an example, most business transactions are regularly carried out in mutual confidence that the other party intends to do what he says he will do. As another example, most of us believe that there is a reasonable probability we will not be murdered or robbed as we walk down the street, even though we know that such things happen.

Adherence to ethical codes is not universally perfect; nevertheless, the genius of civilization and of human progress to date has been man's ability to develop, and to abide by, codes of conduct which successfully advance the aims of most people. The noted philosopher Hans Reichenbach has stated, "The fundamental ethical rules . . . are adhered to merely because human beings want these rules and want other persons to follow the same rules."[25]

Canons of ethics

Engineers have a well-developed set of canons. Indeed, they have several sets of canons, because some engineering societies have individually published their own. The one adopted by the Engineers' Council for Professional Development (ECPD) is the most widely accepted and is reproduced in the appendix.

After the price-fixing scandal of 1960 (which involved U.S. industrial giants like General Electric and Westinghouse), the engineering profession was startled to discover that one of its Canons of Ethics was considered to be in conflict with the U.S. antitrust laws. The Canon was

---

[25] H. Reichenbach, *The Rise of Scientific Philosophy* (Berkeley and Los Angeles, Calif.: Univ. of Calif. Press, 1951), p. 304.

Number 26: "He [the engineer] will not compete with another specialist on the basis of charges for work by underbidding, through reducing his normal fees after having been informed of the charges named by the other."[26]

The preceding is a good example of desirable social objectives in conflict. Canon 26 sought to avoid competition on the basis of price alone among engineers; it was formulated by men who believed that price competition might force engineers into a reduction in the quality of their services to clients. The antitrust laws, on the other hand, were established in order to preserve competition, since the widespread cartels of the late nineteenth century had been manipulated to the enrichment of a favored few and the disadvantage of the general public.

Canon 26 was reworded during a general revision of the Canons: The Canons now prohibit engineers from submitting ". . . price proposals for professional services which require creative effort, on a basis that constitutes competition on price alone."

Many of the duties prescribed by the Canons are also required by law, for instance, the one stating that an engineer will act ". . . as a faithful agent or trustee for each employer or client." In other cases they exceed what the law requires and may operate primarily to enhance the dignity of, and respect for, the engineering profession. However, in the author's opinion, no code of ethics should ever be allowed to become self-serving and to act only to enhance the profession. The objective of increasing public respect is justifiable only if it also increases public trust and confidence (which results in a public benefit) in engineers.

One obligation of a profession is the maintenance of high standards of conduct among its membership, with respect both to its members' relations with the public and to fair practices among the fellow professionals. To this end, the engineering societies appoint special committees to review charges of unethical conduct against individual engineers. Usually, the action taken is merely a rebuke of the offenders and a caution against further offenses. This may sound mild, but within a profession, a rebuke from fellow professionals is a serious thing.

The good of society

If medicine has given mankind improved health, and the humanities have given mankind pleasure, then it can be said that technology has given mankind time.

---

[26] *31st Annual Report.* New York: ECPD, 1963, p. 21.

In many countries of the world today, men exist only in order that they may continue to exist. This was true in our own country not so long ago. There was little time for anything but work—twelve to fourteen hours of it each day, six days a week. It was not only our enlightened visions of right and wrong that caused the forty-hour week to become law in 1938. It was also a *necessity* as machines came, more and more, to replace men at routine tasks. If men had continued to work the eighty-four-hour week of the nineteenth century, the result could have been only the concentration of jobs among fewer people, coupled with rising unemployment.

Ever since 1900, spendable income has continued to rise, so that it has been possible for most Americans to satisfy more of their wants while working less hours. Most of us have heard stories how our grandfather or great-grandfather would work all day cutting a wagonload of wood and then drive to town and sell it for a dollar. A dollar went farther in those days, but as Fig. 1-1 shows, not *that* much farther. In 1909, workers in manufacturing enterprises earned an average of nineteen cents per hour, with no fringe benefits; thus, the average weekly earnings were $9.74 for a 51-hour week.[27]

When these figures are corrected for the cost-of-living increase, it can be seen that such a worker existing in 1963 would have a purchasing power concomitant with a wage of sixty-five cents per hour ($33 weekly). Yet, the average wage in 1963 was $2.44 per hour, plus another 9.7 percent in fringe benefits, constituting a total of $2.67 ($107.36 weekly). This increase in actual purchasing power is an improvement of 325 percent, during a period when the work week was being cut by 22 percent. (An engineer graduated from college in 1963 started at about $595 a month, for a comparable rate of $3.78 per hour.)[28]

This immense improvement in only fifty years did not merely happen. Technology made it possible, and engineers are technology's implementers. Virtually every kind of innovation regarded as beneficial to American comfort has been subject to the influence of engineers: automobiles, airplanes, highways, television, and home appliances, to name the obvious ones. Some less obvious benefits are paper (mill machinery), food (harvesting, processing, and packaging machinery), new art forms (movies and television; or music for mass consumption, made possible by the phono-

---

[27] *The Economic Almanac: 1964*. New York: Nat'l Industrial Conf. Board, 1964, pp. 54, 55, 63, 76, 77, 103.

[28] F. S. Endicott, *Trends in Employment of College and University Graduates in Business and Industry, 1964 (Eighteenth Annual Report)*. Evanston, Ill.: Northwestern Univ., 1964.

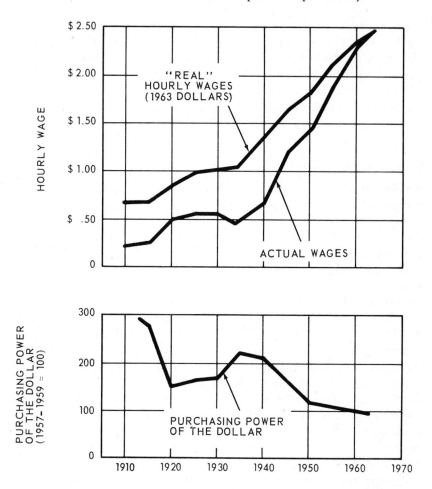

Fig. 1-1 Comparison between wages and cost of living from 1910 to 1963. "Real" wages represent actual purchasing power. Data refers to production workers in manufacturing. (From *The Economic Almanac, 1964*. Nat'l Industrial Conf. Board, New York)

graph and radio), and national security. Although not everyone agrees that engineering contributions to national security benefit mankind, most Americans believe that the production of nuclear missiles and other items for defense preserves their way of life from being disrupted by outsiders.

Even if one disputes that engineers should be proud of their contributions to the art of warfare, it will have to be granted that the freeing of man from a life of hard labor is a magnificent achievement. However, this release has not yet been accomplished throughout the world. In many

Asian countries, three fourths of the population are needed just to produce enough food to support a society existing at the borderline of starvation.[29] In the United States, only one person in six is required for the production of food, and even then our problem has been that we produce too much. In a very real sense, seven out of nine people in the United States can thank their scientists and engineers that they do not have to spend fourteen hours a day laboring in a corn field.

Public responsibility

Coupled with the engineer's enormous influence for good comes a heavy responsibility for human safety. Whenever a dam breaks or a bridge falls, newspapers break out the biggest headline type they own. People simply do not expect such things to happen. One of the most sensational of such events occurred in 1928, when the St. Francis Dam in California burst without warning in the middle of the night and killed nearly four hundred people. The dam had been completed only recently and was the pride of the Los Angeles water system.

Almost as soon as it had been completed and had begun to fill, leakage developed between the dam and the foundation. During its second year of service, several very large cracks formed in the dam. By March 12, 1928, the water below the dam had turned muddy, and William Mulholland, Chief Engineer of the Los Angeles Water Department, personally inspected the situation. He was relieved to find that the muddy water was caused by nearby road construction and decided the dam was not in immediate danger. That same night it collapsed. Mulholland, seventy-three years of age, publicly took full responsibility for the disaster and resigned his post shortly thereafter.[30]

Investigations showed that the dam site was intersected by at least one earthquake fault. Furthermore, when samples of the "bedrock" were tested by immersion in water, they were observed to change into a mushy mass. In the urgency of Los Angeles' need for water, Mulholland had overlooked ordinary engineering precautions. An investigating committee concluded ". . . that the dam was constructed without a sufficiently thorough examination and understanding of the foundation materials upon which the dam was constructed." A coroner's jury found Mulholland responsible for an error in engineering judgment, but no charge of crim-

---

[29] P. A. Samuelson, *Economics* (3d ed.; New York: McGraw-Hill, 1955), p. 397.
[30] R. A. Nadeau, *The Water Seekers* (Garden City, N.Y.: Doubleday, 1950), p. 116.

inal negligence was made. The jury added that construction of a great dam "should never be left to the sole judgment of one man, no matter how eminent . . ."[31]

A more recent incident of almost exactly the same type occurred in France in 1959: the Malpasset Dam collapsed and killed 421 people. In 1961, a government engineer was charged with involuntary homicide through negligence, and in 1964, his case came to trial. He was acquitted. The prosecution stated the engineer had been responsible for seeing that tests of the foundations were adequately carried out and charged that he had not carried them out correctly. However, one of the witnesses testified that the blame really should fall on the designer of the dam, who had been absolved of responsibility for the collapse.[32]

Hardly any bridge failure has received so much publicity as that of the Tacoma Narrows Bridge in 1940. The failure took place in broad daylight, with cameramen present. Fortunately no lives were lost, as the bridge's violent undulations gave ample warning that something was about to happen. This bridge was the most slender large suspension bridge ever built. [33,34] It went down in a moderately strong wind, after having been in service for only four months. The cause of the failure was the creation of "Kármán vortices," which were shed from the leeward side of the deck at a frequency coinciding with one of the natural frequencies of the bridge.[35] Complete destruction of the deck was a result. During the investigation and after, no charges of negligence were made, although it was noted that, "The builders of this bridge, being limited in funds, were anxious to build as inexpensive a bridge as possible in order to build any bridge at all."[36]

Another, and unique, issue in the public responsibility of engineers is the location of nuclear power plants (because of the potential magnitude of a disaster). In late 1964, the Pacific Gas and Electric Company (the world's largest private utility), announced it was cancelling plans to construct a large nuclear power plant at Bodega Head, Calif. This an-

---

[31] "Essential Facts Concerning the Failure of the St. Francis Dam," *Proc. Am. Soc. Civil Engrs.*, vol. 55, October 1929, pp. 2147–2163.

[32] *Engrg. News-Record*, Oct. 29, 1964, pp. 14–15, and Dec. 3, 1964, p. 23.

[33] *Engineering News-Record*, Nov. 14, 1940, p. 10.

[34] Width-to-span ratio for some major bridges: Verrazano–Narrows—1 to 41; Golden Gate—1 to 47; Mackinac—1 to 56; Tacoma Narrows—1 to 72 (original), 1 to 47 (rebuilt). See *Engrg. News-Record*, Aug. 23, 1962, pp. 32–33.

[35] J. P. Den Hartog, *Mechanical Vibrations* (4th ed.; New York: McGraw-Hill, 1956), p. 308.

[36] "Failure of the Tacoma Narrows Bridge," *Proc. Am. Soc. Civil Engrs.*, vol. 69, December 1943, p. 1568.

nouncement climaxed a bitter 4½-year controversy between PG & E and certain segments of the public. Some groups opposed the plant because it would disfigure a portion of California's scenic coastline, but the sharpest battles arose because the plant would be less than a mile from the San Andreas Fault (the fault that had caused the San Francisco Earthquake and Fire in 1906). In matters of this nature, the public must rely for its safety and protection solely upon expert engineering opinion, because no other segment of the population possesses the specialized knowledge about the possible results.

The Atomic Energy Commission, in late 1964, released the report of its Division of Reactor Licensing, concerning the Bodega Head Plant's location. This report stated that the proposed site was unsuitable because of ". . . the lack of any experimental or experience proof–test of the proposed novel method that could form an acceptable basis for the required safety evaluation." It continued: "Because of the magnitude of possible consequences of a major rupture in the reactor containment accompanied by a failure of emergency equipment, we do not believe that a large nuclear power reactor should be the subject of a pioneering construction effort based on unverified engineering principles . . ."

Released at the same time, by the AEC, was a report by the Advisory Committee on Reactor Safeguards, which stated the committee's belief that the reactor could be operated without undue hazard. The Pacific Gas and Electric Company, because of the doubts concerning safety, promptly dropped its plans for a nuclear plant at that site.[37]

Obviously, in cases of this type, the real controversy originates from the ambiguity of terms like "undue hazard," and "safe." During a suit over the Enrico Fermi Power Plant, 29 miles southwest of Detroit, Adolf Ackerman stated (in an *amicus curiae* brief to the United States Supreme Court) that it is the professional engineer's duty ". . . to give overriding consideration to the public safety." He went on to add, "The possibility of an accident or disaster is ever present and the biggest disasters have been the most incredible. Generally, out of a painstaking investigation of a disaster a complex chain of 'incredible' circumstances has emerged to explain the cause."[38]

The author's purpose in recounting the preceding incidents is to emphasize, repeatedly, the profound burden the engineer bears for public safety. Everyone wants the benefits of technical progress, but every step

---

[37] *Nucleonics Week,* vol. 5, Nov. 5, 1964, pp. 1–3.

[38] A. J. Ackerman, "Atomic Power, A Failure in Engineering Responsibility," *Proc. Am. Soc. Civil Engrs.,* October 1961, pp. 43–79.

of progress brings hazards with it. There is no such condition as "absolutely safe." Airplanes, automobiles, and power lines have all caused their share of deaths. Still, it is the engineer's obligation to have an abiding concern for public safety and to place every decision as far to the "safe" side of the spectrum as is possible. Again, desirable social ends are in conflict, and the engineer is in the middle. However, the public is even more in the middle (if such a thing be possible), and has no choice but to trust the engineer.

On a more cheerful note, it must be recorded that engineering also has a great many successes to its credit. Those having obvious dramatic impact (plus excellent press coverage) like satellites, space ships to the moon, and supersonic jet airliners are remarkable enough; but since satellites, space ships, and even jet liners are fairly remote from the lives of most people, the author will, instead, touch upon some commonplace miracles that daily impinge on the lives of everyone.

For example: the availability of pure water is, in itself, something of a miracle. Americans seldom stop to consider the enormous complex of civil engineering works that brings pure water to their sinks, as soon as they turn the tap. Nor do they stop to think of the equally enormous complex that carries it away again. They simply expect it to work—and it does. A comparison of the cost of water with that of any other bulk commodity found in nature (such as sand) will further illustrate this amazing availability. Water generally costs only two or three cents a ton; sand may cost a hundred times as much.

Consider the internal-combustion engine. What more improbable system could one devise for producing rotary motion than that tight little box with its bottled explosions and wildly gyrating assemblage of pistons, rods, and camshafts? Yet it works and works well. Its quiet, smooth, controlled power is a tribute to the perseverence of automotive engineers. Hardly any device has had a more profound impact upon our lives than the automobile: it has vastly increased mobility and wreaked fundamental changes in this country's social mores. Every time an engineer makes a small change that results in a more efficient car, he is also giving a small nudge to the social structure, although he does it unknowingly.

One last example is the telephone. Everybody knows how a telephone works: One talks into it, sound waves push some carbon grains around, an electric current goes out and is perhaps amplified a few times; then an electromagnet wriggles a diaphragm on the other end—and sound is produced.

Although the telephone is a simple enough miracle, how many people have ever thought about the telephone *system*? As *Fortune* puts it, "Indeed, it is now clear that what the Bell System has been doing for the last eighty years is building the world's largest computer."[39] There are 65 million telephones in the United States, plus another 54 million throughout the world, which can be plugged into the system. There are thousands of central offices, each one containing thousands of automatic switches. Most of the system is direct-dialing. When a person dials a number, he is giving programming instructions to the "computer," which must now select a way to solve the problem given it, according to the traffic at the moment. There are an astronomical number of ways in which a long-distance call might be routed, with switch after switch to be automatically selected and actuated. Yet, today, the telephone system is taken for granted, and people probably become choleric if the system doesn't work when they want it. While expanding and improving the telephone system, did the engineers think of the profound social changes they were causing? Probably not. Yet consider the way the telephone has changed our business customs and living habits, by permitting instant information transmittal and, even, facilitating instant date-making.

1.4 The problem of numbers

One of the fundamental facts of life for engineers is that they outnumber every other professional group except teachers. Table 1-1 presents statistics from the 1960 U.S. census:

Table 1-1. Comparison of engineers with other professionals

Occupation	Year 1960	1950	Increase, percent
Accountants and auditors	476,800	385,300	24
Architects	30,500	23,900	27
Dentists	83,200	75,500	10
Engineers	871,600	535,400	63
Lawyers and judges	213,100	182,400	17
Physicians and surgeons	229,600	192,900	19
Teachers (elem. and sec. schools)	1,531,300	1,049,100	46

Source: U.S. Bureau of the Census, *U.S. Census of Population: 1960.* Washington, D.C.: vol. 1, p. 1-522.

[39] F. Bello, "The World's Greatest Industrial Laboratory," *Fortune*, November 1958, p. 150.

620.002   K323e

c. 1

Moreover, the engineering profession is expected to require another 50-percent increase during the decade of the 1960s; it is estimated that, as a result, there will be a total of 1,300,000 engineers in this country by 1970.[40]

For a profession that is based upon individual creativity, such numbers have disturbing implications. Some people doubt that it will be possible for engineers to cultivate individuality or to maintain a sense of personal responsibility under these conditions. They call attention to the masses of technologists employed by some industries (such as aerospace) and despondently conclude that the game is already lost.

The role of the silver-lining seeker is not always an admired one, but it deserves an attempt. Examining the aerospace industry, for example, we ask ourselves, "Where do great achievements originate?" They come from somewhere, for space vehicles do hit the moon, and satellites do orbit the earth. Technical achievements do not merely spontaneously arise from the milling activity, as life was once thought to arise from mouldering humus. Unfortunately, one can rarely recognize technological progress, even when it is taking place under his nose. We perennially seem to expect that idea-generation must occur in huge quantum jumps, but always *in some other place*. The truth is that progress is born out of a ferment of frustration, setbacks, disappointments, and efforts and is rarely recognizable when viewed on the personal level. Added together, the infinitesimal improvements become a veritable avalanche. Remember that an idea cannot occur without an individual human mind for it to occur in.

Before leaving the "Silver Lining Department," the author would like to mention that two of the most massive (and most successful) technological organizations in the world—International Business Machines Corporation and the Bell Telephone Laboratories—make the cultivation of the Individual into almost a religion.

1.5 Engineer shortage: fact or fancy?

Ever since World War II, the engineering profession has been plagued by alternating cries of surplus and shortage. The effects are visible in Fig. 1-2. The U.S. Bureau of Labor Statistics is presumed to have caused the first violent swing in the late 1940s, by its warning of an impending surplus of engineers: In 1950, freshman enrollments fell to their post-war low, only to rise once more as the first "shortage" developed in response to the Korean conflict and the subsequent competition with Russia. Then, in 1957, following some defense industry cutbacks, various articles in the

---

[40] *Scientists and Engineers, 1960–70: Supply and Demand.*

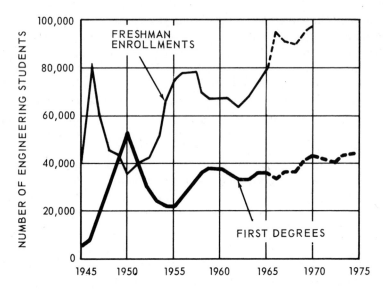

Fig. 1-2   Engineering freshman enrollments and first degrees since 1945, projected into the 1970s. (From *Engineering Manpower Commission, A Statement of Position.* May 1963; courtesy of Engrg. Manpower Com., Engrs. Joint Council, New York. Data for 1963–1965 taken from *J. Engrg. Educ.,* vol. 55, December 1964 and vol. 56, December 1965)

United States press announced that the "engineer shortage" was a thing of the past. What troubled most engineers, however, was the apparent relief with which such announcements were made. This semblance of relief implied that there must have existed a certain amount of submerged resentment against engineers, prior to this time, perhaps stemming from the belief that engineers had been riding the crest of a wave of artificial prosperity to which they were not entitled.

Fortune gave prominent display to the situation in an article entitled "The Turn in the Engineer Market" (subtitled "The postwar 'shortage' of engineers has suddenly disappeared. The question is now whether it is gone for good"). However, in the body of the article, *Fortune* said that some company recruiters still were not able to find all the engineers they wanted and declared that the long-term demand for engineers would continue to be strong, in order to keep productivity and living standards rising.[41]

---

[41] *Fortune,* December 1957, p. 150 ff.

Nevertheless, the adverse publicity appearing in the press created another "shortage." Freshman engineering enrollments dropped from nearly eighty thousand in 1957 to less than sixty-five thousand in 1962. The only conclusion possible is that young men were seriously concerned about the stability of engineering employment.

In 1963, the Bureau of Labor Statistics (BLS), reinforced by the Engineering Manpower Commission, warned that further serious shortages lay ahead, if engineering enrollments did not increase; the BLS projected the demand for new engineers over the 1960–1970 decade at more than seven-hundred thousand, while the number of new entrants into the profession was projected at four-hundred-fifty thousand, or two-hundred-fifty thousand less than the projected demand.[42,43]

Also in 1963, freshman enrollments again began to turn upward. They did so more strongly in 1964, although defense contracts underwent significant cutbacks in that year and were accompanied by engineer layoffs. In spite of this, newly graduated engineers continued to find jobs, even though many of them found it necessary to be somewhat more aggressive than had formerly been the case.[44] By 1966, the demand for engineers had turned upward again.

It is interesting to note that, throughout surpluses and shortages, the starting salaries for engineering graduates have steadily continued to rise, with an average increase of about 6 percent per year since 1950.[45] (Inflation has reduced the effect of this, of course, but even on a net basis, the purchasing power of an engineer's starting salary in 1964 was nearly twice what it had been in 1950.) The *rate of increase* appeared to diminish during the early 1960s, which perhaps is an indication that the supply of engineers was getting reasonably close to the demand, at least at the B.S.

---

[42] *Scientists and Engineers, 1960–70: Supply and Demand.*

[43] *Demand for Engineers, Physical Scientists, and Technicians—1964.* New York: Engrg. Manpower Comm., Engrs. Joint Council, 1964.

[44] *Summary of Engineering Placement Activities, 1964–65.* Berkeley, Calif.: Univ. of Calif. Placement Center. (The conclusion cited here, though based on the experiences of only one university center, has been reflected in the Endicott Report for 1965: *Trends in Employment of College and University Graduates in Business and Industry.* Evanston, Ill.: Northwestern Univ. The reporting companies in Endicott's survey indicated that their need for engineers holding degrees at the bachelor level would increase by 25 percent from 1964 to 1965 and that their need for engineers holding degrees at the master's level would increase 39 percent.

[45] F. S. Endicott, *Trends in Employment of College and University Graduates in Business and Industry.* Evanston, Ill.: Northwestern Univ. (See both the 1963 and 1964 reports.)

level. However, there appeared to be general agreement that serious shortages would persist at the *graduate* levels in engineering and science, at least into the 1970s. This was held to be especially true in regard to men holding Ph.D. degrees in engineering, mathematics, and the physical sciences.[46]

1.6 The challenge

Humanists have often challenged scientists on a fundamental moral issue: allegedly, scientists consider it their responsibility only to reveal truth—how it is used is not their concern. Engineers have a similar problem: allegedly, they consider only the interest (presumably financial) of their client or employer—the broader results of their actions are of no concern to them. One government official has said, "The public administrator finds that when spokesmen for various segments of the economy are identifiable by profession, the engineer all too frequently is spokesman for the specially privileged, or those who seek special privileges."[47]

It is advantageous to technologists that the nation (and the world) has so confidently embraced the god of Research and Development. However, there are some who ask what good the public is receiving in return for picking up an annual multibillion-dollar tab for research and development. The public tends to believe it should be able to perceive some kind of personal benefit, in return for having signed that enormous blank check. "Space is great, and missiles are essential," says John Doe, "but how about some more of those wonderful laborsaving appliances? What about the increasing befoulment of our atmosphere and our rivers, or the clogging of our highways? What about the unemployment created by the automation you engineers are so excited about?" The 1965 preliminary report on "Goals of Engineering Education" suggested that the engineering profession regard problems of the type just mentioned as unique engineering opportunities. The authors of the report urged that engineers take a leading part in improving the quality of human existence, through better urban and regional improvement of transportation, environmental control, the preservation of natural beauty, the enhancement of recreational

---

[46] *Meeting Manpower Needs in Science and Technology*, p. 1.

[47] Arthur C. Stern, "How Professional is Engineering?" *Mech. Engrg.*, vol. 86, June 1964, p. 22. (Mr. Stern is assistant chief, Div. of Air Pollution, U.S. Public Health Service.)

opportunities, and the alleviation of social dislocation resulting from advances in technology.[48]

Because of the seriousness of such problems, the National Academy of Sciences, in 1964, created a National Academy of Engineering, by means of the authority granted it by the United States Congress in its original charter. Since its organization a century ago, the National Academy of Sciences has served, with distinction, in its role of adviser to congress on scientific matters. The organization of a separate engineering academy was a recognition that the engineer stands closer to the public, than does the scientist, in making the fruits of scientific discoveries available to man. Princeton University's Dean Brown has said, "The engineering profession is the channel by which science can greatly improve our way of life, provided it assumes the initiative of leadership rather than the passive role of the hired consultant."[49]

1.7 The future environment

This chapter will close with a list of some of the conditions expected in the world of the future, which were not present in the past. These conditions will largely structure the environment in which the engineer will practice his profession during the next several decades:

The future environment of engineering practice

1. For the first time in history, there is no "free" land of any real, present value.
2. Medicine and hygiene have brought world population growth rates to critical values.
3. A single individual cannot be both broadly and deeply competent in technology.
4. A single, local event can become world knowledge in less than an hour.
5. A single weapon can affect a large fraction of the Earth's surface.
6. Many large weapons can be delivered at long ranges in less than an hour.
7. An aggressive, ruthless government can win World domination, at some sacrifice.

---

[48] *Goals of Engineering Education, The Preliminary Report,* Washington, D.C.: ASEE, October 1965, pp. 15–16.

[49] J. Douglas Brown, "Your Learned Profession," *Mech. Engrg.,* vol. 85, April 1963, p. 43.

8. Rapid technological change accentuates the lag in political institutions.

9. The obsolescence period of a complex device is shorter than its development period.

10. Science is available to all nations. New developments are copied soon after they are marketed. World trade will be won, and held by quality manufacture at low cost.

11. Automation will displace labor. The level of intelligence required to design, manufacture, install, operate, and maintain automatic factories is high. The employment of less intelligent people will become a problem.

12. The new and underdeveloped nations demand, and expect, a better way of life. Their progress, or lack of it, may determine the issue of peace or war in the world.[50]

---

[50] The author is indebted to Richard C. Raymond, Advanced Technology Services, General Elec. Co., New York, for permission to use this list.

2 ▸ | Creativity

2.1 The trouble with words

Creativity

The word "creativity" is in a rather curious state: nearly everybody recognizes creativity when he sees it; yet nobody can define the word in a fully acceptable manner. From such a simple cause, stems much bitter controversy. According to the dictionaries, to "create" means to bring into existence something that did not previously exist; but this definition satisfies almost no one. Therefore, this entire chapter may be regarded as an attempt at a definition.

Invention

In any attempt to discuss "creativity," another term, just as troublesome, almost immediately presents itself: the term "invention." Every layman is instantly confident of the word "invention." He knows exactly what it means; he can think of countless "inventions": the electric light, the safety pin, the phonograph, even the atomic bomb. It is only Patent Office examiners and United States Supreme Court justices who believe there is a problem in defining what an invention is. The legal problems surrounding this word are severe and will be discussed in Chapter 10.

For the purposes of this book, an invention will be regarded as something that is clearly possessed of novelty and usefulness; has identity as a distinct device, process, or system, and has been "reduced to practice." (Even though an idea may have been reduced to practice, it still may not be commercially practical. "Reduction to practice" may consist of nothing more than a written description in a patent, or it may consist of a series of laboratory demonstrations that function only under carefully controlled conditions. The long, and usually painful, task of refining an idea until it reaches the point of commercial realizability is known as "development.")

Patents

It is almost impossible to talk about creativity without also talking about patents. The aforementioned layman, who had no trouble with the term "invention," would probably also assume that "creativity," "invention," and "patent" all refer to essentially the same thing. A slightly better-informed layman would know this is wrong, for he could immediately point out that Einstein could not have patented his theory of relativity, even though the highest possible order of creativity was involved in bringing it into being. Nor would Einstein's theories normally be termed "inventions." As another example, the Golden Gate Bridge represents creative civil engineering of the first magnitude, but it is not an invention, nor is it patentable, because suspension bridges have long been known.

Most important of all to the present discussion: The innumerable innovations and design decisions which go into the final embodiment of a modern-day device (whether it be an automobile, a chemical plant, a satellite, or a zipper fastener) represent acts of creativity of varying degree. Some of these innovations may be patentable and some may not. However, they are all acts of creativity, and it is with creativity *in this larger sense* that we are concerned.

Artistic creativity

Some people will be quick to point out that there are other kinds of creativity than have been mentioned in the preceding sections. For example, authors, artists, and composers are just as concerned with creativity as are engineers and scientists. It may even be that the mysterious fundamental sources of creative potential are the same, whether they are expressed in technological or nontechnological forms. Humanity has an extremely high regard for artistic creativity, but it will not figure in this discussion, except as it impinges upon engineering in the form of the special activity known as "industrial design."

There is one kind of nontechnological creativity with which the author will be concerned: management. It may seem strange to link creativity with management, but as will be shown later, one of the highest rewards of management is the creative content of the job.

2.2 Differing kinds of technical creativity

In the previous section Einstein's theories were given as an illustration of the highest type of creativity. There might be a temptation to rank all new scientific knowledge in this highest category; however, some kinds of scientific effort do not involve much creativity, since they consist of applying a stimulus and observing an outcome. In true scientific creativity, there is a recognition of novel potentialities and a new ordering of the knowledge that permits significant and enlightening generalizations (in other words, the statement of a theory).

For instance, the formulation of Newton's laws and that of the laws governing the behavior of charged particles, fall into this highest category of creativity. In each of these accomplishments, the establishment of a set of mathematical relations between observed experimental results constituted the central act of creation.

Some examples, drawn from the history of science, will help to illuminate, and emphasize, the differences among the various kinds of creative activity:

Quantum mechanics

Many informed persons regard the formulation of the theory of quantum mechanics as of even greater importance than Einstein's theories of relativity.[1] The greatest contributors to quantum mechanics were Planck, Heisenberg, Schrödinger, and Dirac. The essence of their contributions is that the earlier image of a universe in which every effect had its cause was replaced by the image of a universe governed by the laws of probability. A critic of their theories (Einstein was one) would no doubt have used the phrase, "laws of chance." Most of these new ideas were introduced in the 1920s, at a time when the science of physics was paralyzed by confusion resulting from the overturn of the convictions of the nineteenth century. It is because quantum mechanics dispersed the confusion and refocused the energies of physicists, that these theories are assigned a more significant role than that of relativity.

No one would seriously question that the formulation of the theory of quantum mechanics was creativity of the highest order.

---

[1] *Great American Scientists* (Englewood Cliffs, N.J.: Prentice-Hall, 1961), pp. 15–16. By the editors of *Fortune*.

Cyclotron

The cyclotron is a very interesting example of creative activity because it necessitated that a scientist, E. O. Lawrence, do some engineering (that is, design the cyclotron) in order to continue with his scientific research concerning high-energy particles. It is unlikely that anyone but a nuclear physicist would ever have conceived of the cyclotron, both because it would require a person of such background to recognize the need and because it would require training in nuclear physics before one could know how to go about making it.

Magnetic recording

Magnetic recording differs from the preceding examples, because it derives from an application of previously known scientific knowledge. Hence, it is more representative of the kind of creativity with which *engineers* are usually concerned.

Magnetic recording was invented by Valdemar Poulsen in 1898.[2] However, the process did not become of general use until the invention of a-c biasing in the 1920s; many subsequent engineering improvements (by many individuals), as well as much additional scientific research, were required before the public could reap the full benefits. Today, of course, magnetic recording is taken for granted and is central to the rapid development of digital computers. But it should be noted that full commercial utilization did not take place until more than fifty years after the original invention.

Mechanical calculator

When a member of the general public thinks of an invention, he generally envisions some sort of a mechanical device. Very few mechanical devices have ever been created that are more elaborate than modern calculating machines.

Charles Xavier Thomas, a Frenchman, might be regarded as the "father" of modern calculating machines, since he developed the first commercially useful calculator (in 1820). His basic mechanical principle is still used today in one of the leading American-made calculators, although it is applied in modified form.

---

[2] J. Jewkes, D. Sawers, and R. Stillerman, *The Sources of Invention* (London: Macmillan; and New York: St. Martin's Press, 1958), p. 326. Used by permission.

Some desk calculators contain more than eight thousand individual parts, and it must be clear that such a device does not spring into existence, all in one conception, as a finished "invention." A great many inventions are involved, and an innumerable set of other creative acts in addition. Most of these are unpatentable but, nonetheless, essential.

Classifications of technical creativity

The foregoing examples permit us to classify technical creativity in the following ways:

1) *New scientific theories and knowledge.* This is the domain of scientists. Some engineers—those previously identified as "engineering scientists"—are engaged in this activity, also.

2) *The "frontier"* where new knowledge is being sifted, explored, expanded; and, in other ways, made usable to society. Here, scientists, engineers, and engineering scientists mix almost indistinguishably; and here, most of the confusion arises as to what is "engineering" and what is "science."

3) *The development of new devices, systems, and structures.* This is the region in which the vast majority of engineers work. Here, the task is to apply scientific, mathematical, economic, and social knowledge to satisfy specific needs. At this point, matters of human usability and of economics become paramount.

Essentially the same breakdown is given by Peck and Scherer, who identify four steps or kinds of creativity: Step I, or Basic Research—knowledge of the physical world; Step II, or Applied Research—a concern with radically new concepts and devices, (Examples: How can steel be made strong at high temperatures? How can atomic energy be turned directly into electricity?); Step III, or Advanced Engineering and Development—provision of distinctly new applications utilizing known concepts, with emphasis on performance and cost; Step IV, or Product Engineering—relatively minor modifications to improve performance or reduce cost or to do both.[3,4]

---

[3] J. Peck and F. M. Scherer, *The Weapons Acquisition Process: An Economic Analysis.* Cambridge, Mass.: Grad. School of Business Admin., Harvard Univ., 1962, pp. 27–37.

[4] In terms of the definitions introduced in the first chapter, the activity identified as "engineering science" would be concerned primarily with Peck and Scherer's second step. (Most engineers would be concerned with Steps III and IV.) Since Peck and Scherer recognized that ". . . one man's science is often another

Design of new products

Within the author's third category, many gradations of creative ability are exercised. At the uppermost levels lie such activities as problem recognition and definition, schematic (or "logical") design, and basic *scheme* selection. More will be said about schemes later in the book, but, basically, selection of a scheme means deciding what the method of solution will be, in terms of actual structure. This is the most crucial stage in the life of any embryonic new product and is the phase that will be most critically examined by the Patent Office.

Once a basic scheme has been chosen, there is much additional work to be done in the selection and arrangement of components; these activities involve even the most junior designer, whose only "creative" act may be to decide whether to use five screws or six. All such decisions have their effect: Sometimes a whole project fails because of insufficient attention to detail. It is common knowledge that some of our missile troubles have been caused by "minor" components.

2.3   Sources of creativity

The creative person

Everybody is creative to some degree: Creativity is not a step function, so that one is either a thoroughly creative person or else a person completely lacking in this quality. Creativity is distributed by degrees among humanity and is very likely to be closely associated with intelligence.[5]

Psychologists have shown considerable interest in this last point, and some research seems to indicate that there is no correlation between intelligence and creativity. In such cases, however, "intelligence" is likely to mean intelligence *as measured by an I.Q. test* and I.Q. tests measure only certain kinds of intelligence. As Getzels and Jackson put it: "I.Q.

---

man's engineering . . .," they cited the development of radar to illustrate their meanings. Most of the work on radar falling under Steps I and II had been accomplished before the Second World War, while the magnificent wartime work of MIT's Radiation Laboratory would be classified, for the most part, as Step III. See Peck and Scherer.

[5] C. W. Taylor and F. Barron, eds., *Scientific Creativity: Its Recognition and Development* (New York: Wiley, 1963). See "The Personality and Motivation of the Researcher from Measurements of Contemporaries and from Biography," by R. B. Cattell, p. 122.

tests tend to reward 'convergent thinking,' since they are largely framed in terms of 'acceptable' answers."[6] Since I.Q. tests tend to emphasize such matters as reading comprehension, vocabularly, and recognition-patterns, it can readily be seen that those qualities regarded as "creative" generally are bypassed.

To most people, the term "intelligence" has a much broader scope than the one gauged by current I.Q. tests. We would probably include imponderables like alertness; insight; comprehension; cleverness; wisdom; and above all, originality, in our net judgment of a person's intelligence.

There is some psychological evidence that our educational system may tend to inhibit the development of creativity in individuals. Anne Roe, of Harvard University, suggests there is a "subtle something" about the way in which elementary subjects are taught that may have a stultifying effect upon original thinking. She says, "Teaching these subjects in terms of 'right' and 'wrong' answers carries a strong moral connotation of considerable significance." Unconventional answers from children may be sweepingly denounced by teachers as "wild" or "silly," but may actually be indications of creative potential. In addition to this, children usually impose sanctions against members of their group who are "different." As a result, potentially creative children often are subjected to severe repressions and frequently develop into isolates.[7]

Some people appear to be natural creators; that is, ideas seem to come forth almost automatically. Others have to engage in deliberate, conscious effort to develop their creative potential. Obviously, there is a limit to each person's ability, but one should take heart from the findings of a California psychologist, that ". . . the actual creative productivity of almost every individual falls far short of his own level of creative capacity."[8]

Clearly, the ideal would be to find ways to induce each individual to utilize more of his natural potential for creativity. Certain techniques have been suggested for this and will be mentioned later, but the first step is to realize that everyone has far more creative capacity than he generally uses. Simple awareness of this can open the door to more effective creative activity. There is no more poetic advice to the would-be creator than that of Ralph Waldo Emerson, who says, in his essay on "Self-Reliance":

---

[6] J. W. Getzels and Philip W. Jackson, *Creativity and Intelligence* (New York: Wiley, 1962).

[7] *Scientific Creativity: Its Recognition and Development*. See "Personal Problems and Science," by Anne Roe, pp. 133–134.

[8] *The Creative Person*. Berkeley, Calif.: Inst. of Personality Assessment and Research, Univ. of Calif., 1961. See "The Creative Process," by R. S. Crutchfield, p. VI-2.

A man should learn to detect and watch for that gleam of light which flashes across his mind from within, more than the lustre of the firmament of bards and sages. Yet he dismisses without notice his thought, because it is his. In every work of genius we recognize our own rejected thoughts; they come back to us with a certain alienated majesty. Great works of art have no more affecting lesson for us than this. They teach us to abide by our spontaneous impression with good-humored inflexibility the most when the whole cry of voices is on the other side. Else tomorrow a stranger will say with masterly good sense precisely what we have thought and felt all the time, and we shall be forced to take with shame our own opinion from another.

The importance of the individual

It is amazing how people fall prey to various catch phrases, repeating them to one another, over and over, until they come to believe they are true.

One such bromide is that "the day of the individual inventor is past." Presumably, the day of the Organization has taken over, with rank upon rank of white-coated lab technicians standing poised, their miracles to perform. Probably, what was originally meant by the trite phrase just cited is that the day of the untutored, unwashed inventor–mechanic, laboring alone in his basement, is past. No doubt it is. In fact, as one reads the case histories of great inventions, he wonders if such a type ever existed.

In *The Sources of Invention*,[9] the suggestion is offered that the once-popular stereotype of the inventor as a misunderstood genius laboring under extreme adversity, may have been strongly influenced by a nineteenth-century industrial biographer, Samuel Smiles. Though virtually unknown today, Smiles was extremely popular and widely read in his time. He made a specialty of writing about inventors, and preferred writing about underdogs. He is reputed to have had a positive distaste for writing about inventors who were blessed with so much success as to make them colorless biographical subjects.

The other side of the stereotype—that innovation is the exclusive property of the Organization—was augmented by the publicity concerning the development of nylon. This is regarded as the classic case of concerted effort by a large industrial laboratory resulting in a new product. Yet, as the story unfolds, the name of one individual, Dr. Wallace H. Carothers, appears again and again as the central driving spirit and the supplier of the crucial ideas.[10]

---

[9] Jewkes *et al.*, p. 70.
[10] Jewkes *et al.*, p. 337.

The transistor is another new development that came from a large research complex, this time the Bell Telephone Laboratories. But again, it was *individuals* who did the work; who had the ideas, the imagination, and the tenacity to carry through with them. William Shockley, John Bardeen, and Walter Brattain did the major creative work leading to the transistor and, in fact, won the 1956 Nobel Prize for their achievements. *Fortune* has stated, "Bell has cultivated, perhaps more diligently than any other industrial firm, an atmosphere that stimulates and prizes individual creativity."[11]

One of the most dramatic modern cases in which a lone inventor persisted against great obstacles is that of the jet engine. The hero of this story is Frank Whittle (now Sir Frank Whittle). Whittle began thinking about jet engines in the 1920s, but found British industrial apathy so profound that he almost gave up in 1935. However, he continued to persist, obtaining financial backing wherever he could. Then, in 1939, the apathy suddenly disappeared as World War II burst upon Britain. In Germany, a somewhat similar set of events took place, with individual inventors attempting to convince government and industry to pursue their ideas. In both countries, fruition did not come until near the end of the war.[12]

The essential point of these paragraphs is that ideas still must come from individual minds, even though the expense of developing today's new products may be so vast that only large corporations can afford the development.

Group action: "brainstorming"

For a few years after "brainstorming" was invented, the idea caught fire. It was fun, and marvelous results were claimed. Everybody sat around the table and gushed forth ideas without restraint. (Indeed, the less restraint exercised, the better.) Then a reaction against brainstorming set in, which was almost as extreme as the enthusiasm had been; heated debate arose as to whether brainstorming was or was not a useful creative tool.[13]

Attempts have been made to establish brainstorming's effectiveness by means of controlled tests; unfortunately, these tests have not been conclusive. Donald W. Taylor of Yale University conducted one such study and decided that brainstorming "... *inhibits* creative thinking." In his

---

[11] Francis Bello, "The World's Greatest Industrial Laboratory," *Fortune*, November 1958, p. 150.

[12] Jewkes *et al.*, pp. 314–321.

[13] B. S. Benson, "Let's Toss This Idea Up . . .", *Fortune*, October 1957, pp. 145–146.

research, individuals working alone produced more ideas, and more *quality* ideas, than the same number of individuals working as a group under brainstorming conditions.[14]

In another case, two engineers spent more than a month in conceiving twenty-seven possible solutions to a given problem. Then, eleven young engineers having no prior acquaintance with the problem came up with all twenty-seven of these ideas, plus many more, in a twenty-five-minute brainstorming session.[15]

In still a third instance, a pair of psychologists repeated Taylor's tests on different subjects and, this time, found no significant differences between the performance of groups and that of individuals.[16] The major finding of this study was that the key influential factor is the employment of *deferred* judgment, as opposed to *concurrent* judgment, whether used by groups or by individuals. In the exercise of deferred judgment, ideas are generated without any attempt at evaluation until later; under concurrent judgment, ideas are evaluated as they occur.

This, then, is the thing of value that brainstorming can teach us about creativity, on a larger scale: in any such deliberate attempt to be creative, the focus should first be on the generation of a large number of ideas including even some superficially foolish ones. Later, after the flow of ideas has ceased, judgment can be employed while each idea is carefully examined for new leads and hidden possibilities.

The rules of brainstorming essentially restate this procedure, as follows:

1) Criticism of ideas must be temporarily suspended.
2) "Free-wheeling" is welcome: the wilder, the better.
3) Quantity is wanted.
4) Combination and improvement of individual ideas are encouraged.

Proponents of brainstorming maintain that the use of Rule 4 causes a group to be more effective than an equal number of persons working individually. However, as we have seen, it has not been possible either to prove or to disprove this point by means of controlled tests. Nevertheless, most engineers agree that group discussion is a powerful lubricant to creative thought. The attempts at verbalization serve as a stimulus toward

---

[14] *The Creative Person.* See "Environment and Creativity," by D. W. Taylor, p. VIII–5.

[15] E. K. Von Fange, *Professional Creativity* (Englewood Cliffs, N.J.: Prentice-Hall, 1959), p. 51.

[16] *Scientific Creativity: Its Recognition and Development.* See "Development of Individual Creative Talent," by S. J. Parnes and A. Meadow, p. 318.

illumination. The participants can subsequently retreat to mental privacy, if they wish, and explore the new avenues of thought that discussion has evoked.

Perspiration and inspiration

Thomas Edison is often quoted as having said, "Genius is 99 percent perspiration and 1 percent inspiration." There is another maxim that "inspiration most often strikes those who are hard at work."

Outstandingly creative persons are almost always noted for their great energy and drive.[17] Nevertheless, many people still believe that inspiration comes unbidden, at idle moments, and can strike only those who are blessed with a mysterious "gift" of some sort. At one time, the United States Supreme Court even clothed this notion with official dignity, by insisting that each potential patent be tested to determine if the invention resulted from a "flash of genius." Fortunately, by act of Congress, this idea has been discarded, and inventions are no longer tested on the basis of the manner in which they were made, but on their intrinsic nature.[18] Even so, investigations made by psychologists show that there actually is something called inspiration, although it most certainly does not come unbidden. Instead, it requires a most strenuous preparation period.[19]

This preparation (the "perspiration" part) consists of an intense period of study and search, while one learns everything he possibly can about the subject, followed by a period of extreme concentration and effort during which the "creator" makes repeated attempts to solve the problem. A long-time associate of Edison's told of coming in on the great inventor one night, to find him surrounded by piles of books he had ordered. "He studied them night and day. He ate at his desk and slept in a chair. In six weeks he had gone through the books, written a volume of abstracts, made two thousand experiments . . . and produced a solution." Edison was twenty-four at the time.[20]

---

[17] *Scientific Creativity: Its Recognition and Development.* See "Report on Creativity Research by the Examiner's Office of the University of Chicago," by R. S. Bloom, pp. 253–258.

[18] *U.S. Code,* title 35, chap. 10, par. 103. The "Legislative History" of this section states, ". . . it is immaterial whether it [an invention] resulted from long toil and experimentation or from a flash of genius."

[19] *Scientific Creativity: Its Recognition and Development.* See "The Creative Process and Its Relation to the Identification of Creative Talent," by B. Ghiselin, p. 356.

[20] From *Edison,* by M. Josephson. Copyright 1959 by Matthew Josephson; New York: McGraw-Hill, p. 94. Used by permission.

Another example of such diligence is the discovery of vulcanization by Goodyear: The United States Commissioner of Patents declared in 1858 that Goodyear had made himself such a master of the subject of rubber that nothing could escape his attention.[21] Thus, the "accidental" discovery of vulcanization was preceded by an intense period of preparation.

W. H. Easton, in "Creative Thinking and How to Develop It," gives this graphic description concerning the occurrence of inspiration (called "illumination"):

> In this case, the thinker encounters a problem of great difficulty; but, as he has no way of knowing this in advance, he proceeds as usual, expecting to clear up the matter without much trouble. This, however, he fails to do. The problem resists all of his initial efforts to solve it, and before long, he discovers he has run into a serious obstacle.
>
> This is a critical point in his work. If he were like most people, he would stop here, giving up the problem as hopeless. But, being a creative thinker, he refuses to accept defeat, so he works on.
>
> But no amount of deliberate thinking gets him anywhere. He develops and applies every promising method of solving his problem he can imagine, but all prove failures.
>
> After struggling for hours, he runs out of ideas. Further thinking is useless, but his intense interest in the matter prevents him from stopping. Yet all he can do is to mill old ideas around in his mind to no purpose. Finally, frustrated and utterly disgusted with himself, he throws the work aside and spends the rest of his day in misery.
>
> Next morning he wakes oppressed. His problem is still on his mind and he thinks about it gloomily. But as the fog of sleep clears from his brain, the tenor of his thoughts changes.
>
> If, now, nothing distracts his attention, he soon finds that exactly those ideas he strove so hard to grasp the day before are now flowing through his mind as smoothly and easily as a stream flows through a level meadow. This is illumination.[22]

Easton, in analyzing the phenomenon of illumination (or inspiration), says the following elements are necessary:

1) One must have a difficult problem to solve.
2) One must think deliberately and intensely about the problem.
3) The deliberate thinking must *fail* to solve the problem. [Obviously true; otherwise, there is no need for later illumination.]
4) Interest in the problem must be maintained.
5) The mind must be relaxed and unwearied, as upon awakening from a night's sleep.

---

[21] Jewkes *et al.*, p. 50.
[22] *Creative Engineering.* New York: Am. Soc. Mech. Engrs., pp. 6–7.

2.4 Blocks to creativity

Probably the most frustrating block to creativity is what psychologists call "persistence of a misleading set."[23] This means that one solution to a problem is already known and, try as one might, he cannot get his mind past that particular solution to see what other (and perhaps better) solution might exist. He says to himself, "all right, here we go for a solution of a totally different sort," but though he strenuously resists it, his mind circles about and comes to rest directly upon the old familiar solution. Successful creative people say they sometimes get around this kind of block by forcing themselves to adopt extravagantly unorthodox viewpoints of their problem, such as, "Suppose I completely inverted this structure and made the output into the input?" or "Now that I have a mechanical solution to this problem, suppose I deliberately try to make one that is completely electronic?"

A related method is the use of forced-relationship techniques. In this approach, a list of ideas is first generated; then each idea is arbitrarily associated with others in an attempt to stimulate the mind into perceiving new relationships.[24] Eugene Von Fange suggests the use of the following check-list, to generate new aspects of an idea:

1. Put to other uses?
2. Adapt? Copy good ideas from other objects?
3. Modify? Change color, sound, odor, shape?
4. Magnify? Thicker, heavier, multiply components, exaggerate?
5. Minify? Subtract, condense, lighten, streamline?
6. Substitute? Other ingredients, processes, or approaches?
7. Rearrange? Interchange, change sequence, transpose cause and effect?
8. Reverse? Backward, upside down, transpose positive and negative?
9. Combine? Blend, or produce assortment?[25]

Although artificial approaches of this sort may not lead directly to explicit solutions, they sometimes serve to break the misleading set.

Closely allied to the block of a misleading set is the one called "functional fixedness." Here, a potential new use for a familiar object is obscured by its present use. An excellent illustration of this kind of block is given by Harold Buhl:

---

[23] R. S. Crutchfield in *The Creative Person,* p. VI-8.
[24] S. J. Parnes and A. Meadow in *Scientific Creativity: Its Recognition and Development,* p. 311 ff.
[25] Eugene K. Von Fange, *Professional Creativity,* © 1959. Reprinted by permission of Prentice-Hall, Inc., Englewood Cliffs, N.J.

Some students were once given the task of removing a ping-pong ball from a rusty pipe that had been bolted upright to the floor. In the room with the pipe, students found hammers, pliers, soda straws, strings, pine, and an old bucket of dirty wash water. After fishing vainly with the various tools most of the students finally saw a solution; they poured dirty water into the cylinder and floated the ball to the top. Then the experiment was repeated on other students with one important change; instead of the bucket, there was a crystal pitcher of fresh ice water surrounded by shining goblets on the table with a gleaming white cloth. Not one student solved the problem because no one could connect the beautiful pitcher and its clean water with the rusty pipe.[26]

Premature criticism has caused many an idea to be stillborn. It is better for the potential creator to adopt an attitude of optimistic reserve, always expecting the most favorable results from new avenues of thought. This, of course, is nothing but the application of deferred judgment. Eventually a choice must be made from among the various alternatives, but a possibility should not be eliminated too early by someone's saying, "Oh, that's ridiculous!" For it just might not be so absurd as it seems.

Last, and most pernicious of all, is the block of fear: primarily fear of social disapproval, or perhaps, of supervisorial disapproval. Undoubtedly, fear is at the root of human tendencies to conform. Many writers of the "social protest school" have lashed out at conformity. It should suffice to say that anything really new is a departure from past practice and, therefore, represents some individual's nonconforming. If a person is so afraid of failure as to be unwilling to depart from tradition, he will never be very creative.

2.5 Recognizing creativity

Nonconformity

In recent years, the public has caught hold of the idea that the typical creative person is a nonconformist. And so he is—by definition. However, as is so often the case, the form has been identified with its substance. As a result, many people envision the typical creative genius as one who is unkempt; uncombed; perhaps unshaven; pretentiously independent in social behavior; and, even, rude and arrogant like the creative heroes in Ayn Rand's *The Fountainhead*. Conformity, on the other hand, is assumed to be an indication of an uncreative person.

[26] H. R. Buhl, *Creative Engineering Design* (Ames, Iowa: The Iowa State Univ. Press, 1960), p. 55.

Concern over conformity has typically expressed itself in apprehension about the Organization Man; he is identifiable by his uniform, the Gray Flannel Suit. Such a person's strong urge to conform in external matters has been held sufficient cause to suspect that internal conformance is also taking place. The suspicion is justifiable in many cases and often is especially applicable to hopeful junior executives.

Nevertheless, there is no valid reason why an individual cannot display external conformance and still be highly creative. Some of the most progressive companies in America set quite a store by a man's neat appearance. The International Business Machines Corporation is one of these; and, as if to underscore the point that a creative outlook is prized at IBM, their chairman of the board T. J. Watson, Jr., says, "Every time we've moved ahead in IBM, it was because someone was willing to take a chance, put his head on the block, and try something new."[27]

There is a great deal of evidence that a correlation between creativity and an independent spirit does exist. This is as it should be. However, wild hair and an arrogant manner are not necessarily a guarantee of an independent mind. Moreover, we are entitled to ask: "Which is cause, and which is effect?" Is a man creative because he is independent? Or is he independent because he is successfully creative and *can afford* to be independent? As Getzels and Jackson put it, "We need to distinguish between independence and unruliness, between individuality and rebelliousness."[28]

Ideas

Some supervisors of creative people complain that they are literally swamped with ideas from their subordinates—that ideas are the cheapest thing in the world. Such supervisors are quick to acquire the reputation of being unsympathetic to creative people, but one should look to see if any substance underlies their complaints.

Most often, their irritation centers upon the creative individual who places such a high value upon his ideas that he believes the organization should permit him to operate as a pure idea-generator. Once he has expressed an idea, he is through with it. It is someone else's role to bring this man's ideas to the level of utilizability. His ideas pour out in random fashion and without regard to whether they fit the company's current line of activity or not. Such individuals are "starters" *par excellence,* but have

---

[27] From *A Business and Its Beliefs, the Ideas that Helped Build IBM,* by T. J. Watson, Jr., p. 60; copyright 1963 by McGraw-Hill, New York. Used by permission.

[28] *Creativity and Intelligence,* p. 124.

no interest in being "finishers." To them, the first idea is all-important. It is a curious paradox that such men generally regard Thomas Edison as their patron saint and exemplar. Yet it is obvious that they could never have read the story of Edison's life, since Edison's fame and his career derived from his ability to carry through and *perfect* good ideas, his disregard for the enormous difficulties along the way, and his reluctance to rest until the job had been finished.

Corporations are often derided for the good ideas they have passed up that later become smashing successes in someone else's hands. Nobody mentions the enormous number of *bad* ideas they have also rejected. A corporation is in a difficult position when it is asked to venture millions of dollars on a new, untried idea: Although it may net them millions of dollars, there is also the possibility that the company will not even realize its investment.

Corporations also must be careful not to spread themselves too thin. If successful, they will be praised for being "diversified"; if not, they will be criticized for "scattering their fire." Consider the quandary of a corporation in the scientific instrument business, for example, when one of its idea-men proposes an unorthodox type of movie camera. Just because the idea shows promise, is the company expected to branch out abruptly into the photographic business? There are almost always far more time and many more dollars involved in developing an idea than anyone suspects (sometimes, even years of effort may be required). Once the development phase has been completed, enormous sums will be required for tooling, production start-up, finished-goods inventory, sales training, and *market development*. This last item is one that many creative people never appreciate. The public is just perverse enough so that it will *not* beat a path to the door of the man who builds the better mouse trap. It is the other way around: the company must beat a path to the door of every potential customer, and keep everlastingly after him, to create an awareness of the new product and effect an attitude of acceptance toward it.

From the foregoing, it may appear that companies are both in favor of new ideas and against them. However, any seeming contradiction can be resolved by the simplest statement: Companies want ideas *that will solve their problems*. In other words, they want ideas that are to the point—that will help their existing line of activity, improve it, expand it, and make it more profitable. Whenever the opportunity for diversification is on hand, as a result of available capital, the best ideas are those that will permit the company to make the greatest possible use of *existing* talent and equipment in expanding into the new field.

Some supervisors are willing to have a few idea-men in the organization for the sake of the occasional usable ideas they produce. How to keep the idea-man happy (his ability to produce is likely to be dependent upon his happiness) is still an open question, since he is continually faced by the fact that only a small fraction of his ideas are ever actually put into use.

Before the author leaves this subject, a distinction must be made between engineering creativity and scientific creativity. In the foregoing discussion, it was argued that engineering creativity should be strongly directed to a company's problems. However, in scientific creativity, strong direction might inhibit productivity. A large portion of scientific activity should be *undirected:* this is usually termed *basic* research, as opposed to *applied* research. Until World War II, Europe dominated the world in scientific discoveries, and also had a strong tradition of undirected scientific research. Today, many scientists fear insufficient funds are being committed to undirected research in the United States and that, as a result, technical progress will lag.

Characteristics of creative people

Much psychological research has been focused upon identifying the characteristics of outstandingly creative people, especially those outstanding in the context of scientific creativity. A common and consistent core of characteristics has been discovered through these investigations.[29] Briefly, as compiled from studies made by Roe, McClelland, Barron, Saunders, MacCurdy, Knapp, and Cattell, the typical traits of the productive scientist are:

1. Self-sufficiency and capacity for self-direction
2. Preference for mental challenges; detached attitude in social matters
3. A high ego
4. Preference for exactness
5. Preference for isolation, as a defense mechanism
6. High personal dominance, but a dislike for personal controversy
7. High self-control, even overcontrol; little impulsiveness
8. A liking for abstractness
9. Independent thinking; rejection of group pressures
10. Superior intelligence
11. An early interest in intellectual matters
12. Comprehensiveness and elegance in explanation
13. An enjoyment of pitting himself against uncertain circumstances[30]

Other researchers have noted that outstandingly creative people gen-

---

[29] By inference, these same characteristics would be representative of creative engineers.

[30] *Scientific Creativity: Its Recognition and Development.* See "A Look Ahead," by C. W. Taylor and F. Barron, pp. 385–386.

erally exhibit great drive and voluminous productivity. Harrison Gough, of the University of California Institute of Personality Assessment and Research, has reported the results of studies on groups of research scientists and engineers. He found that the most outstanding characteristic indicative of creative potential is that of the "Zealot." The Zealot, he writes, is "a driving, indefatigable researcher, with exceptional mathematical skills and a lively sense of curiosity."[31]

In the same study, Gough compared value-judgments made of scientists and engineers (the appraisals were by other men in the same field) with evidences of the study subjects' creative potential. The highest positive correlations occurred with the men described as "clear-thinking," "insightful," and having "wide interests." The highest negative correlations involved men who had been termed "undependable," "pessimistic," and "lazy."

2.6 A "formula" for creativity

Besides the exhortation to work hard, other specifics may help to stimulate one's creative capacities. To begin with, a simple *awareness* of the different phases[32] of the creative process may be valuable:

1) **Preparation.** It is essential to obtain every possible scrap of knowledge concerning the specific problem, that one can. In opposition to this, some people point out that many technical bottlenecks have been broken by men who were novices in the particular fields of their accomplishments. Such successes may be attributable to these individuals' freedom from functional fixedness and from misleading sets. Despite this, most engineers will be more successful at being creative if they first go to the trouble of making themselves *knowledgeable*. The popular supposition that most great inventors of the nineteenth century were lacking in scientific knowledge stems from today's lack of appreciation of the possibilities of self-education.[33] Most of these nineteenth-century inventors were as knowledgeable in their chosen fields as the leading scientists of their day and, in fact, were to a large degree in intimate association with the scientists. Edison, one of the most prolific inventors the world has ever seen, generally avoided *scientists,* but made it a rule to gain access to every bit of

---

[31] *The Creative Person.* See "Techniques for Identifying the Creative Research Scientist," by Harrison Gough, pp. III–11.

[32] D. W. MacKinnon is source for names of the five phases of creativity. See "The Study of Creativity," in *The Creative Person,* p. I–1.

[33] Jewkes *et al.,* p. 64.

scientific knowledge he possibly could. Whenever he moved into a field with which he was unfamiliar, he first collected all of the published material on the subject that he could, and then digested it in an orgy of reading.

2) Concentration. One way of getting started at being creative is to sit down with the intention of being creative. At first, there may be no discernible result, but each step is a necessary precursor to those which follow. One way or another, one must get himself thinking, long and hard, about possible solutions to his problem, and developing as many promising leads as possible. Concentration is the hardest part of being creative, but it is also the most characteristic.

3) Incubation. Incubation is defined as a temporary withdrawal of the conscious mind from the problem while the subconscious continues to work on it. Some psychologists question the necessity for an incubation period. However, it is probably not accidental that the term to "sleep on it" has become common in our language.

4) Inspiration. As previously described, inspiration is the sudden appearance of new insight, accompanied by exhilaration and elation. One psychologist points out that the elation is generally accompanied by feelings of certainty, which are not always valid.[34]

5) Verification. This final period requires steady nerves and enormous determination as one "proves out" his idea, both to stave off despair as obstacles are encountered and to prevent oversights that might result from too much mental intoxication carrying over from phase 4.

Deliberate attempts have been made to teach the creative problem-solving process. Parnes and Meadow report that research on the effectiveness of such courses has been conducted at the University of Buffalo, with strongly encouraging results. In the teaching of creative problem-solving, various blocks to creative thinking are first discussed. Some of those cited are difficulty in isolating the problem, rigidity of narrow viewpoints, trouble identifying fundamental attributes, conformity, excessive faith in logic, fear, self-satisfaction, perfectionism, negativism, and reliance on authority.[35]

---

[34] B. Ghiselin in *Scientific Creativity: Its Recognition and Development,* p. 356.
[35] S. J. Parnes and A. Meadow in *Scientific Creativity: Its Recognition and Development,* pp. 311–320.

After the blocks have been identified, the principle of deferred judgment is introduced, together with practice in "attribute listing" and the forcing of new combinations. (The author has already described the last item.) In "attribute-listing," the student is taught to look for *fundamental* attributes of an object, rather than to focus on its known functions. For example, in considering a piece of paper, a student might discover potential new applications for paper by studying such fundamental attributes as its whiteness, its square corners, its straight edges, or its translucence. This exercise is expected to help him avoid functional fixedness, an evil that might easily occur if he were to focus prematurely upon the known function of paper as a material for writing.

Students are also taught to keep notes on all ideas that come to them and to allocate definite times for deliberate idea production. They are urged to list all conceivable facts that might relate to their problems, together with lists of questions and possible sources of answers. Potential answer-sources are then followed up. Many people have reported amazement at the number of answers that can be obtained simply by consulting a library. (For some perverse reason, libraries are often among the last sources tapped for answers.)

In the University of Buffalo research on the effectiveness of such courses in creativity, individuals were tested on their creative abilities both before and after taking creative problem-solving courses. The results were then compared with control groups. The findings were that a significant increment in creative ability was produced by taking a problem-solving course; follow-up research showed the effect was a lasting one.

Environment

The most critical factor in the encouragement of creativity is generally conceded to be *environment*. What is meant is not physical environment, however, but mostly the supervisor's *attitude*. For instance: Is the supervisor receptive to new ideas? Does he encourage public recognition of his men for their contributions? Does he thoroughly understand the creative process? Does he use the principle of deferred judgment? Is he a creative person himself? Is he prepared to accept the fact that honest mistakes will occur when people depart from convention? Finally, will the *company* indorse the supervisor in all these admirable attitudes?

It might as well be recognized that the preceding recital of supervisory virtues is in direct conflict with the previously described dilemma of what a company should do with a flood of disassociated new ideas. If you are the supervisor, you are in a tough spot indeed: knowing full well that only a small fraction of your men's ideas will be used (and creative people *do* like to see their ideas utilized), you must nevertheless maintain an atmosphere of encouragement and receptivity. Otherwise, your company will not have the opportunity to acquire even that small fraction. This is a difficult task, of course, but no one has ever claimed that a supervisor's role is easy.

2.7 Rewards for creativity

Entrenched in American folklore are stories of lone inventors who became rich. There certainly have been a few such men; there have even been some "Cinderella cases" in which huge financial judgments were granted to inventors after lengthy court battles. However, the chances of someone's being successful in this way are about the same as his getting to be a world-famous movie star or circus acrobat.

A large proportion of inventive people eventually decide to give up such tenuous chances of striking wealth and become corporation inventors. In exchange for their creative talents, they receive a regular salary and fringe benefits, plus a reasonable amount of security. Often the salaries are excellent and may even permit a moderate amount of luxury; this is especially the case when the inventive person displays high-level creativity at regular intervals.

Such arrangements are made because it is virtually impossible for the lone person to underwrite and develop an idea by himself, no matter how good his idea might be. Despite this unavoidable truth, many corporation inventors believe they have been somehow cheated if the company makes big profits on one of their ideas. Such injured feelings stem from a basic philosophical consideration: the idea did not exist until the inventor conceived it and gave it to the world. This is an important thought and one not to be passed off lightly.

Another thought, also to be weighed, is as follows: material progress in this world is completely dependent upon the provision of capital;[36] therefore, the risk capital put up by a corporation is at least as essential to success as the idea itself.

It would be foolish to ask, "Which point of view is right?" For there is no issue of "rightness" here, but only one of scarcity. As long as both capital and inventive talent are scarce, a high premium will be placed on both. A few decades ago, fundamental economic thought held that all desirable commodities exist in insufficient supply—a sort of law of scarcity. Today, many economists have abandoned this idea and believe the American people are turning into an "affluent society," whose problem is becom-

---

[36] Here, the author uses capital in its broadest sense, to include money, plant, materials, and labor.

ing how to consume what it produces. If widespread affluence is the result of an increasing supply of expansion capital and of creative talent, then one can hardly be morose about it. Creative ability is not likely to become so common, however, that it will fail to be in demand. Furthermore, there is sufficient hard work involved in creativity for most people to shun it.

Patents again

Sometimes the *quantity* of patents stemming from a given individual is taken as a measure of his creative ability. But patents are not a reliable indicator. For one thing, too many worthless patents have been, and are being, issued. For another, many important kinds of creative activity do not culminate in patents. The correct analysis of a crisis on the production line and the subsequent discernment of its solution can require great creativity (and may save the company as much money as several patentable ideas would earn for it); yet, the result probably will not be patentable.

In the author's opinion, the use of patents as badges of status within an organization is highly pernicious. Such a practice can gain a hold quite readily, especially if it reflects the attitude of one of the executives. The producer of *good* patents is a valuable man and is to be highly respected. However, if patents become an end in themselves, rather than a means, and especially if the practice of *counting* patents takes hold (either officially or unofficially), then trouble will follow. Creative people may begin to favor ideas that will cause patents to be issued in their names, rather than ideas of intrinsic value to the company. If both ends are simultaneously served, there can be no objection; but the leverage encourages the policy of "patent first; company second."

Perhaps the most dishonorable miscarriage of justice takes place when a person misuses a position of authority to see that patents bear his own name. The practice of insisting that the supervisor's name be included on every patent stemming from the group is bad enough, besides being illegal; it is much worse when a supervisor with creative ability uses his authority to insure that *his* ideas are the ones that are used and patented. It is the constitutional purpose of patents to promote progress through creativity. Yet, the preceding injustice clearly interferes with progress, for what creative person would willingly work under such a supervisor?

Royalty systems

Some people strongly believe that inventors are legally and morally entitled to share in the profits made from patents, on a royalty basis. Some foreign countries have such plans, but they have not become popular in the United States. In America, many companies pay a token sum (perhaps $50 or $100) to an inventor upon his filing a patent application and a similar amount when the patent is issued. However, the most commonly held belief in this country today is that creative contributions should be compensated in the form of salary.

A 1964 survey investigating the patent practices of 251 American industrial concerns, disclosed that three fourths of the companies replying made no cash award whatsoever to their inventors, for patentable ideas. Nearly all of the remaining 25 percent had moderate awards of the type just described. A conspicuous exception was IBM, who had installed a plan in 1961 that awards $5000 and more for significant inventions.[37]

Suggestion systems

Most companies have, at one time or another, considered the possibility of installing a suggestion system. The purpose of such systems is to tap hidden wells of creativity in the organization (presumably outside the normally creative departments) and, thus, to gain costsaving ideas. Sometimes the cash awards from suggestion systems have been of sufficient magnitude to make newspaper headlines and, upon rare occasions, have been truly spectacular.

It is to be wondered if sufficient consideration has been given to the effect such awards may have upon the departments that are in the daily business of improving the company's products and of conceiving, and putting into practice, costsaving ideas; a few departments of this type are: development engineering, production engineering, manufacturing engineering, and industrial engineering. To a person in such a department, it seems that an outsider can receive an award, amounting perhaps to a year's salary, for an idea that is no better than the ones the "creative engineer" turns out every week. If such a man feels sufficiently outraged, he might even threaten to quit the engineering department and go to work in the shop so that he can be better paid for his engineering ideas.

Coupled with this is the embarrassingly small number of really good ideas acquired through suggestion plans: Inevitably, there will be a veritable avalanche of ideas at the inception of one of these plans. After the sifting and sorting, the evaluation committee will generally have nothing to show for its efforts, except a feeling of harrassment. Of course,

---

[37] C. G. Baumes, *Patent Counsel in Industry*. New York: Nat'l Industrial Conf. Board, 1964, p. 35. (One hundred eighty-three companies responded to the question about cash awards.)

there is always the chance of a really good idea coming along. This chance is what keeps the committee going; meanwhile, the engineering departments, which justify their existence because of their ability to produce workable ideas on a routine basis, feel overlooked, unappreciated, and jilted.

If an evaluation committee is prepared to cope with the frustrations resulting from having to reject 999 suggestions out of 1000 and if the cash awards are not set so high as to bring about internal struggles, then there is nothing inherently wrong with a suggestion system. The rare occasions upon which the committee members discover a good idea are sufficient to give them heart and hope, as they brace themselves to face the rest of the pile.

In 1951, a major oil company issued an invitation to inventive Americans to send their ideas to the company's new multimillion dollar research laboratory, where the ideas would be evaluated and the promising ones selected for further development. Three years and thousands of suggestions later, the company concluded it had essentially nothing to show for its efforts. Out of the thousands of ideas submitted, only three had seemed worthy of further testing. Two of these were judged impractical, and the third was turned back to its submitter for development.[38]

---

[38] *The Mighty Force of Research* (New York: McGraw-Hill, 1956), pp. 74–75. By the editors of *Fortune*. See "The Inventor in Eclipse," by E. L. Van Deusen.

3 ▸ | Engineers in industry

It is expected that, by 1970, one million engineers will be employed by American industrial firms. This figure is nearly 75 percent of the 1,300,000 engineers predicted by the U.S. Department of Labor for that year. Of the remaining 300,000 engineers, 11 percent will be in government; 6 percent will be in consulting service; and 4 percent, in education. (See Table 3–1.)

The engineer is almost always an employee of someone else. This fact, in itself, makes the engineering profession distinctly different from the three classical professions of law, theology, and medicine. Since he is a professional, and yet an employee, the engineer represents a special and perplexing problem in employee relations.

3.1 Problems of professionals

Some managers believe engineers show more loyalty to their profession than they do to their companies. One top manager is reported to have said, "Engineers do not think of themselves as working for the company, but have the attitude that the company is a laboratory operated for their own special benefit." In a survey, the editors of *Machine Design* sought reactions to the statement just quoted, from 1000 engineers in industry, half of them in supervisory–management positions.[1] Most of the nonsupervisory respondents disagreed with the statement; some did so vehemently. The supervisory engineers were more cautious: only about a third said they believed the statement is false. A large segment of both groups

---

[1] "Management Charges . . . Engineers Deny," *Machine Design*, Jan. 7, 1965, pp. 102–104. Survey performed in cooperation with Princeton Creative Research, Inc., Princeton, N.J.

Table 3-1. Estimated distribution of engineers in 1970

Field of engineering	Number	Number	Percent
Mining		27,900	2.0
Construction		102,000	7.4
Manufacturing			
electrical equipment	178,200		13.1
metal products and machinery	175,000		12.8
aerospace	155,600		11.3
chemical	67,500		4.9
autos and other transportation	55,000		4.0
instruments	43,100		3.1
primary metals	41,000		3.0
petroleum	25,900		1.9
rubber, stone, and glass	18,300		1.3
lumber and paper	15,300		1.1
other manufacturing	48,900		3.6
		823,800	60.1
Services			
transportation	16,900		1.2
communication	31,600		2.3
utilities	27,400		2.0
		75,900	5.5
Government			
federal	80,200		5.8
state	34,800		2.5
local	32,100		2.3
		147,100	10.6
Education		52,000	3.8
Engineering and architectural services		88,000	6.4
All other		58,000	4.2
Total engineers		1,374,700	100.0

Source: U.S. Dept. of Labor, Bureau of Labor Statistics, *Scientists and Engineers, 1960–70: Supply and Demand*. Washington, D.C.: November 1963.

thought the statement is true of some engineers, but very few said it is true of the majority.

At this point, a comment seems to be in order upon the basic assumption that a man must be loyal *either* to his profession *or* to his company and that he cannot simultaneously be loyal to both. This assumption could be a major cause of misunderstandings between engineering and management. It might help to clarify these issues, if we distinguish between loyalty to professional goals and the blind pursuit of selfish objectives. It is the latter kind of behavior to which management generally objects and which gives rise to the kind of statements that stimulated *Machine Design*'s survey. True professionalism would require that the interests of the client (in this case, the employer) be primary.

The newly graduated engineer is generally unaware of the kinds of crosscurrents described in the preceding paragraph. He is likely to be much more concerned with his own personal problems and is eager to prove himself and find his place in the industrial world. Considering the intense anticipation that builds up in the mind of the student as the change to industrial life approaches, it is not too surprising if some subsequent disillusionment occurs.

One factor that may make the transition awkward is this: the new engineer starts his first job with a salary that often exceeds the amount paid to nonengineering employees in the organization who have had many years of experience. Some people might take the stand that the new engineer should immediately start making significant contributions in order to justify his high salary, but this point of view would be inconsistent with the frequently recorded opinions of engineering supervisors that it takes one or two years for a man to become a fully producing member of the team.

Some serious attempts have been made to identify and analyze the problems of young professionals. In his book *Characteristics of Engineers and Scientists,* Lee Danielson reports the results of interviews with 367 engineers and scientists, conducted by the Bureau of Industrial Relations at the University of Michigan. Danielson found the following to be the most frequently mentioned problem areas of young professionals, in order of their frequency of mention:

1. Adjusting to company practices
2. Advancement slow or uncertain
3. Accepting routine jobs
4. Learning what is expected
5. Finding one's own niche
6. Unrealistic ambitions
7. Lack of initiative
8. Gaining social acceptance
9. Lack of specialized courses
10. Lack of recognition[2]

Problems 4, 5, and 8 undoubtedly would diminish with the simple

---

[2] L. E. Danielson, *Characteristics of Engineers and Scientists.* Ann Arbor, Mich.: Univ. of Mich., 1960, pp. 55–78.

passage of time. Problem 1 can be helped by company training programs (about which more will be said later). The remaining items are probably the most important ones on the list and are, also, the most difficult to deal with constructively.

The essence of some of these points is that the young engineer is simultaneously being criticized for not being ambitious enough (Problem 7) and for being too ambitious (Problem 6). Great things are expected of him because of his education; at the same time, he is told that he does not know enough to handle anything important and he is given routine tasks. As an example, comments from two of the respondents in Danielson's survey are given below:

> I think most of the people think they are more important than they really are. This is the college build-up, once again. You are important eventually, but not immediately.

> Their biggest difficulty is having to start on a low plane.

Remarks of the same sort turn up, again and again, in surveys and commentaries. They occur so frequently that a person wonders if these traits are often discovered in new graduates because they are so confidently expected to be there. On the other hand, there must be some substance to these criticisms, since they are reported so often. Perhaps the colleges *are* partially to blame, as suggested by the following quotation:

> We feel there is a strong need for the college to provide students with a more realistic image of the engineer on the job. Young engineers come to us with their heads in the clouds, looking only at the glamour of engineering. They should also appreciate the need for pick and shovel work, to get their hands dirty, and be practical.[3]

To achieve the desired amount of humility, and yet avoid the wallows of torpidity poses a considerable problem for the young engineer. One writer warns against ". . . producing the apathetic, uncreative, passive kind of employee whom most organizations seem to welcome at the outset but regret being saddled with at a later time."[4]

The author believes that a young engineer's enthusiasm is one of his most valuable assets. Yet, it is this very enthusiasm that might sometimes

---

[3] I. L. Herman, *A Frontier Industry, and Personnel Development Implications (A Report to the California Commission on Manpower, Automation, and Technology)*, Dec. 11, 1964. Mr. Herman is manager of Personnel Development, for Aerojet-General Corp., Sacramento, Calif.

[4] E. H. Schein, "How to Break In the College Graduate," *Harvard Business Rev.*, vol. 42, November–December 1964, pp. 68–76.

be interpreted as overaggressiveness and unrealistic expectations. If consistently rebuffed, enthusiasm can easily degenerate to a permanently low level. This would be a tragedy, because enthusiasm is too precious a national resource to be smothered—and eventually lost—in this fashion. Colleges and universities can perform the service Mr. Herman implies by teaching their students a simple formula: one of the best ways to move out of routine assignments is to handle each of them with as much skill, dispatch, and enthusiasm as one has at his command. There are few, if any, better ways in which to come to the favorable attention of management.

The problem of slow promotions is something else. Probably no one is ever promoted as fast as he would like to be. Moreover, most young men very quickly learn that a complacent attitude toward promotions may make them come slower than would otherwise be the case. Many have heard the adage that "squeaky wheels get the grease" and are not unwilling to test its truth in practice. But they may also learn that management is generally unimpressed by any agitation for promotion unless it is coupled with proved ability and achievement.

All these factors create problems, but they are not unique to engineering: They are human problems, and probably are permanently with us. The engineer can improve the situation through a desire to do the best job possible plus a reasonable amount of patience. On the company's part, more specific actions are required, and these will be dealt with in the next section.

3.2 Constructive action by the company

Although not all the fault for the existence of problems lies with the companies, there are more avenues for improvement open to companies than there are to individuals. Once the individual engineer has diligently equipped himself with all the right attitudes—patience, enthusiasm, diligence, alertness, thoroughness—the next moves are up to his corporation.

The proposals advanced by some writers will be very hard for many managers to accept. For example, Danielson's prescription is that management assume the role of "helper" in order to maximize the contributions that the professionals can make.[5] In effect, he is suggesting that

---

[5] Danielson, p. 76. [Others have made proposals that are essentially similar—notably, Peter F. Drucker in "Management and the Professional Employee," *Harvard Business Rev.,* vol. 30, May–June 1952, pp. 84–90; and William H. Whyte, Jr., in *The Organization Man* (New York: Simon and Schuster, 1956).]

management treat itself as a service to the engineering function. However, he does not mean engineers should become arrogant and irresponsible and demand that management serve their wants. What Danielson does suggest is that both sides adopt the following viewpoint: the engineer's responsibility is to do a good job of engineering; management's responsibility is to do everything possible to help the engineer do that job. Fortunately for national well-being, most of this country's more progressive companies appear to follow the latter line of thought.

One constructive point upon which everyone appears to be agreed (at least in principle) is that good communication must be maintained between engineering and management. Principally, this means the engineers must be supplied with information concerning company objectives, particularly those which affect engineering projects. There is a natural limit to the degree that such a program can be pursued, however. Much information about company objectives may also be precisely that kind of information that will aid and comfort the competition, if it should come into their hands. Management can hardly be blamed if it tends to hold back on such sensitive information, since it knows, full well, that engineers do quit the organization from time to time, and sometimes join competitors. Unfortunately, this sensitive information is the very kind that is of greatest interest. Hence, the goal of complete communication is never achieved, although with honest effort it can be approached.

Another important problem area is that of salaries,[6] reviews, and promotion. It is generally agreed salaries should reflect the contributions made by the engineers. This is by no means an easy task, and many companies do a less than adequate job in this area. In one survey involving 350 engineers and engineering managers, 88 percent of the engineers thought it was imperative for their companies to establish salary progressions that faithfully reflect engineers' contributions; when asked if their companies realistically followed such a policy, only 23 percent answered in the affirmative.[7]

Good facilities are also emphasized in virtually every list of recommendations. Facilities include such things as secretarial and clerical support, provision of technicians and draftsmen, equipment, telephones, and reasonably private quarters. The day of the giant "bullpen," with engineers stacked at desks ranged row on row, is nearly a thing of the

---

[6] The subject of salaries is so important that Chapter Eight has been devoted to it.

[7] *Engineering Professionalism in Industry*. Washington, D.C.: The Professional Engrs. Conf. Board for Industry, 1960, pp. 35–37.

past. Most companies have gone to considerable trouble and expense to provide semiprivate quarters for engineers, with perhaps two or three persons per office.

It is often assumed that the purpose of such accommodations is to generate high morale. This is only part of it, however, for there is not necessarily a correlation between morale and productivity: high morale— if it is based too much on comfort and pleasurable surroundings—can be remarkably sterile. From the stockholders' point of view, the only possible economic justification for providing a good environment for engineers is that such conditions enable them to produce more and better work.

The Engineers Joint Council (EJC), which represents engineering societies having a combined membership of more than 500,000 professionals, has adopted the following recommendations for improving management–engineering relations.

The EJC recommends that:

(1) Management utilize the services of engineers more effectively and thereby afford them opportunity for advancement and economic improvement.
(2) Management recognize its responsibility to make engineers feel that they are a part of management.
(3) Management survey areas of communication, recognition, and salaries, and where found wanting, correct to conform with standards of professional practice.
(4) The engineer take inventory of his services and his actions to make sure that he has a professional attitude toward his work.
(5) Engineering societies establish and employ appropriate means to maintain high standards of ethical conduct for professional achievement.
(6) Engineering societies encourage the professional development of their members and promote proper recognition of the profession.
(7) Engineering educators emphasize the characteristics of the profession.[8]

3.3 About training programs

Probably, no company will readily admit it does not have a training program, although the term "training program" covers an immense spectrum. At one end of the spectrum are formal programs that combine work with periods of full-time study leading to advanced degrees. At the other, is "on-the-job training," wherein the new employee is put directly to work and is taught by his supervisor as the need arises. Just why the

---

[8] *Raising Professional Standards and Improving Employment Conditions for Engineers.* New York: EJC, 1956, p. 14.

latter type of approach should merit the title "training program" is unclear, since this is the way new employees have been broken in since time began.

Contrary as it may seem to expectations, on-the-job training appears to be more popular with new graduates than do many types of formal programs. A survey of more than 1000 participants in 26 different training programs showed that on-the-job programs far surpassed the more formal types in the esteem of the participants.[9] This survey did not include any programs leading to advanced engineering degrees, however. Mostly, the intent of the "formal" programs was to prepare young men for the ultimate assumption of managerial duties.

According to the National Industrial Conference Board, the differences between formal and on-the-job programs are approximately as follows:

Formal training. May last one, two, or even three years. Time is spent in several different departments, mostly observing. Written reports and examinations are included. The emphasis usually is on preparation for management.

On-the-job training. Duration of program is generally less than that of formal programs. The training usually focuses more on a particular job, at the expense of a broader orientation, and involves actual work participation.

One explanation offered for the greater popularity of on-the-job training is that the new graduate, saturated with formal classroom education, is eager to get started in actual productive work. The strongest criticism of some "formal" programs were that they were not challenging enough, moved too slowly, or did not contain enough actual "doing."

Edgar H. Schein, professor of Industrial Management at the Massachusetts Institute of Technology, listed the following kinds of "induction strategies" used by organizations:

1. *Sink or Swim.* The new graduate is simply given a project and is judged by the outcome. If he is given little information to guide him, then he is partially judged by how good a job he does in structuring his own assignment. This requires the new employee to take vaguely stated objectives and translate them into specific tasks that can be dealt with, one by one.

---

[9] S. Habbe, *College Graduates Assess Their Company Training, Personnel Policy Study No. 188.* New York: Nat'l Industrial Conf. Board, 1963, pp. 45–46.

2. *The "Upending" Experience.* The intent of this type of strategy is to jar the new employee loose from the presumed "impracticalities" he acquired in college and to confront him with the "realities" of industrial life. In one approach of this nature reported by Schein, each new engineer is given a special electric circuit, which violates several theoretical assumptions, to analyze. When the new man reports that the circuit will not work, he is shown that it not only does work, but also has been in commercial use by the company for several years. Chastened, he is then asked to find out *why* it works. When he finds he cannot do this, he becomes thoroughly depressed and is now considered "ready" to tackle his first real assignment.

3. *Training While Working.* This is the typical on-the-job type of induction program. The new man is given an assignment, commensurate with his experience, and carries it out under the close guidance of his supervisor.

4. *Working While Training.* The new man is considered to belong to a formal training program, but is given small projects involving real work. He may be rotated through several different departments during the course of the program. It is sometimes difficult to decide whether programs of this type should be classified as "on-the-job" or "formal."

5. *Full-Time Training.* These programs clearly belong in the "formal" category. They usually involve class work and rotational assignments that call for the trainee to observe the work being done by others: Direct participation is minimal. Schein observes that some trainees criticize such observational activities as mostly meaningless, or "Mickey Mouse."

6. *Integrative Strategies.* In approaches of this type, an attempt is made to adjust to the different needs of different trainees. In one such program, the new employees are given regular job assignments for a year and then are sent to a summer-long full-time university training program. A key feature of the initial assignments is that the supervisors have been specially selected and trained to be sensitive to the new man's problems. Some of these programs lead to advanced degrees.[10]

Of Schein's six "strategies," the first two ("Sink or Swim," and "The Upending Experience") would seem to show little appreciation for the proper objective of any inductive strategy, which should be to turn a new man into a productive employee as soon as possible. It should be mentioned, also, that Schein did not imply endorsement of these two strategies:

---

[10] See E. H. Schein's "How to Break in the College Graduate," *Harvard Business Rev.,* vol. 42, November–December 1964.

he merely recorded them. Moreover, Schein argues that initial assignments should maximize responsibility to the highest degree possible, for the sake of both the man and the organization. Admittedly, there is risk in such an approach because the new man could fail an important assignment. However, there is much to gain by using men at their highest potential, and much to lose by using them at their lowest.

With regard to the "upending" experience especially, the author would like to offer his opinion that there is a great deal to condemn it. No doubt, the purpose of such an approach is to demonstrate to the new man that all knowledge is not contained in textbooks and that nature still insists on behaving the way she wants to, without necessarily feeling constrained to conform to the behavior prescribed by men. While the purpose may be worthwhile, an "upending" experience is a poor way to achieve it. As a result, the new man often abandons "theoretical" approaches in favor of "practical" ones. A further-reaching consequence is that he has thus unknowingly limited himself in his professional development at a time in our history when an increasing number of important problems are proving to be solvable only by people having an excellent command of theory.

More will be said on this subject in a later chapter, but the moral is this: all theories developed to date have proved limitable in their applicability; regularly, we witness the spectacle of old theories being replaced by new and better ones. For from having a discouraging effect, such a state of affairs should give engineers strong encouragement, for it means we are constantly improving and extending our abilities to predict the behavior of engineering systems *before* they are built. This ability to predict behavior carries with it the capacity to optimize and make things more efficient. Western technology has already passed beyond the point where engineering can be performed on an intuitive basis; continuing advancement will be increasingly dependent upon the widespread application of theoretical understanding.

3.4 Women in engineering

Upon occasion, the observation has been made that the most discriminated-against minority group in the United States is the female sex. In engineering, there doubtless are some men who believe women have no business being engineers. Fortunately, such discrimination is waning.

Whether discrimination is the cause or not, relatively few American women are engineers. It has been estimated that less than 1 percent of the engineers in this country are women; in 1965, out of the nearly quarter of a million students enrolled in engineering schools, only about 1900 were women.[11] In 1963 and 1964, respectively, 130 and 159 bachelor's degrees in engineering were awarded to women.

Women have shown they are capable of performing very well as engineers. It is probably not aptitude, so much as custom, that deters women from engineering. Engineering education is strongly oriented in an occupational direction, and Western society generally expects that men will be the breadwinners. However, as a result of the general trend toward more women in business and professional careers of every kind, it can be expected that more women will enter engineering.

Somewhat surprisingly, the greatest concentration of women engineers is in industrial engineering.[12] Many people have expected that women would gravitate more to research and analysis jobs, since industrial engineering is fairly close to the hurly-burly of the factory. As a matter of fact, one of our best-known woman engineers, Dr. Lillian M. Gilbreth (of "Cheaper by the Dozen" fame) is an industrial engineer.

In Schenectady, New York, Mrs. Nancy D. Fitzroy is an engineer specializing in heat transfer, for General Electric. In 1963, Mrs. Fitzroy was elected chairman of the Hudson-Mohawk Section of the American Society of Mechanical Engineers, the first woman engineer to be so honored by ASME.

As an example from a different field, Mrs. Carol Schumaker is a senior highway engineer for the California Division of Highways, which employs no less than 22 women engineers.[13]

Several engineering colleges have women engineering professors on their faculties. Among such women are Dr. Irene Peden, at the University of Washington, Dr. Irmgaard Flügge-Lotz, of Stanford University, and Dr. Madeline Goulard, of Purdue University. Dr. Goulard offers this advice to young women thinking of careers in engineering: "If a woman is going to work in predominantly male surroundings, she must above all be herself, accept herself, and not try to reject or suppress her femininty."

Returning to the matter of discrimination, Miss Gail Burnham, who is a mechanical engineer working for the United States Air Force at Sacramento, California, was asked if she had encountered any discrimination because she was a woman in a profession that some would consider to be a man's field. Replying in the negative, Miss Burnham said, "They not only don't discriminate, they actually go out of their way to be helpful!"

[11] H. A. Foecke, "Engineering Degrees (1963–64) and Enrollments (Fall, 1964)," *J. Engrg. Educ.*, vol. 55, February 1965, pp. 190–203.

[12] J. R. Whinnery, ed., *The World of Engineering* (New York: McGraw-Hill, 1965), p. 277. See "Women in Engineering Careers," by I. C. Peden.

[13] "Women in a Man's World?" *The Engineerogram*, Sacramento, Calif., vol. 27, March 1965, p. 8.

A worry expressed by some employers is that women may not prove to be permanent employees. It is feared that they will marry, have babies, and retire to home life at just the time they should be entering the most productive phases of their careers. The risk is undeniable; however, the counterargument has been presented that large numbers of young *male* employees do not prove to be permanent, either, but move to other employers after a few years.

To help answer some of the questions concerning engineering careers for women, the Society of Women Engineers (organized in 1952) published the results of a survey of 600 women engineering graduates. The survey revealed the following information:

1) Eighty percent were married, with an average of two children; over half of these were married to engineers or scientists.
2) Fifty-three percent were employed, of which 81 percent were employed full time; most of those who were not employed had small children;
3) Sixty-eight percent of the women not working said they were interested in retraining programs.
4) Seventy percent of the women working thought they had been given every opportunity for professional advancement.[14]

It has repeatedly been pointed out that a large percentage of engineers in Russia are women. This has caused responsible groups in our country to look critically at our projected engineer shortages and to ask: "Why don't we encourage more women to take engineering and, thus, help reduce the shortage?" To this end, a conference met in 1962 at the University of Pittsburgh, Pennsylvania, to deal specifically with the role of women in professional engineering. A few of the conference's principal conclusions were: 1) the greatest loss of productive talent in the United States is that of talented womanpower; 2) the role of women in professional engineering is increasing, but at too slow a pace; and 3) better cooperation is needed among parents, counselors, educators, employers, and other interested groups, concerning the role of women in engineering.[15]

One significant fact must be emphasized: scarcely any field open to women pays them better than engineering. In a 1963 survey, the Society

---

[14] *Preliminary Report of the Survey of Women Engineering Graduates.* New York: Soc. Women Engrs., June 1964.

[15] W. G. Torpey, "The Role of Women in Professional Engineering," *J. Engrg. Educ.*, vol. 52, June 1962, p. 656.

of Women Engineers reported a median salary of $9000–$10,000 a year
for the survey participants.[16] This is approximately the same median
salary earned by all engineers during 1963, and would imply that women
have not experienced any financial discrimination in engineering. Moreover, in occupations customarily staffed by women (secretarial or clerical
work, for instance), the salary potential is less than half the amount paid
women engineers.

3.5 Other engineering activities

It was observed, earlier in this book, that the characteristic activity of
the engineer is *design*. However, there are other kinds of technical activity
that have traditionally been regarded as part of the engineering scope,
even though they are not involved with design.

Construction. Many engineers go directly into construction activities
and operate more as managers than as engineers. Nevertheless, because of
the highly technical content of their jobs, these men generally need
engineering backgrounds, think of themselves as engineers, and belong to
engineering societies.

Operations. Substantially the same remarks could be made about many
engineers in manufacturing or processing companies who fill combined
technical-managerial positions. In this case, they are usually industrial or
mechanical engineers. Industrial engineers, for example, are often concerned with the organization of work activities, as in time-and-motion
studies or work-simplification studies. They may also be involved with
machine-evaluation studies aimed at obtaining maximum efficiency from
a process. In some organizations, especially those concerned with processing, engineers may not only have technical responsibility for an operational unit, but may also have supervisory responsibility for the men who
operate the unit. Many mining engineers, for example, fit into this
category. Men performing such operational functions probably act more
as managers than as engineers, but are very likely to think of themselves
as the latter.

Sales engineering. Many engineers move into activities that clearly
consist of straight sales work and thus, completely lose contact with
engineering activities. However, this is not what is generally meant by

---

[16] *Profile of a Woman Engineer.* New York: Soc. of Women Engrs., May 1963.

"sales engineering," which is a province truly intermediate between sales and engineering. In fact, sales engineering occasionally involves engineering design. Such opportunities normally arise in enterprises that sell and produce custom-designed systems. In a typical case of this nature, a fully operating system, put together from off-the-shelf components, may be offered in a way that is unique to the customer. In some instances, it may be necessary to include a special component that has not yet been designed. The sales engineer works with the customer and essentially makes the sale, but he also designs the system to meet the customer's needs and when necessary, works with his home engineering office to develop hitherto nonexistent components. Not only do such people usually regard themselves as engineers, but indeed their work does have considerable engineering content.

4 ▸ Engineers in private practice and in government

4.1 Engineers in private practice

The number of engineers in private practice is small, compared with the total number of engineers. For example: In 1964, the Consulting Engineers Council and the American Institute of Consulting Engineers had memberships of only 1700 and 375, respectively.[1] Obviously, not all consultants are necessarily members of these two organizations, but the figures are significant when compared with the membership totals of The Institute of Electrical and Electronics Engineers and The American Society of Mechanical Engineers for the same year—155,000 and 59,000, respectively.[2]

It is erroneous to think of a consulting engineer as an individual who typically offers his services to the public for a fee, like a doctor. There are some who function like this, of course, especially among those who are just starting out as consultants. But the "consulting engineer" usually is an organization that hires engineers, architects, accountants, draftsmen, clerks, and men of similar skills. Some consulting services are very large indeed and hire hundreds of engineers of all kinds: chemical, civil, electrical, mechanical, and nuclear, among others.

It is unlikely that engineers who are employees of such firms would see their positions as much different from those of engineers in industry. It is only the principals—the partners or officers of such companies—who have problems substantially different from other engineers. The bulk of their problems are typical of any businessman and involve finances, sales, legal

---

[1] *Register and Directory.* New York: Engrs. Joint Council, 1965.
[2] *Register and Directory.*

responsibilities, and personnel. Yet, in reality, their position is different from that of other businessmen, because their business responsibilities are coupled with *personal* responsibilities for the services they hold out to the public. This accounts for the frequent organization of large consulting services into partnerships or proprietorships: in a partnership or in a proprietorship (that is, a firm with only one owner), each principal is directly responsible for the firm's activities, whereas there are limitations to the liabilities officers of a corporation can incur. As a result, the corporate form of organization for engineering concerns has been the subject of controversy: opponents of such a form have argued that a corporation cannot legally be held responsible for services that are essentially personal in nature. Generally, for corporations engaged in consulting, it is required at least that the officer directly responsible for the engineering work be a registered engineer.

4.2 Becoming a consultant

A person beginning consulting work is much more likely to fail because of a lack of business ability than because of a lack of technical ability. Virtually all consultants warn the prospective newcomer about "that depressing first year." Some even declare that the lean period is apt to be three years, instead of one.[3]

Some of the things the beginning consultant may neglect relate to such ordinary business matters as accounting, collections, overhead, taxes, and insurance. *Overhead,* for example, includes many items often overlooked. Vacations, sick leaves, insurance, and social security taxes may add from 10 to 15 percent of the direct costs. Rent, supplies, telephone service, and secretarial service may come to as much as 30 or 40 percent of the direct costs. If there are more than six or eight employees, additional supervision may be required; this may add another 15 percent. Finally, there is the often belatedly recognized factor of *nonproductive time,* which involves stand-by, fill-in, and other lost time, and may add another 10 percent. Thus, the direct engineering costs may have to be increased by as much as from 65 to 80 percent of the original estimate, with no allowance made, as yet, for profit.[4]

Probably, not even a determination to work extra hours would compensate for a lack of good business ability and adequate financial reserves,

---

[3] J. S. Ward, "Starting Your Own Consulting Practice," *Civil Engrg.,* vol. 35, January 1965, pp. 53–55.

[4] A. J. Ryan, "Operating Your Practice," *Amer. Engr.,* November 1955.

because extra hours and consulting work appear to go hand in hand as the normal situation. One consultant writes,

> If you object to working long hours and if you intend to dismiss all the business problems from your mind when you leave the office, don't try to be a consulting engineer, for the problems will be with you 24 hours a day.[5]

The same writer has offered the following list of *minimum* qualifications for the aspiring consultant:

(1) Appropriate education, including humanities
(2) Engineering registration
(3) Confidence in his professional ability
(4) Broad prior experience in responsible discharge of engineering work
(5) Business acumen
(6) Financial reserves to last at least six months (other writers say a *year* or longer)
(7) Ability to get along with people, especially clients and employees

The basic problem of the new consultant is simple: to acquire his first project, he is expected to demonstrate his competence by pointing to projects he has completed in the past. Given such circumstances, getting the first job could be understandably difficult. Yet, every consultant in business today has had to get past this barrier.

Some consultants have attained their start by quitting their jobs and taking one or more of their former employers' clients with them. However, besides being obviously severely frowned upon, such a practice is unethical. Other aspirants have associated themselves with an established consultant, as a junior partner. This is certainly ethical, but offers a difficulty in that the senior man has to be convinced he has something to gain by taking on a new partner.

4.3 Compensation for consulting engineers

The size of the fee the consulting engineer receives will depend, not only upon the size of the job, but also upon what kinds of services he agrees to perform. His typical services include the following, for engineering jobs involving constructed works:[6]

1) Advice on feasibility*
2) Preliminary studies and cost estimates*

---

[5] J. B. McGaughy, "So You Want to Open a Consulting Office—By Way of Qualifications," *Amer. Engr.*, October 1955.
[6] The items marked with an asterisk usually are contracted for separately from the main job.

3) Collection of basic data: surveys, borings, traffic census, etc.*
4) Preparation of plans and specifications
5) Assistance and advice in awarding construction contract
6) Interpretation of plans during construction
7) Checking shop drawings
8) Approval for payments to contractor
9) Resident engineering service*
10) Inspection upon completion and supervision of tests
11) Preparation of final record drawings
12) Assistance during start-up
13) Consultation as needed[7]

Methods for establishing compensation

In the past, the engineer's fee was often calculated as a percentage of the final construction cost, but there now appears to be a trend away from this. One of the arguments against this historical practice is that it penalizes the engineer for producing an economical design, when he should actually be rewarded.

Following are a few of the methods employed today, for establishing the consultant's fee:

Lump sum. When the services to be performed are known with considerable precision, it may be possible to agree upon a fixed sum as the engineer's compensation. The obvious disadvantage is that the consultant may incur serious loss if the job has been underestimated.

Payroll cost times a multiplier. Under this method, the client essentially pays the engineering costs as they occur, including a sufficient amount to cover overhead and profit.

Per diem. If the job is a short-term one, a fixed daily rate may be charged; this is known as a *per diem* arrangement. Direct out-of-pocket expenses, such as travel costs, are reimbursed in addition to the per diem payments.

Percentage of construction cost. Even though the "percentage of construction cost" method is not so widely used as it once was, such a calculation is often used to check the overall amount arrived at by means of one of the other methods. Charts in general use by some of the professional

---

[7] *Guide for Selecting, Retaining, and Compensating Professional Engineers in Private Practice.* Washington, D.C.: Nat'l Soc. Professional Engrs., 1963.

societies indicate that the engineering fee might be $80,000 to $100,000 for a million-dollar construction job and $500,000 to $600,000 for a ten-million-dollar job.

Many kinds of consulting engineering services do not involve construction. For example, some consulting concerns make a business of performing product-development services for clients. Often, firms of this type, upon request, will also place their own personnel within a client's firm, to work side by side with the client's engineers. In this fashion, the client can absorb unexpected peak workloads without hiring and training people who may become surplus when the peak has passed. Consulting companies of the type just described usually charge a fixed rate per hour per person employed on the jroject, for as long as the client employs their services. The rates are set high enough to enable the consulting company to recover all costs, including overhead, and to provide it with a profit.

4.4 Ethical problems in consulting practice

A special problem that besets engineers in private practice has to do with competitive bidding. Bidding on the basis of price alone is held to be unethical. To persons who have been raised in an economic society founded upon competition, an ethical sanction against competitive bidding may seem eccentric. However, consulting engineers point out that people do not ordinarily select a doctor or a lawyer on the basis of price alone. They assert that the personal nature of the services offered by an engineer places him in a similar position.

The American Institute of Consulting Engineers' position on competitive bidding has been aptly phrased by its president, F. S. Friel:

> Competitive bidding for engineering services is not in the public interest since it may lead to the employment of the engineer least qualified for the particular work under consideration instead of the best qualified, which should be the objective.[8]

As an alternative to competitive bidding, the Coordinating Committee on Relations of Engineers in Private Practice with Government[9] recommended the following procedure:

---

[8] F. S. Friel, "Ethical Problems," *Amer. Engr.*, December 1955.

[9] The Coordinating Committee is composed of representatives from the American Institute of Consulting Engineers, American Road Builders Association, American Society of Civil Engineers, Consulting Engineers Council, National Society of Professional Engineers, Engineers Joint Council. (The EJC is an observer.)

(1) Examine the qualifications of several potential engineering firms who may have the desired capabilities.
(2) Select up to six firms with acceptable qualifications, and investigate them carefully, including the use of personal interviews.
(3) Rank the firms in the order of their desirability, and commence negotiations with the top-ranked firm.
(4) If the negotiations are not successful, then open negotiations with the second-ranked firm, then the third, and so on, until negotiations meet with success.[10]

Engineers and architects

Another unusual problem of consulting engineers involves their relationships with architects. Both groups are legally entitled to offer somewhat similar services; however, it is also recognized that each group possesses special competence in certain areas and that it is to their mutual advantage to work together. Furthermore, the public benefits by such cooperation.

Unfortunately, the relationships between these two professions have not always been smooth. As an example, a headline in *Engineering News-Record* for July 9, 1964, read, "NSPE Irked by AIA Ethical Standard."[11] The standard in question appeared to prohibit architects from working as employees of engineers. In replying to the article, the AIA claimed its standards had been misinterpreted.[12] The institute explained that its objection primarily focused on architectural–engineering concerns that employed registered architects only as minor employees. Architectural services should be performed within an established architectural division of the company, under the responsible direction and control of a registered architect, said the AIA.

4.5 Legal responsibilities

In the course of carrying out a contract, an engineer can sometimes acquire unexpected and unwanted legal obligations. "Supervision" and "inspection," two words frequently used in engineering contracts, frequently also cause trouble.

---

[10] *A Guide for the Selection of Engineers in Private Practice*, Sept. 28, 1961. (Available from the Nat'l Soc. Professional Engrs., Washington, D.C.)

[11] NSPE stands for National Society of Professional Engineers; AIA stands for American Institute of Architects.

[12] "AIA Clarifies its Ethical Standards," *Engrg. News-Record*, July 30, 1964, p. 12.

Supervision. Many contracts in the past have used the phrase, "the Engineer (or Architect) shall have general supervision and direction of the work." In some recent court decisions, it has been held that the design professionals (a term embracing both engineers and architects) were responsible for defective construction techniques in cases where they undertook the responsibility of supervising.[13] In 1961, a joint professional committee of architects and engineers recommended that all reference to "supervision" be omitted from contract documents. The matter remains controversial, however, for many consulting engineers believe that supervision of the work is an engineering service to which the owner is traditionally entitled.

Inspection. The work "inspection" has caused trouble because it has sometimes been interpreted to mean exhaustive and continuous inspection of all details of the construction. Most often, this has not been the type of function the engineer had in mind when he agreed to "inspection of the work." More likely, he envisioned some kind of educated spot-checking; hence, the word "observation" has been proposed as a substitute that more accurately describes the service intended. If actual detailed inspection is desired, then it is recommended by professional groups that the contract provide for a full-time Project Representative whose task it is to perform detailed and continuous inspections.

Special legal hazards are involved in the use of new materials or equipment. Courts have generally held that the engineer or architect is obliged to conduct tests of the new material or to have reliable information concerning the results of tests conducted by others. Sole reliance upon manufacturers' sales literature and specifications has been held insufficient. The question of the obligations of the design professional, in the use of new materials, remains a tricky legal matter.

The foregoing paragraphs describe some of the legal hazards involved in offering consulting services. Any one of them could be financially catastrophic for the consultant. Because of this, professional groups recommend that architects and engineers maintain professional liability insurance, often known as "errors and omissions" insurance. It is further pointed out that the written language of the contract may be insufficient

---

[13] J. R. Clark, *Concerning Some Legal Responsibilities in the Practice of Architecture and Engineering.* Washington, D.C.: AIA, 1961. This publication is the source for most of the information contained in Section 4.5. (Mr. Clark is a partner in the well-known legal firm of Barnes, Dechert, Price, Meyers & Rhoads, of Philadelphia, Pa.)

to protect the engineer, if he attempts to perform services in an area beyond the scope of the contract. J. R. Clark says, "Having once moved into that area he may be charged with the responsibility for all of the functions involved, such as failure to exercise reasonable care in performing the services or failing to do what one experienced in the field would do in the exercise of reasonable care."[14]

4.6 Engineers in government

Many engineers in the federal government, and some in state governments, are engaged in research, design, and development. As a result, they probably would not perceive their situation as being much different from that of engineers in industry. Yet, there are areas of engineering activity in government that have little or no counterparts in private industry; these contribute to the formation of public policy and law enforcement, as in environmental regulation, operation of public utilities, and public transportation.[15] While jobs in such areas require engineering backgrounds, they frequently do not involve the basic engineering function of design. Much of the typical activity of government engineers has to do with the preparation of functional specifications for public works and with supervision of the resulting construction and operations. In the federal government, engineers have participated at high levels in policy matters, since the government has increasingly come to recognize that many decisions of national importance rest primarily upon technical considerations.

Nevertheless, much design is being carried out at all levels of government: federal, state, and municipal. An especially important example is the planning of highways and expressways. The arrangement and utility of our highway system have a subtle and long-range impact upon the nature of our environment and upon the very quality of our existence.

The direct involvement of government engineers in design activities has led to complaints by some consulting engineer groups against the use of government engineers in the design of public works. The consultants maintain they can offer greater economy in performing engineering services for the various governments than can the engineers who are *in* government. However, professionals on the opposite side disagree. This dispute—which actually is only one facet of a larger problem; namely,

---

[14] Clark, p. 23.

[15] A. C. Stern, "When Government Hires an Engineer," *Mech. Engrg.*, vol. 86, June 1964, p. 22.

which services will be performed by the public sector of the American economy and which by the private sector—will probably continue to be troublesome in years to come.

The federal government has recognized that it has just as much need for high-quality engineering talent as does private industry. It has also shown concern that its image is not so favorable as could be desired. As a result, the Federal Council for Science and Technology in 1962 published a series of recommendations for the improvement of the technological environment in government. Among other things, the council recommended that the federal government:

1) Provide for greater participation by scientists and engineers in the making of decisions
2) Delegate more administrative authority to technical directors
3) Provide a clearer picture of the opportunities and challenges in a government career
4) Improve recruiting procedures
5) Provide better fringe benefits[16]

---

[16] *The Competition for Quality.* Fed. Council for Science and Technology, Washington, D.C.: April 1962.

5 ▸ | Management

5.1 The meaning of management

It is interesting that many engineering students do not really want to be engineers: they want to be managers. However, they are generally quick to admit that they do not have a particularly clear picture of what being a manager would be like.

When asked why they want to be managers, engineering students may have some interesting answers: "Because I'm mercenary," says one; this is merely a way of stating that the prospect of large financial rewards is one of the traditional attractions in management. "Because managers run things," says another; this man's answer shows that he is getting very close to the core of the matter. An especially interesting reply is, "Because I don't believe I have what it takes to be a good engineer." Nevertheless, most students take the view that nearly everyone wants to grow in stature throughout his career and management is the traditional route for such growth.

What do managers really do?

There is a simple answer to the question of what managers do. It can be answered that they manage money, materials, and men. However, this is little help to the potential management aspirant. He wants to know what it would *feel* like to be a manager: Would he like it? Would he be engaged in a daily rapid-fire round of decision-making à la Hollywood? Would he be constantly embroiled in dirty political in-fighting, dramatized in "Executive Suite" and "The Carpetbaggers"? Would he be required to ride the social merry-go-round regardless of his own wishes? Would he find it necessary to discipline his wife, at intervals, regarding proper corporation-wife behavior? The answer need not necessarily be "yes" to *any* of these questions. However, any given individual could make it "yes" to all of them, depending upon the level of the job and upon his own characteristics.

Up to a certain level, a man can belong to himself. That is, he can be fully loyal to his company, have high devotion to duty, be on the firing line to meet every crisis, and, yet, never seriously be placed in a position where he must choose where his greater loyalty lies—with his family or with his company. However, if he truly aspires to a high-level post he should not have any delusions: it will be necessary for him to marry the job.

The editors of *Fortune* estimate a fifty-seven- to sixty-hour average work-week for executives, including the effect of take-home work and business entertaining. Furthermore, *Fortune* suggests that, while corporations may publicly deplore the pressure placed upon their executives, they privately do everything possible to increase it. One executive is quoted as saying, "What it boils down to is this: You promote the guy who takes his problems home with him."[1]

A large part of any executive's time is taken up by reading letters, memos, company reports, policy statements, proposals, specifications, laws, regulations, contracts, analyses, magazines, and newspapers. In addition, he must write (mostly memos), although he has a dictation machine and a secretary to ease this part of the chore for him. Much of this reading and writing is done at home, because the executive's day is almost monopolized by meetings.

During the office day, the executive is seldom alone. If he is not involved in a formal committee meeting of some sort, he is informally engaged with one or more associates, because the executive is primarily concerned with *people.* This brings the author to the single most characteristic thing about an executive's job: he must somehow be able to get numbers of people moving in the same direction; hopefully, he gets them to move on a willing basis.

Once a given corporate objective has been formulated, a manager is faced with the task of getting others to attain it. He may feel himself more capable of carrying out any given task than the person to whom he

---

[1] *The Executive Life* (Garden City, N.Y.: Doubleday, 1956), p. 65. By the editors of *Fortune.* This book, plus Vance Packard's *The Pyramid Climbers* and William Whyte's *The Organization Man,* should be required reading for every management aspirant.

assigns it, but being only one man, he cannot do everything himself. Therefore, he uses all those techniques that, collectively, are in the area of human relations. Some of these are good; some are bad. The executive suggests, recommends, persuades, urges, or directs (all good); or he may order, command, demand, fume, bully, or rage (listed in order of their decreasing desirability).

J. Irwin Miller, chairman of the board of Cummins Engine Company, has graphically described the immense multiple pressures that operate on an executive:

> To illustrate, let us suppose we can see inside the head of the president of a large manufacturing organization. His company employs 20,000 persons and operates half a dozen plants. It distributes its products in every state and in many foreign countries, and—most frightening of all—it has competitors.
>
> Now let us suppose that these competitors are extremely vigorous, and that our president knows that to maintain his share of the market and to make earnings which will please his directors, he must accomplish the following very quickly: design and perfect a brand-new and more advanced line of products; tool up these products in such a way as to permit higher quality and lower costs than his competitors; purchase new machinery; arrange major additional long-term financing. At the same time his corporation's labor contract is up for negotiation, and this must be rewritten in such a way as to obtain good employee response and yet make no more concessions than do his competitors. Sales coverage of all customers has to be intensified, and sales costs reduced. Every one of these objectives must be accomplished simultaneously, and ahead of similar efforts on the part of his competitors—or the future of his company is in great danger. Every head of a corporation lives every day with the awareness that it is quite possible to go broke. At the same time he lives with the awareness that he cannot personally accomplish a single one of these vital objectives. The actual work will have to be accomplished by numerous individuals, some actually unknown to him, most of them many layers removed from his direct influence in the organization.[2]

The second most characteristic thing about a manager's job is decision-making. As the author will show, the *engineer* is a decision-maker, too, and by virtue of this function, is also a manager; however, the effects of decisions made by a person directly in management are more immediately apparent than those made by an engineer. The effects of an engineer's decisions may ultimately be far-reaching, but they are usually subtle.

---

[2] J. Irwin Miller, "The Dilemma of the Corporation Man," *Fortune,* August 1959, p. 103.

In fact, the engineer may never become fully aware of the ultimate effects of his own actions. This is not the case with the executive, who may be acutely aware that his decision, today, to cut back production means that hundreds of people will be out of work tomorrow.

Making decisions is a lonely privilege. Inevitably, there comes a time in the career of every person who follows the management route, when he realizes there is no one to whom he can turn for help in making his decisions. Before this point, there always was a boss to whom he could go for advice. Suddenly, he realizes that he himself is the boss to whom *others* are coming for advice. Worse: in considering the possibility of going to his own boss for assistance, he may realize, with a shock, that his boss cannot help him. There are many possible reasons why this might be so: the boss may be too far away; he may not have the special background necessary to understand the situation; he may not have the necessary time—or the manager may fear his boss will not *take* the time. Finally, it may simply be that the boss has delegated major responsibilities to the manager and *expects* him to make decisions. This is complicated by the fact that one of the hardest decisions to make, is the decision of what to take to the boss and what to determine for one's self.

In the effort to ease this loneliness, executives may turn to committees to help them make decisions. It may even be possible for executives to bury the responsibility for their decisions in the anonymity of committee action. But, under the methods that govern American business, this is feasible only to a limited degree. Even if a decision has been made by a committee, the ultimate responsibility for a bad decision will probably come to rest upon the individual executive who originally had the responsibility for acting. Knowing this, most executives will use a committee in two major capacities: 1) as a sounding board to enlarge their own perceptions of the problem, and 2) as a means to involve their associates and subordinates in the decision-making process and, thus, to approach unity of purpose as nearly as is possible. Following a committee meeting during which the problem has been thoroughly aired, the executive will then make the decision himself.

Levels of management

So far, the author has spoken of management as though it looks and feels the same wherever it is found. It does not: it varies considerably, depending upon the level of management. A list of some management levels, together with typical titles of the men in each category, follows:

Executive. Chairman of the board, president, vice-president (of manufacturing, of engineering, of marketing, of finance, and so forth), general manager, treasurer, controller.

Manager. Plant manager, chief engineer, director of engineering, general sales manager, personnel manager.

Superintendent. Chief project engineer, chief industrial engineer, purchasing agent, group head, regional sales manager, assembly-line superintendent.

Supervisor. Project engineer, foreman, office manager.

In *The Executive Life,* the editors of *Fortune* list the five characteristic functions of an *executive* as 1) setting policy, 2) making major decisions, 3) coordinating, 4) organizing, and 5) delegating responsibility. The term "top management" is frequently used to identify this level.

According to *Fortune,* a man at the *manager* level does not set policy, but interprets and carries out policies formulated by others. He may have the authority to make decisions of considerable importance, for instance, approval of union contracts, but he makes these decisions within the limits set by top-executive policy.

A *superintendent* differs from a manager primarily in the magnitude of the decisions he may make and, from the category beneath him, by virtue of his function as a *supervisor of supervisors.* The term "middle management" generally encompasses the two categories of manager and superintendent.

A *supervisor* enforces rules; sees that quotas are met; administers personnel matters; and, in other ways, operates within fairly narrow and well-defined limits. Usually the term "first-line supervisor" is employed to describe his activities; this phrase signifies that the people under him are the productive workers themselves. (It should be noted that the "project engineer" is included in this lowest category of management. On the other hand, as will be explained in Section 5.5, the project engineer actually is in a position of critical importance and may be considered a member of one of the most influential classes of people in industry. However, the purely supervisorial portion of his activities correctly belongs at this level.)

Generally, when a person says he wants to go into "management," he means he wants to be an "executive" or a "manager"; he is likely to regard the positions of supervisor or superintendent as way-stations on the road to ambition's fulfillment. Most of the author's discussion will be relevant to these two higher categories, since these are the levels where money, prestige, and influence (all highly desired) and stress, politics, and loss of personal freedoms (deterrents) are most in evidence.

5.2 Attractions to management careers

Financial gain

Everybody knows that executives make plenty of money. Probably the only question that remains to be answered is the personal one, "How much am *I* likely to make?" It is interesting that the salaries of the top moneymakers are public knowledge.[3] These are the "six-figure men," some of whom make four, five, and six hundred thousand dollars a year. But there are only a handful of such; very few aspiring managers—even ambitious ones—really expect to make the six-figure group. It is more probable that they are thinking of the jobs in the $25,000-plus category, perhaps extending up to $100,000.

According to *The Executive Life,* there seems to be some kind of unwritten formula for determining executive salaries. If the Number 1 man gets $100,000; the next man is likely to be paid $75,000; the third $50,000; and the fourth man from the top, probably $35,000. This top-paid group typically will include the president, the executive vice-president, the marketing vice-president, and the financial vice-president. The annual salary of a manufacturing or an engineering vice-president generally would be below this—perhaps at the $25,000-to-$30,000 level. There are no hard and fast rules, and company size is an important deciding factor. In an extremely large company like General Motors, there would be many levels, including half-a-dozen jobs in the $400,000-plus category. However, General Motors can hardly be considered a typical corporation.

Dean Rosensteel, of the American Management Association, has been keeping track of executive compensation trends for more than twenty-five years. His studies show that companies in the $50–$75 million bracket might pay their presidents $50,000 to $75,000 per year, while a company would probably need annual sales in excess of $300 million to pay a salary of $100,000 to its top man.[4] There are less than two hundred such companies in the United States.[5] A somewhat sobering statistic is that most

---

[3] "Biggest Salaries Get Bigger," *Business Week,* May 23, 1964, p. 81. Every year, *Business Week* publishes the earnings of the 400 top-paid executives in the United States. In 1963, Frederic G. Donner, chairman of General Motors, was top earner with a total of $800,000-plus, including bonus and contingent credits.

[4] "Executive Pay Trends Changing," *Nation's Business,* vol. 46, December 1958, p. 48.

[5] "The Fortune Directory—The 500 Largest U.S. Industrial Corporations," *Fortune,* July 1964, pp. 179–198.

top executives are in their sixties and, so, do not reach the big-money brackets until they are nearly ready for retirement.[6]

While on the subject of pay, it is important to note that the $15,000-to-$20,000 bracket has been invaded, in recent years, by people in purely technical categories who have no administrative responsibilities. Obviously, this is partly the result of inflation: $15,000 today buys what $12,000 did in 1950. However, there is a more important reason: as industry increases in technical complexity, there is a tendency to give greater recognition to the technical specialist. (Usually such a specialist possesses a doctor's degree.) A 1964 survey showed that the median salary of engineers with doctor's degrees and with no supervisory responsibilities was over $15,000 per year.[7] It wasn't too long ago that a salary of $10,000 or $12,000 per year was considered to be in the executive category, but now the median pay of all engineers exceeds $10,000 and a brand-new Ph.D. can *start* at $12,000 or higher.

Management creativity

Many observers have noticed the following trait among management men: after they have earned all the money they can possibly use, they keep right on working as hard as ever. When asked about this, some executives readily admit that salary itself becomes unimportant above a certain point—that it is only a way of "keeping score."

The real motivation of such men must be something other than money and is usually nothing less than a manifestation of our old friend, creativity. A systems engineer has said:

> Before you reach a certain salary level, money is the important thing. After that, job satisfaction takes over.[8]

And from a company president:

> ... I dearly love this work. You live only one time and you might as well do something you like.[9]

---

[6] "When *You* Will Hit Your Peak," *Nation's Business*, vol. 51, January 1963, pp. 64–66.

[7] *Professional Income of Engineers, 1964*. New York: Engrg. Manpower Com., Engrs. Joint Council, p. 21. This survey included 4549 engineers with doctor's degrees, among the total of 231,618 engineers surveyed.

[8] W. Guzzardi, Jr., "Man and Corporation," *Fortune*, July 1964, p. 148.

[9] *The Executive Life*, p. 69.

From a labor union vice-president, who talks just like any other executive:

> I'm working harder than I ever have in my life . . . The incentive isn't monetary gain . . . I feel I'm part of a crusade, making the world a better place in which to live.[10]

When a management man says his job is creative, he is not just giving idle play to a fashionable word: he means it. He enjoys seeing programs that he originated take shape and prosper, accompanied by organizational flowering and growth. Nor should it be dismissed that many men are motivated by a genuine desire to give service. Almost every human being wishes to feel that his existence has meaning and value to the rest of the world, and managers are no exception.

It is indeed fortunate for the rest of society that the highest reward in management has all the worthy overtones the word "creativity" implies. It certainly provides today's executives with a better motivational creed than the simple one of "profit," which was pursued with such undiluted enthusiasm by the industrial barons of the nineteenth century and led to excesses of greed.

Many executives today—especially those in large companies—believe that corporations have a specific responsibility to the public; they believe that corporate profits must be accompanied by social benefits, and that this must be made a conscious part of company policy. However, there are others who deny that the consciousness is necessary. They believe that only pursuit of the profit objective is necessary and that social benefits will be a natural consequence. In reply, many management men point out that the constrictive government regulations under which businesses must operate today are the direct result of the actions of previous generations of management who believed they had no obligations to society other than the pursuit of profit. Some comments on this subject are thought-provoking:

> It is not that they don't care but rather that they tend to assume that the ends of organization and morality coincide, and on such matters as social welfare they give their proxy to the organization.[11]

Louis E. Newman, President, Smithcraft Corporation, has said:

> No greater responsibility do we have than seeing that the skill of manag-

---

[10] William H. Whyte, Jr., *The Organization Man* (paperback ed.; Garden City, N.Y.: Doubleday), p. 160. Orig. publ. Simon and Schuster, New York, 1956.
[11] Whyte, p. 8.

ing helps provide a better world than simply reinforce the permanence of power of each manager.[12]

From Thomas J. Watson, Jr., chairman of the board, International Business Machines Corporation:

> Historically, I think we can show that restraints on business have not come into being simply because someone wanted to make life harder for us businessmen. In almost every instance they came about because businessmen had put such emphasis on self-interest that their actions were regarded as objectionable and intolerable by the people and their elected representatives.[13]

From a man identified only as a "thoughtful executive":

> The corporation lives only through the toleration of the people . . . The more estranged the corporation becomes from the majority of people the more likely is the corporation to be the goat when someone wants to make political capital.[14]

Fortune sets up the two opposing ideas in the following way:

1) The main role of management is to do justice between the competing claims of stockholders and other groups.
2) A long-range concern for profits is enough to guide managers.

Fortune then says, "We suggest that the second view is the right one and that it makes the first unnecessary."[15]

Does this seem confusing, since there appears to be no consensus? But why should a consensus be expected? This particular subject is one of the most controversial in the modern world; the viewpoints of the two opposing camps have merely been exposed. The author suggests that it is impossible to select either extreme and blindly cling to it and that, therefore, businessmen must strike a balance between the two objectives. *Both* of them bear upon the long-range stability and profitability of the organization. T. J. Watson, Jr. (previously quoted), who is one of the most

---

[12] L. E. Newman, "Managing In a Changing World," *Mech. Engrg.*, vol. 86, April 1964, p. 112.

[13] T. J. Watson, Jr., *A Business and Its Beliefs* (New York: McGraw-Hill, 1963), pp. 90–91.

[14] V. Packard, *The Pyramid Climbers* (Crest paperback ed.; New York: Fawcett World Library), pp. 254–255. Orig. publ. McGraw-Hill, New York, 1962.

[15] "Have Corporations a Higher Duty than Profits?" *Fortune,* August 1960, p. 153.

outspoken proponents of statesmanship in corporate management, adds this caution to ensure that the picture remains in balance: "If the businessman fails at business, then all his other concerns will mean nothing, for he will have lost the power to do anything about them."

The tacit motivations: status and power

One of the most damaging labels that can be fastened onto an aspiring manager is that he is "status-conscious." Yet, virtually everyone is constantly seeking to improve his status, and most human beings enjoy having an influence over their environment; that is, they enjoy the use of power.

The word "status" has acquired undesirable connotations for many people: snobbishness, conceit, egotism, unworthiness, vanity, sham, falsity, pretension, affectation, ostentation. All of these do violence to the basic ideal that all men are created equal. But instead of deliberately choosing unpleasant adjectives to equate to our ideas of status, we could just as well have chosen the words importance, honor, value, esteem, distinction, significance, greatness, quality, respect, and excellence. Expressed in this fashion, a desire for status no longer would seem so ignoble. Put it yet another way, it can be said that virtually everybody desires recognition; he wants his existence and efforts to be recognized by others as having value. This wish is simply a desire for status, but in more euphemistic dress.

Most people object to the word "status," because they equate it to the activity known as "company politics," wherein advancement through personal accomplishment is abandoned in favor of the more direct techniques of political maneuver, rumor, and insinuation. Yet, it is the *methods* they object to, and not the validity of the goal. Most of mankind has only respect for people of truly outstanding ability, such as great writers, great composers, and—naturally—great engineers and scientists. There are also many industrial managers who have gained public respect, primarily on the basis of their creative accomplishments.

It could be said that, if the motivations to achieve status and power did not exist, no one would seek top industrial or political posts. Instead, everyone would seek middle-level positions, where the pecuniary rewards would be adequate, but the exposure to responsibility not so great. This produces an amusing vision in which hopeful managers would seek to be *over* some people, but always *under* someone else. However, the rest of the vision has sobering (and even frightening) implications, since it would imply a complete absence of competence at the top.

Every fourth year brings the emergence of many aspirants for America's top job: the presidency. Money must be dismissed as a motivation, since most of these aspirants are already wealthy. It could legitimately be asked: "Why would anyone seek to be President?" The responsibilities are almost intolerable. The sacrifice of normal family life is legendary. The physical danger is real and ever-present, as has been demonstrated many times in American history. In the face of these drawbacks, we can be thankful that the job nevertheless attracts men of top ability. Consequently, what can possibly be the explanation except the desire to achieve recognition, honor, and a place in history—plus the aspirant's supreme confidence in his ability to handle matters better than someone else? These motivations are nothing but the desires for status and power stated in a way that avoids disagreeable connotations.

Challenge

After the most basic human wants—food, shelter, and security—have been satisfied, man looks around for new worlds to conquer. If there are no natural obstacles to be overcome, he will invent some. Thus, men compete in business, fight wars, climb mountains, and engage in sports; many undertake difficult educational programs that go far beyond what would be necessary solely for economic survival.

All these things are manifestations of *challenge,* which, in itself, is one of the most compelling urges that propel men into management careers. It is the excitement and exhilaration of the game itself that some men enjoy. A high level of energy and drive are universally recognized as essential ingredients for management success. A person who does not have this high level of drive, but who aspires to a management career, has already made his first mistake.

5.3 Drawbacks in management careers

In any recounting of the "bad things" about management, the following should be recognized: not everyone will agree that these things exist, or even that, if they do exist, they are necessarily bad. Probably, most people who are emotionally equipped to find satisfaction in management would believe these factors to be minor, or perhaps not even relevant to their own cases. A decision concerning the direction of a man's career is, after all, a personal one and will be made according to each person's own value judgments about all the advantages and disadvantages of a given set of alternatives.

Loss of personal freedoms

One infringement on a manager's freedom concerns the right to select social companions as one pleases. Some managers even make it a rule never to socialize with other company people, for fear that such an arrangement might some day prove embarrassing. Conversely, others feel *compelled* to socialize with company people, especially if the company is in a small town. Both conditions are a curtailment of freedom. The greatest casualty is often the executive's wife. Upon her husband's promotion, she is universally advised by management consultants to cut off any friendships she may have made with the wives of men who are now subordinate to her husband. If she finds such action beyond her surgical powers, then she may be subject, later, to vexatious strains generated from the husbands' relationships at work. An equally serious threat is that subconscious compulsions will devolve upon her husband to show favoritism. In any of these events, there has been a curtailment of freedom.

The young executive may find that much of his socializing is in the form of company obligations. For example, he may be required to entertain out-of-town VIPs and may wonder just what all this has to do with his job. Nevertheless, it must be recognized that many executives enjoy this part of their work. While some would regard it as a curtailment of freedom, others would look upon it as a kind of fringe benefit.

Even in such minor matters as personal appearance, there are erosions of freedom. As mentioned elsewhere, conformance of dress in itself is not a serious thing; yet, it seems that a man's chances of advancement *are*, to some extent, influenced by whether he has a crew cut or wears the right kind of ties, or shirts with French cuffs, or (continuing to the extreme of trivia) long hose. For, if minor things like this grate on the boss, they can interfere with a man's promotion. It has been said that "before the boss will promote you, he first has to be able to envision you in his mind's eye as an occupant of the prospective job."

Of a much more serious nature is the demand of practically all companies that an executive give total allegiance to the organization. One student of management behavior has stated, "To get to the top a man must put on a pair of blinders and shut out everything except business . . . In others words, the corporation must become the life of the man."[16]

While some people would not consider that they had lost anything by fulfilling this demand, others might consider it a loss of freedom.

---

[16] Benjamin G. Davis, "Executivism: How to Climb the Executive Ladder," *Mech. Engrg.*, vol. 86, July 1964, pp. 22–25.

Supression of emotion: stress

The executive with ulcers is a standard fixture in the popular image of the modern business world. Like all stereotypes, this one is often false; nevertheless, many managers do experience physical disorders that have their origin in emotional stress. It is pressure, of course, that causes this situation; but what causes the pressure?

In some instances, pressure has been used by the "higher-ups" as a conscious management tool to maintain an atmosphere of urgency and to make sure everyone is working at his maximum output. If a manager objects to the strains on his nervous system, he is likely to be met with the admonition, "If you can't stand the heat, get out of the kitchen." Hence, he is likely to keep his feelings under wraps. The result is more stress.

There are many other well-known sources of stress, such as anxiety concerning job security, or slowness of promotion, or intense competition with rivals, as well as the classic case of the man who is "in over his head" and is struggling to conceal it.

Not so well known, but probably one of the biggest ulcer-producers, is the requirement that the ideal executive always present a calm self-assured façade. Even though, internally, the executive may be as much assailed by feelings of weakness and self-doubt as anyone, he can never allow these to show, or he invites others to trample on him.

Chris Argyris of the Yale Labor and Management Center, who has been very active in research on managers and management characteristics, offers the following as some of the important qualities of the executive:

1) He has high tolerance for frustration.
2) He permits dissection of his ideas without feeling personally threatened.
3) He engages in continual self-examination.
4) He is a strong, cool competitor.
5) He expresses hostility tactfully.
6) He accepts both victories and setbacks with controlled emotions.[17]

After such studious suppression of his emotions as is implied by the characteristics compiled by Dr. Argyris, the executive is then surprised when they flare up in the form of a physical disorder.

Promotion to a position of increased responsibility often brings on a state of mind *Fortune* calls "promotion neurosis," in which the subject experiences great anxiety and emotional conflict. The most common sufferer from this neurosis, says *Fortune,* is the engineer or scientist who

---

[17] C. Argyris, "Some Characteristics of Successful Executives," *Personnel J.,* vol. 32, June 1953, pp. 50–55.

has been forced into an administrative job. *Fortune* quotes a psychologist (Harriet Bruce Moore) who says one of the troubles of the engineer-turned-manager is that ". . . he has a very real tendency to regard people (especially his subordinates) as complicated machines which are different from his tools primarily in two ways—they are harder to renovate and more costly to oil."[18]

Family impact

The previously noted demand that the executive put his job before everything else means his family life is often a casualty. In saying this, it must be recognized that not all people assign the same values to the same things. Many men will accept the minimal family life that frequently goes with being an executive and never feel they have missed anything.

One of the things young men very quickly learn is that corporations generally expect instant mobility in their management hopefuls. If a man is in Phoenix and his company wants him to go to Omaha (presumably a promotion), it expects him to go without hesitation, and preferably tomorrow, although next week will probably have to do. If he declines, or probably even if he pleads for a delay until June when "the kids" are out of school, then the next man on the list will be chosen, and it can be assumed that this man's climb up the promotion ladder has ceased. Most companies make this clear: mobility is held up as a prime virtue.

The man in question must realize that his wife will have some opinions on this subject. If he has to be in Omaha next week, his *wife* has to stay to look after all the affairs, sell the house, and arrange for moving. If it is deemed important for the children to finish out the year at their present school, she is the one who must stay behind, perhaps even for several months, while her husband makes hurried "commuting" trips home on occasional week ends. Understandably, family relations could become strained under such circumstances, unless both husband *and* wife are thoroughly sold on the same objectives.

The Executive Manpower Corporation, a national recruiting organization, recently reported a trend of increasing balkiness on the part of wives regarding relocations. The president of Executive Manpower Corporation said that some re-educating of wives might be desirable, so that they would be more receptive to geographical changes.[19]

A man must examine his (and his wife's) scale of values very closely. As mentioned earlier, up to a certain level (probably through the "super-

---

[18] *The Executive Life,* p. 87.
[19] "Executive Trends—Wives Balking at Job Moves," *Nation's Business,* August 1964, p. 14.

intendent level" described in Section 5.1 of this chapter and, in rare cases, even into the "manager level") a man can "have his cake and eat it too." If he has advancement aspirations beyond this, but insists that his family come before the company, he will almost inevitably come to the point where he will be forced to choose.

Politics and jungle-fighting

Politics and "jungle-fighting" do exist, although not to the extent suggested by popular fiction. Since they are probably the most thoroughly publicized and well understood of management drawbacks, the author will spend little time on them. Nothing can protect a man from falling into the mistake of using these fabled evils, except a strong sense of personal integrity. If a man should discover that he is spending more of his business day with actions that have "getting ahead" as their object, rather than doing the job well, he is in danger of taking the next step into the arena of political maneuver.

Among the commonest of such maneuvers is the skillful discrediting of an opponent by any one of many techniques, such as planting rumor, sowing doubts, withholding information, maneuvering him into an untenable position, and methods of a similar nature. An equally common maneuver is the seeking to make one's self more apparent; that is, to attract favorable attention from one's superiors. The techniques are almost as numerous as are their practitioners. They include such procedures as marking the boss's *boss* for copies of memos, finding excuses to visit headquarters (in the case of a branch office man), currying favor with the boss, or being especially agreeable to the boss's secretary.

There are even coaching services available to executives who feel deficient in political skills. Vance Packard reports on one firm that instructs its clients, among other things, to keep a file of index cards on "important people" and to edge out into social spheres. This firm goes so far as to suggest, "Follow your immediate vice-president into your favorite bar and have a drink with him." Packard flatly gives his opinion that if the man dutifully follows these precepts, ". . . the coaches will have succeeded in producing a real grade-A corporate creep."

A conflict of moralities

A serious potential difficulty in a management career arises in the sphere of moral action. The problem comes into being because many companies demand that their managers follow a rule of seeking only the good of the company, to the exclusion of other considerations. A three-year study, conducted at the University of California, Los Angeles, on executives and how they get ahead showed some executives were not sure that the usual moral standards observed by most people in their personal lives are applicable to business.[20]

That such a policy often backfires, has already been mentioned. When the policy expresses itself in the form of trusts and cartels, society reacts by passing antitrust laws. When the policy results in the exploitation of working men, labor reacts by forming unions. When it expresses itself in the form of cheap, unsafe equipment, government agencies step in with restrictive laws.

In the price-fixing suits against the electrical industry in 1961, the presiding judge described the individual defendants as "torn between conscience and an approved corporate policy . . . the company man, the conformist, who goes along with his superiors and finds balm for his conscience in additional comforts and the security of his place in the corporate setup." It was shown that, within the organizations, managers who believed in obeying the law were sidetracked from promotions; their respect for ethical behavior was mocked as "religious." One of the defendants stated: "I was to replace a man who took a strictly religious view of it; who, because he had signed this slip of paper wouldn't contact competitors or talk to them—even when they came to his home." He added, "I was glad to get the promotion. I had no objections."

Fortune commented on these suits: "No thoughtful person could have left that courtroom untroubled by the problems of corporate power and corporate ethics. . . . Big business . . . establishes the kind of competition that is typical of our system and sets the moral tone of the market place."[21]

It should not be inferred that a man must discard his moral code to succeed in management. Encouragement can be drawn from the fact that some of America's most successful managers are also well known for their adherence to high sets of standards.

5.4 Getting there

Best routes to management

Compare the following statements:

Forty percent of management is recruited from the ranks of the engineers.[22]

---

[20] R. M. Powell, "How Men Get Ahead," *Nation's Business*, vol. 52, March 1964, p. 58.

[21] R. A. Smith, "The Incredible Electrical Conspiracy," *Fortune*, April 1961, p. 132 ff.

[22] H. W. Dougherty, *Your Approach to Professionalism*. New York: Engrs. Council for Professional Development, 1959, p. 43.

Some time ago I noticed that appointments to top-level positions were seldom going to engineers, but were going to finance men, marketing men, and lawyers.[23]

The proportion of top industrial management with a background in science and engineering will have risen to more than 50 percent by 1980. U. S. industry is indeed coming under new management.[24]

Despite the swift advances of technology, there has apparently been a drop-off in the proportion of industrial scientists and engineers who reach the position of chief executive officer.[25]

Strangely enough, *all* of these apparently contradictory statements are true. As might be expected, the paradox results from the interpretation. A study of top executives made by *Fortune* in 1952 showed that only 10 percent of them came up through engineering; the same study showed that 46 percent of them had studied science or engineering in college.[26] Yet, 25 percent of the top executives had risen through sales, 23 percent through production, 17 percent through finance, 16 percent through general management, and 8 percent through law. What accounts for the apparent contradictions in the statements at the beginning of this section, is an ambiguity in the use of the word "engineers." In one case it means those who are actually working as engineers in the company, while in the other, it means all those who may once have studied engineering. The implication is that it is fine to take engineering while in college, if you yearn for the corporation president's job; but you should not have very high hopes of getting there through the engineering department.

A Scientific American study made in 1963 gave the results in Table 5-1. (The study included data on 800 executives, selected as the top two men in each American firm having annual gross sales of $100 million or more.)

Scientific American's studies show that the percentage of top corporation officials with a background in science or engineering has risen from 20 percent in 1950 to the 1963 level of 37 percent. From the composition of the pool from which future management will be drawn, Scientific American predicts that this percentage will increase to more than 50 percent by 1980.

The view has occasionally been advanced that there is something about

---

[23] "Executivism," p. 22.

[24] *U. S. Industry: Under New Management, A Scientific American Study,* Publ. by Scientific American, New York, 1963, p. 33.

[25] *The Pyramid Climbers,* p. 170.

[26] *The Executive Life,* pp. 31–34.

Table 5-1. Executive backgrounds

Science or engineering	Percent	Totals, percent
Bachelor's degree	26	
Graduate degree	6	
No degree	5	
		37
Nonscience		
Business degree	6	
LL.B. degree	12	
Other college degree	23	
No degree	22	
		63
		100

Source: *U.S. Industry: Under New Management.* Publ.
by Scientific American, New York, 1964, p. 31.

an engineering education which gives one a special advantage in a managerial career; further, the inference is drawn that engineers hold such an advantage because they can apply the "scientific method" to their management activities. In the author's opinion, the inference is unwarranted. Yet, the results of the Scientific American study cannot be denied. What does it all mean?

Part of the explanation is that science and engineering are difficult courses of study, and successful completion of a college program in one of these curriculums means that the student has learned to work hard and successfully. He has already developed, to a high level of proficiency, his personal initiative and his ability to finish the jobs he has undertaken. These statements could apply equally well to a law degree or to a master's degree in business administration; however, these two educations take longer than four years and, thus, attract fewer people.

What really gives science and engineering the edge is the growing technical complexity of industry. This statement should not be misunderstood: it does *not* mean that the top-level manager must have a large fund of detailed technical know-how. It means that the top man in a technically based industry needs a technical background as part of his *cultural* understanding. The word "cultural" is used here in the broadest possible way: it refers to all the knowledge and experience a man possesses, against which he compares his current situation in order to make value judgments. Many industries today completely depend upon rapid technological change for their well-being; it seems inevitable that managers of such enterprises will possess considerable technical understanding, and that this trend will increase.

If an engineering education is at least as good as any other preparation for a man who wants to be a company president, then what comes next? Finance and law would appear to be closed routes for the engineering graduate, although they are classic routes to the top. Still, *Fortune's* 1952 study indicates that sales and production are even better routes than finance and law; almost half of the executives studied by *Fortune*[26] had achieved their positions through the sales and production departments. These two routes are wide open to the engineer, and in fact, many new engineering graduates go directly into one of these fields.

Many young men ask if it would be wise to get a Master of Business Administration degree, if they are interested in management. Insofar as a general answer to such a question is possible, this would probably be it: if a man feels he is destined for top management, an M.B.A. would be extremely useful to him. However, many companies seem to believe that a B.S. is just the ticket for management aspirants. In any event, it should be remembered that an individual's personal characteristics and drive are more important than mere possession of degrees.

What it takes

Many of the essential managerial characteristics have already been discussed. To summarize, these have been:

1) A willingness to place the company first
2) A high degree of agressiveness and drive, including a willingness to work long hours
3) An ability to handle others
4) A strong desire for personal status and economic gain
5) A desire to be in control
6) A high degree of tolerance for frustration and disappointment

To these should be added the following:

7) Persistent optimism (no matter how bleak things look, the ideal management man always has a constructive program on tap for which he entertains the highest hopes. The cynic is unpopular in management circles.)

8) The ability to *finish* a job, as well as to initiate it (Actually, this characteristic is in demand at all times and places, and not just for management positions. It is among the rarest of the world's commodities, and its absence is seldom detected by people who do not have it.)

9) Good judgment and logical thinking ability (These qualities are sometimes known simply as "intelligence." In a complicated situation, the manager must be able to sort things out into their proper relationships and to dig beneath surface irrelevancies to get at the heart of issues. This having been accomplished, he must forecast the future and be right most of the time.)

10) The ability to communicate, not only in writing but above all, orally

Vance Packard offers these four basic "survival" rules for managers:[27]

RULE ONE:	Be Dedicated
RULE TWO:	Be Loyal
RULE THREE:	Be Adaptable
RULE FOUR:	Be Quietly Deferential

Concerning Rule Four, the author would like to add that, while nobody likes a "yes-man," nobody likes a "no-man," either. This is a ticklish matter and can cause a man a certain amount of ethical queasiness. In essence: a man must appear, to the Boss, to be on the Boss's team most of the time and use his own creative input with discrimination.

A prominent question in management is how much importance should be attached to technical know-how. In recent years, there has been a tendency to disparage the need for subject-matter competence on the part of a manager. Instead, it is claimed that the manager should be an expert at "management skills"; presumably, these include proficiency in such things as human relations, budgeting, and planning. When applied to a *general* management job, the advice makes considerable sense; when applied to the manager of one of the functional branches of the company, the advice seems defective.

A *general* manager, who must simultaneously manage several functional branches (for instance, sales, finance, manufacturing, and engineering), will find it a physical impossibility to be expert in all of the departments he is managing. If he should persist in acting as an expert in the one he does know (the branch through which he came up), then he is a thorn in the side of everyone who must work under him in that branch. Obviously, he needs *some* background in all branches (gained partly through college course-work, but more importantly through experience); however, he cannot be an expert in all. Here the advice at issue is good.

---

[27] *The Pyramid Climbers*, pp. 103–110.

Many promoters of this advice insist that it should apply to *all* levels of management, but the reasoning applied here to general management jobs is not necessarily applicable to managers of the functional branches, such as general sales manager, director of manufacturing, or chief engineer. In these cases, it is preferable to have a manager who is technically competent in his own area, as well as in possession of the requisite management abilities. Of course, he must be capable of suppressing the urge to function in a technical operating capacity himself. He must get others to do the actual operations, but he will be a better manager if he himself thoroughly understands those operations.

Advice of the opposite extreme, which holds that the *best* technical man should be chosen leader, is equally bad. This point of view is usually espoused by someone who thinks *himself* to be the best technical man. The notorious failures of this approach have undoubtedly helped to form the opposite attitude. The following procedure would seem to make the most sense (at least until the level below that of general manager): first, select a group of men for their thorough competence in the subject-matter to be managed; then, from these, make a final selection on the basis of their managerial skills.

One last matter is the question: Should a man join one company and stick with it, or should he shift around a little during his early working years? Nobody knows for sure. The *Fortune* study on executives[26] revealed that a full third of the subjects had never worked for another company and an additional 27 percent had worked for only one other company. Almost half of the subjects had been with their current employers more than thirty years. The least mobility was shown by those in the oil industry. The most mobile were steel executives, with automobile executives close behind them.

The biggest single danger in staying with one organization is that a person could find himself becoming more and more highly specialized in one particular thing and, correspondingly, more and more narrow. Most organizations will encourage such specialization as long as it is useful, but will be quick to amputate it when it is no longer needed. This practice is the main worry that causes young men to move during their early years, and many companies combat it by offering unusually high salaries for the specialties currently in demand.

Some large companies are in a position to avoid these disadvantages. They can transfer their men frequently among divisions and, thus, give them the same broad experience the men would acquire if they were to work for many different employers. This is great for the management-bound man, provided he is "geographically flexible." On the other hand, a capable young man can often shine to better advantage if he is in a small company, especially if the company is a fast-growing one.

Will computers replace managers?

Obviously, computers will not completely eliminate management jobs, but most assuredly, they will reduce these jobs in number, especially at the middle management level. According to *Fortune,* this trend is already taking place.[28]

The reasons are fairly simple: Organizational subdivisions are created only so that the activities with which each manager is directly concerned can be brought within the attention span of which a human being is capable. But a computer can have a vast attention span. The result of increasing computerization will be a reduction in the number of levels between top management and the productive workers; many middle management positions will disappear. Much information that formerly had to filter upward through layer after layer of organization (and which sometimes arrived too late to be useful) will be made directly available to top management almost as soon as an event has happened. Already, computer systems have been applied to such things as ordering, shipping, production scheduling, and sales analysis.

Staff jobs will suffer heavy attrition in the process of computerization. In the past, many companies have maintained large departments for purposes such as production control, sales analysis, and cost accounting. As these activities shrink, many middle management jobs will disappear. Other quasi-management staff jobs, for instance, those in market research and value analysis, are sure to diminish.

As a countertrend, systems and computer engineers are coming in at the levels formerly occupied by many middle managers. It has been suggested that these engineers might prove to be in an excellent spot to move into top management, because of the broad knowledge and creative attitude required by their systems activities. Says *Fortune,* "The computerized world would be an oyster for the young man with brains, judgment, personality, education, ambition—and a good knowledge of computers."

5.5 Engineering is management

Management action

There is sufficient similarity to give substance to the assertion that engineering is part of management. Consider the president of a corporation: In his daily activities, he must conserve money; conserve time;

---

[28] G. Burck, "Management Will Never Be the Same Again," *Fortune,* August 1964, p. 204.

maximize effort; increase the competitiveness of his company's products; and, finally, satisfy the conflicting internal requirements of the company's various departments, such as sales, service, manufacturing, finance, and engineering.

The preceding is also a fairly accurate enumeration of the opposing forces the engineer must balance in fulfilling *his* responsibilities. The president has additional responsibilities, of course. No one would seriously suggest that the engineering department duplicates the president's function, but there is an especially important characteristic belonging to the president of the corporation which is worth noting: he is a man who *cares*. In this crucial aspect, the engineer's outlook should exactly match the president's. He must care deeply about what is going to happen to the organization. Without any exaggeration, it can be said that the future of the company has been laid in the hands of its engineers, for the future consists of the new products the engineers will create. It is entirely possible for the engineering department to make or break a company.

Is it the conception of spectacular new inventions that has so great an influence? Although such conception is essential, it is by no means the whole story. A program may begin with a concept for a great new product, but there are numerous places along the development route where it can be ruined. Probably the most sensitive moment in the entire life-history of a potential new product occurs during the selection of the basic physical method by means of which the functional objectives will be achieved (previously referred to as the selection of a *scheme*).[29]

No doubt it will be argued that higher management will have the ultimate word on these matters and that the only function the engineering department can have is to make proposals. This is true, but higher management can operate only on the proposals submitted. They can refuse bad proposals, but the act of refusing does not create good ones. If the engineers are unable to create good proposals, there will be no new products—unless higher management is willing to accept the least objectionable of the poor proposals, perhaps never even knowing these are poor proposals, since they will not have seen any better ones.

After several possible schemes have been generated, another critical phase is approached. It is at this point that the engineer's knowledge of mathematics and science comes into play. Somehow, each scheme has to be reduced to an estimated cost, since it is upon *cost* that higher management's decisions will be based and it is also upon *cost* that the ultimate competitive vitality of the product will depend. To get this information,

---

[29] See sec. 2.2.

each scheme must be analyzed on paper before anything is actually built. Later, limited experiments may be conducted to settle some fine points, but at this stage, everything depends upon what goes on in the engineers' heads. What are the most influential parameters in the system, and how might one select a reasonable criterion for optimizing them? How many components, and of what quality, will be necessary to accomplish each scheme? What will be the influence upon performance (and cost) if the component characteristics vary from their nominal values? What about strength, wear, corrosion? How much additional (and expensive) quality is justifiable in the initial manufacture of the product so as to avoid undue field service costs later?

Nobody can duplicate the engineers in this role, unless he himself sits down and repeats the whole process, step by step. If the engineers do their job wrong it will not be of much help that everyone else has done his right. Moreover, nobody will know if the engineer's job has been done right or wrong until it is too late.

A key man in the national economy: the project engineer

In any given engineering department, it is usually easy to determine who the key people are. It should not be supposed that the key group consists exclusively of supervisors. Many key people will turn out to be supervisors, of course, but not all. However, all the key people are distinguished by two important characteristics: first, they will be outstandingly competent at the *technical* aspects of their work; and second, they will be men of such stature and authority that they are the ones to whom people naturally turn for direction. For the most part, they will be first-line *engineering* supervisors, a category the author will refer to as "project engineer." (However, it should be noted that this particular title has widely varying meanings in different companies.)

Project engineers make the real engineering decisions. Engineers at a *higher* administrative level are usually too remote from daily activities to be able to bring sufficient detailed technical understanding to the decision-making process. Engineers at a *lower* level lack the authority and overall knowledge to be able to make decisions that will stand up in the long run.

Key men like these fill the pivotal posts of engineering, throughout America. Collectively, their actions have an almost incalculable effect upon the rest of the country, since they possess a combination of technical knowledge and authority which is sufficient to control the directions that engineering technology will take and, hence, to determine the nature of the goods that will be made available to society.

It would be a strong temptation simply to classify these men as managers, for they usually do have others working for them—as few as three or four, or as many as fifteen or twenty. But it is essential to note that at least 50 percent of project engineers' time is spent in directly technical affairs. This is what makes them influential: they are fundamentally *creators*.

6 ▸ | Business organization

6.1 Business structure

There are three fundamental forms of business organization: the proprietorship, the partnership, and the corporation.

In a *proprietorship,* there is only one owner. All the profits of the business belong to him (as do all the losses). Within the limits of the law, he is the undisputed master of his business. If he wishes to expand, he can hire a group of new people tomorrow—and let them go the next day, should he change his mind. Two disadvantages of the proprietorship form of business organization are: 1) there is a rather severe limit to the amount of capital a proprietorship can collect for investment and 2) the proprietor has "unlimited liability" for the debts of his business. The latter means that, should the business fail, all of the proprietor's personal assets (except for a negligible minimum) may be impounded to satisfy his creditors.

In a *partnership,* there is more than one owner. In some giant brokerage firms, there are scores of partners (although such firms are unusual). There are few formalities involved in forming a partnership. Two partners could operate on the basis of a simple oral agreement if they wished; however, they would be ill advised to do so, since written agreements generally prevent later misunderstandings. At the minimum, a partnership agreement would probably state the resources that each man is putting into the business and would specify the manner in which profits are to be distributed. The agreement also would provide for the distribution of the assets, should the partnership be dissolved.

The principal disadvantages of the partnership are: 1) by law, *any* partner can be held liable for *all* the debts of the partnership; 2) each partner can individually bind the other partners in the business; 3) in the event of the death of a partner, or the dissolution of the partnership, there are severe problems in maintaining the continuity of the business.[1] The principal advantage of a partnership is that it can bring together a greater amount of capital than can a proprietorship.

By far the most important form of organization, for engineers, is the *corporation*. The corporate form of organization came into being as an answer to some of the problems that exist in the other two forms of organization. The corporation can collect vast amounts of capital; the liability of its owners is limited to the amounts they have invested in the business. Finally, the continuity of the corporation is ensured by the ease with which certificates of ownership (that is, stock certificates) may be bought or sold. The principal disadvantage is the number of procedural regulations that must be complied with, in the formation and operation of a corporation. Some people believe that another disadvantage is that the corporate form of organization causes income to be subjected to double taxation: the income of the corporation is taxed once at the corporate rate and then, again, as personal income when the profits are distributed in the form of dividends.

In most cases, the officers of modern corporations are not the owners. Although the officers frequently own a certain amount of stock, it is seldom that they own enough even to assure working control (which usually requires about 20 percent of the stock).[2] Control, then, stems from the consensus of some group that can command the backing of the stockholders. Ultimate control, of course, is vested in the stockholders themselves, but there may be thousands or even millions of these, and they may be scattered all over the world. Thus, it is meaningless to speak of control by the stockholders unless there is some person, or group of persons, upon whom the stockholders can focus their wishes. Because there is a natural tendency for human beings to trust a known quantity more than an unknown one, stockholders are inclined to give their proxies to the current officers, who then vote them as a block. This inclination is especially pronounced when the group in control has been performing in a creditable fashion. For these reasons, annual stockholders' meetings are often formalities, held because they are required by law. To such meetings, the management group can come with predetermined programs and in possession of enough votes to ensure their passage.

If the stockholders have become disenchanted with the current management, occasionally a group of outsiders may arise and seek to take control

---

[1] W. Edgar Jessup, Jr., and Walter E. Jessup, *Law and Specifications for Engineers and Scientists* (Englewood Cliffs, N.J.: Prentice-Hall, 1963), pp. 432–435.

[2] P. A. Samuelson, *Economics* (3d ed.; New York: McGraw-Hill, 1955, pp. 88–89).

by means of a "proxy fight." Members of such a group may purchase large holdings of stock themselves and may also seek to sway other stockholders to their side and, thus, gain a sufficiently large block of votes to take over corporate power. Such fights will generally make newspaper headlines, at least on the financial pages, because they are waged "in the open" at stockholders' meetings.

Every corporation has a board of directors, the members of which are the legal representatives of the stockholders. They have ultimate authority over all affairs of the corporation, with the exception of certain matters which, by law, must be submitted to the stockholders themselves. Within any board, there is almost certain to be a group that, because of the confidence placed in it by the rest of the board, represents actual control of the company. Frequently such a group will include the president of the company and some key vice-presidents; sometimes it is formally organized as an executive or a finance committee.

Probably no two corporations in the United States are organized exactly alike, but they do tend to fall into two broad groups: the centralized and the decentralized. In the *centralized* form of corporate organization, the principal functions of the company (sales, finance, engineering, and production) are split at a level close below the presidential level, and lines of responsibility extend directly from that level to all activities of a similar type in the company, wherever the activity may be located. For example, chief engineers at plants on opposite sides of the continent would both report to an engineering vice-president at headquarters and would only have minor administrative responsibilities to the local managers.

In the *decentralized,* or "profit-center" type of organization, the company is essentially broken down into a number of smaller companies, each of which is equipped with a general manager and its own functional branches. A high degree of autonomy is then granted to these small "companies," coupled with full accountability for profitable operation. The function of headquarters is to ensure coordination, prevent duplication, and make sure that growth capital is channeled into divisions that merit special nurturing.

The general trend, at least for large companies, inclines toward decentralization. General Motors, for example, is well known for its emphasis upon decentralization. The enormously successful Texas Instruments is said to consist of "fifty little businesses," each with its own engineering, manufacturing, and marketing capability.[3] However, there is

---

[3] J. McDonald, "Where Texas Instruments Goes From Here," *Fortune,* December 1961, p. 236.

no general agreement among businessmen as to which of the two methods is better. Recent years have even revealed the somewhat startling spectacles of companies that have just completed centralization, turning about-face to begin the task of decentralization and vice versa.

6.2 Profits (and losses)

The author once knew a corporation president who was fond of stating that his only business principle was "to make a profit." Such a policy does correctly describe the justification for a corporation's existence. It is for just such a purpose that the stockholders put their money into the business.

In the larger socioeconomic sense, a corporation's purpose is to supply the goods needed by people. In Russia, the entire economy is run like a single gigantic company, with managerial directives and a system of merit awards relied upon to achieve efficiency. In the United States, it is believed that the economic system works better when it is based upon privately owned competitive business units, coupled with the incentive of profits. To keep the greed for profits from overbalancing the benefits to society, Americans attempt to regulate the system by means of taxation and regulatory laws.

In Chapter 5 it was mentioned that a preoccupation with short-range profits can bring a company to grief. Short-range profits are important, of course; without them a company will find it unnecessary to worry about long-range profits because it will soon have ceased to exist. But corporations are presumably in business on a long-range basis, and for this reason, the managers worry about the status of the corporation as a good "citizen." They wish the company to be well thought of for a variety of reasons: so that it will inspire the confidence of customers; so that it will attract, and hold, good employees; and so that it will avoid the unfavorable attention of legislative bodies. However, the managers of a corporation are entitled to worry about such things only because they believe this is the best way to ensure the long-term profitability of their organization.

Viewed in this light, engineering must be regarded as a very heavy expense item that is justifiable only if it improves chances for future profit. Yet in recent years, virtually all manufacturing companies have been energetic in increasing this expense item, because they know they cannot have new products without engineering—and they know, further, that their future depends upon new products. In 1964, Booz, Allen, and Hamilton stated that many companies were finding that more than half their sales were coming from products which had been unknown ten years previously.[4] Furthermore, on the basis of their wide management consulting experience, Booz, Allen, and Hamilton asserts that, on the average, only one idea out of every fifty-eight evaluated actually becomes a successful product. Even worse, they state that, out of every three products that are "successful" at the Research and Development (R & D) stage, there emerges only one commercial success. Obviously, then, it becomes of overriding importance to improve the initial product selection processes to the highest degree possible, *before* projects get into the costly R & D stage. It has been pointed out that any reasonable improvement in the *commercial*-failure-rate of "successful" R & D projects (67 percent) would go a long way toward alleviating national engineer shortages. Various approaches to achieving such improvements will be treated later, in the section on "Developing New Products."

6.3 Reading the corporate report

Since engineering is so intimately related to the profitable operation of a company, it is highly desirable for engineers to have some appreciation of the manner in which financial reports are prepared and presented. Peter F. Drucker has reported that, in his experience, professional employees have the most favorable attitude of all employee groups toward company reports and figures. Furthermore, says Drucker, the professional employee typically rejects anything that smacks of "popular writing," and ". . . demands the original version, however difficult and unreadable it may be."[5]

Publicly held corporations are required to publish annual reports setting forth their financial condition. Such reports typically contain much detail, and are excellent sources of information for persons seeking employment, as well as for prospective investors. As a general rule, they are available from companies merely for the asking. Understandably, a corporate report will be written in a way that casts the most favorable possible light on the corporation's activities.

The most important pieces of information in an annual report are the *operating statement* and the *balance sheet*. The operating statement (sometimes called the "statement of profit or loss") essentially shows the income and expense for the year. The balance sheet shows the financial

---

[4] *Management of New Products.* Booz, Allen, and Hamilton, New York, 1964. Booz, Allen, and Hamilton are a prominent engineering consultant service.

[5] P. F. Drucker, "Management and the Professional Employee," *Harvard Business Rev.*, vol. 30, May–June, 1952, p. 89.

condition at the end of the year: how much the company *owns,* how much it *owes,* and how much is left over (the stockholders' equity, otherwise known as *net worth*).

Tables 6-1 through 6-4 are typical examples of these two statements in condensed form. Research and development expenses are included in the category of "Selling, general, and administrative expenses." All four statements were taken from actual annual reports, but have been disguised to conceal the identity of the companies. Obviously, Company "A" is in good condition. It made a handsome net profit for the year (5.9, as a percent of sales), paid a dividend to its stockholders, and retained a large share of its earnings to assist in company growth. Furthermore, a glance at Table 6-2 shows that its long-term debt is small in relation to its net worth.

Table 6-1. Operating statement of Company "A"

Net sales		$94,000,000
Cost of sales	$48,000,000	
Selling, general, and administrative expenses	34,000,000	
Other expenses	1,000,000	
		83,000,000
Profit before taxes		$11,000,000
Federal income taxes		5,500,000
Net income (profit)		$ 5,500,000
Retained earnings (earned surplus) at beginning of year		21,000,000
Cash dividends paid out		1,500,000
Retained earnings (earned surplus) at close of year		$25,000,000

A look at Tables 6-3 and 6-4 will show that Company "B" has financial troubles. This company apparently also made a profit during the year. However, its profit was less than that of Company "A," even though its sales volume was larger: the net profit, as a percent of sales, was only 2.1. But there are deeper troubles. Evidently the company found that it had vastly overstated the value of its inventories in previous years, because in the current year it has found it necessary to take an extraordinary adjustment of 5 million dollars, which amounts to a staggering loss. In essence, this means that profits in previous years were overstated and it is now time to "face the music." Note, however, that the operating statement still

Table 6-2. Balance sheet of Company "A"[a]

Assets	
Cash	$ 9,500,000
Accounts receivable	16,000,000
Inventories	22,500,000
Other current assets	2,000,000
Total current assets	$50,000,000
Property, plant, and equipment	15,000,000
Other	1,000,000
Total assets	$66,000,000
Liabilities and stockholders' equity	
Current liabilities (accounts payable)	$10,000,000
Long term debt (notes payable)	5,000,000
Stockholders' equity (net worth)	
Capital surplus	26,000,000
Retained earnings (earned surplus)	25,000,000
Total liabilities and stockholders' equity	$66,000,000

[a] Balance sheet presents figures as of end of year (with 3,830,000 shares of stock outstanding).

Table 6-3. Operating statement of Company "B"

Net sales		$119,000,000
Cost of sales	$86,000,000	
Selling, general, and administrative expenses	21,000,000	
Other expenses	7,000,000	
		114,000,000
Profit before taxes		$ 5,000,000
Federal income taxes		2,500,000
Net income (profit)		$ 2,500,000
Retained earnings (earned surplus) at beginning of year		25,000,000
Extraordinary adjustment for overevaluated inventory, less applicable income tax credits		5,000,000
Retained earnings (earned surplus) at close of year		$ 22,500,000

Table 6-4. Balance sheet of Company "B"[a]

Assets	
Cash	$ 5,000,000
Accounts receivable	19,000,000
Inventories	34,000,000
Other current assets	2,500,000
Total current assets	$60,500,000
Property, plant, and equipment	25,000,000
Other	3,000,000
Total assets	$88,500,000
Liabilities and stockholders' equity	
Current liabilities (accounts payable)	$31,000,000
Long term debt (notes payable)	21,000,000
Stockholders' equity (net worth)	
Capital surplus	14,000,000
Retained earnings (earned surplus)	22,500,000
Total liabilities and stockholders' equity	$88,500,000

[a] Balance sheet presents figures as of end of year (with 2,950,000 shares of stock outstanding).

declares that the current year was a profitable one and resulted in a "profit" of $2,500,000. Furthermore, in former years when profits were being declared, the management probably genuinely believed the corporation was experiencing profitable years, whereas in actuality, it was probably losing ground. Items produced in those years, but still held by the company, were carried as an asset on the balance sheet (which is acceptable accounting procedure) instead of being charged off as cost of sales. Now, when it has suddenly been discovered that the value of these particular assets has been overstated (perhaps because nobody will buy them at their stated value), there is no choice but to write them off as a loss.

From this last example, it should be noted that it is impossible to tell the true financial status of a company by looking at just one year's report. There are too many variations possible in accounting policy that might produce an apparent profit in any given year, or even in a few sequential years. For this reason, at least five consecutive years should be examined. The key figure is "retained earnings." If this figure increases each year, the company is growing; if it decreases, the company is shrinking, no matter what the current year's operating profit may appear to be.

Several indexes are commonly used as a rough measure of the financial health of a company; some of the more important of these follow:[6]

Profit margin. This is the ratio of net profit to net sales, expressed in percent. It is important to designate whether the figure being given is the profit margin "before taxes," or "after taxes."

Current ratio. This is the ratio of current assets to current liabilities. The New York Stock Exchange states that 2:1 is generally accepted as standard.

Book value. When the net worth of a company is divided by the number of shares of common stock outstanding, the resulting amount is the book value per share. It is the presumed amount a stockholder would receive per share if all the assets were disposed of (at the value shown on the balance sheet), and after all the debts were paid.

Market value. This is the amount for which shares of stock are currently being sold on the stock exchange. For many reasons, some of them emotional, the market value and book value may be widely divergent.

Earnings per share. This is the ratio of the net dollar income to the number of shares of common stock outstanding. A prospective investor might compare this value against the price he must pay per share of stock, as a measure of the profitability of his investment.

Common stock ratio. This is most simply expressed by the following formula:

$$\text{Common Stock Ratio} = \frac{\text{Capital surplus} + \text{Retained earnings}}{\text{Long term debt} + \text{Capital surplus} + \text{Retained earnings}}$$

This ratio expresses the share of the overall financing actually owned by the stockholders, as compared to the total amount of long-term financing. A common stock ratio of only 50 percent would probably be considered alarmingly low for most industries, but might be reasonable for such industries as utilities.

---

[6] For more details, see D. T. Canfield and J. H. Bowman's *Business, Legal, and Ethical Phases of Engineering* (2d ed.; New York: McGraw-Hill, 1954), pp. 109–113. Also, see *How to Understand Financial Statements*, New York Stock Exchange, June 1963.

A comparison of the two companies being used as examples results in the following:

	Company "A"	Company "B"
Profit Margin (after taxes)	5.8 percent	2.1 percent
Current Ratio	5	1.9
Book Value	$13.30	$12.40
Earnings per Share	$1.44	$0.85
Common Stock Ratio	91 percent	63 percent

It is clear that Company "A" is in a more favorable situation on every count. A profit margin of 5.8 percent after taxes would generally be considered good, although in 1963 General Motors made a profit of 9.7 percent, and International Business Machines Corporation made 14.1 percent. However, such margins are high. In the same year, Westinghouse, Lockheed, and North American all made 2.2 percent; Boeing made 1.2 percent; and Sperry Rand 1.1 percent.[7]

6.4 Organizational relationships

Occasionally, people have been known to ask, "Which is the most important branch of a company: sales, engineering, or manufacturing?" One might as well ask, "Which is the most important leg of a three-legged stool?" Obviously, all are essential. Briefly, each group's special functional contributions to the organization are as follows:

Engineering *defines* the product.
Manufacturing *makes* the product.
Sales (or marketing) *distributes* the product and is the income-producing agency of the company.

These distinctions may seem obvious, and even simple-minded, but it is precisely because many people overlook such fundamentals that strife sometimes occurs among departments. Two examples will suffice to give an idea of the manner in which problems can arise and the ways in which they may be avoided:

Example 1. Engineering releases a set of drawings for a new product. After a lapse of time, Manufacturing reports that Engineering's design

---

[7] "The Fortune Directory—The 500 Largest U.S. Industrial Corporations," *Fortune,* July 1964, pp. 179–198.

cannot be produced. The engineering department, which has anticipated this, whips out a pre-prepared method by which production can be accomplished. Manufacturing, after due examination, declares the method impractical. Engineering thereupon announces that it will establish a model department of the proposed process and prove its practicality. If it turns out to be successful in this endeavor, Engineering now finds itself in the production business and is faced with two alternatives: a) it can remain permanently in the production game or b) it can somehow convince Manufacturing to assume control of the "orphan" department. Either way, relations between the two departments are apt to be less than cordial. Earlier consultation and cooperation with the manufacturing department would have avoided most of the trouble.

Example 2. On a new design, Manufacturing suggests some changes and claims it will reduce the cost of the product. After examination, Engineering declares the original design is better and rejects the proposed changes. Manufacturing, without authorization, makes the changes anyway. The changes prove successful, and Manufacturing continues to produce the article the new way and says nothing to Engineering. Manufacturing is now in the engineering business, but nobody else knows it. If this situation occurs very often, confusion and costly errors lie ahead, plus an inevitable blowup and deterioration of relations between the two departments.

The prescription for improvement is simple; it is based upon only two principles: a) each department should bear constantly in mind what its basic function is and adhere to it; b) each department should respect the special competence of the other and seek the consultation of the other on a continuing basis.

Some attempts have been made to circumvent these problems by placing a small engineering group *within* a manufacturing department, with authority to make changes on products. However, this usually changes nothing. The new engineering group soon develops its own sense of identity, and the same kinds of problems can take place as before, except this time they occur between the new group and the rest of Manufacturing. The prescription for improvement is the same as that previously given.

The greater burden for preserving effective relations rests upon Engineering. The very nature of their relationship places manufacturing departments in the position of continually receiving "orders" from Engineering, in the form of drawings and specifications. Furthermore, most engineers have college degrees, whereas most manufacturing men do not, even though they may possess the native ability to succeed in college had they gone there. For these reasons, manufacturing personnel automatically are likely to feel at a disadvantage. The slightest indication of superiority on the part of engineering personnel may be enough to tip the scale in an unfavorable direction. Almost every manufacturing organization can cite examples of engineers who are unable to work with manufacturing personnel, usually because of an unconscious (sometimes *conscious*) attitude of superiority which they convey.

A senior student in engineering at the University of California, Davis, chose the subject of engineer–machinist relations for an oral report he was to present to a group of classmates. To prepare for his talk, this student solicited responses from twenty machinists working at various experimental shops in northern California. He was hardly prepared for the emotionally charged responses he received. Following are representative answers to his question, "What, in your opinion, is the typical engineer's attitude toward machinists?"

> That we are dirt under his feet—that the machinist doesn't know anything.
>
> Lacks respect for machinists. That machinists are inferior.
>
> In too many cases the actual design is done by the machinist and the engineer takes the credit for it.

On the other hand, virtually all the respondents expressed high respect for engineers who act as though machinists have something of value to contribute, but implied that engineers of this type are too rare.

Engineering's relationships with Marketing tend to be of a more subtle variety than are those it maintains with Manufacturing. Here, if any conflict arises, it is likely to be over product function and customer acceptance. For example, Marketing is apt to believe it has a better appreciation of what the customer wants in a product than does Engineering, while the engineering department may think the customer's demands are illogical. Having been encouraged all his life to think logically, an engineer may believe it only reasonable that customers should do the same. Customers, of course, remain unimpressed; they simply buy a competitive product if they feel so inclined.

The matters in question may be things like appearance, color, noise, arrangement of controls, and the method of use. These items definitely come under the heading "defining the product," which is Engineering's basic responsibility. No clear-cut boundary is possible, yet marketing people generally believe that their department should be the principal authority on features such as those just mentioned, all of which profoundly affect marketability. To justify this view, one marketing vice-president of a national company was fond of relating a story whenever his engineer associates were proving to be contrary in yielding a point. His anecdote concerned a dog food company that had invested a considerable sum of money in developing the perfect dog food. After years of effort, the company's scientists at last proclaimed success. Their new product consisted of a carefully balanced formula of proteins, fats, and carbohydrates and contained all the essential vitamins and minerals. Close attention had been given to the perfect blending of many savory aromas and the achievement of an attractive texture. Furthermore, it was economical to manufacture. "The only trouble," said the marketing vice-president, "is that the dogs wouldn't eat it."

6.5 Developing new products

This section will deal with one of the most difficult problems facing modern industry: how one goes about developing successful new products. Today, it is well known that any successful product has only a limited life. Booz, Allen, and Hamilton claim that when a product reaches its peak in terms of sales volume, it has already started its downhill slide in terms of profits.[8] In the current world, a continuing stream of new products is absolutely essential to the well-being of a business.

Good sense indicates that every new product proposal should be analyzed in terms of its prospective return on investment. Those products with the greatest apparent return and the lowest apparent risk are selected for development. Although fine in theory, this precept requires prediction of the future, and just how does one predict the future?

Corporations' usual answer to the preceding question is to carry out a survey. But market surveys are generally successful only in ascertaining the *current* state of affairs and then, only moderately so: often, they are useless at predicting what the customer will do in the future[9]—the customer himself does not know what he will do. If the proposed product under survey is *really* new, so that nobody has ever heard of it before, then a market survey will generally produce nothing but a vacuum—precisely because nobody ever heard of the product before. If a sizeable market is forecast, it at best represents someone's guess, however intelligent and informed such a guess may be. Yet, how can one calculate a return on his investment (which is a reasonably scientific process) when he can't get a

---

[8] *Management of New Products,* p. 4.

[9] See, for example, *Developing a Product Strategy* (E. Marting, ed.: New York: Amer. Management Assoc., 1959), pp. 134, 137, 141, 154, 336.

scientific grip on the size of his market? If there is a shortage of capital, which is often the case, the pressure may be all but irresistible to put available funds into the area of greatest certainty; this probably means following a trail someone else has blazed; and if the organization yields, it has then chosen to be a follower instead of a leader, however unwilling its decision may have been.

There is hardly any doubt that an organization must take chances, if it wants to be a leader. Thus, the element of risk enters, since a company must be willing to spend large amounts of money today on the strength of the best vision of the future it can obtain within its own doors. Risk means that some will fail; others will succeed, largely because of their skill in forecasting the unknown.

Top management usually takes the viewpoint that one of its most important functions is to foster, analyze, and develop new product ideas. Hence, there is a tendency to keep the new product function very close to the top, organizationally. If the new products in question are mostly extensions of the present product line, these responsibilities may be entrusted to the marketing vice-president. However, if the new product investigations reach into areas that are completely unexplored, such responsibilities more likely will be given to a new products department, sometimes directly attached to the president's office.

The new products department

Generally, the functions of a new products department will be to:

1) Generate new ideas
2) Analyze and screen ideas from all sources
3) Coordinate market needs with research and development ideas
4) Conduct pilot tests of new products, under market conditions

Of these four functions, the most important is probably the second. Most often, companies rely upon their research and engineering departments to generate new ideas (function 1).[10] Sometimes new ideas come from outside the company, but nearly all observers agree this is a minor source. Other possible sources of new ideas are:

1) **Unused patents.** A veritable avalanche of new patents is issued every year; very few of these patents see commercial use because for nu-

---

[10] In the American Management Association's book, *Developing a Product Strategy*, thirty-four executives from twenty-nine different organizations have presented their views on the new products function. This book is an important source of the information in this chapter.

merous reasons, patent owners may find themselves unable to press ahead with commercial development. As a result, many patents are available for license or sale. In addition, an examination of issued patents may generate entirely new product ideas. If one wished to find a route to the largest number of creative minds in this country, the trail of issued patents would surely be his best starting-place. The Small Business Administration, Washington, D.C., regularly publishes a *Products List Circular* containing abstracts of patented inventions available for sale or license.

2) Government needs. Supplying goods needed by the government is big business. The gigantic weapons industry completely depends upon the government as its principal customer. Major weapons development companies have special Washington offices, whose purpose it is to maintain constant contact with government agencies, in order to ascertain their needs and to anticipate trends. Each year, the government issues a publication, *Inventions Wanted by the Armed Forces,* which can be an important stimulant to new product ideas.

3) Top management. In some organizations, particularly those which were founded by creative technical people, a major source of new ideas continues to be the top man or men.[11]

Whatever their source, after a group of ideas has been collected, they must be carefully screened. Out of this group, an average of only one in fifty-eight actually becomes a successful product, as the author has already mentioned.

In the screening process, new ideas are first compared against the company's technical capabilities, manufacturing resources, and existing market coverage. An idea that does not fit with existing company capabilities in any of these three categories will probably go no further. If the idea matches with at least one existing resource, or better yet, with two, then it will probably be considered further, perhaps with a view to acquiring the missing faculties. Probably the most troublesome missing capability to acquire is in marketing and distribution coverage.

Ideas that survive the screening step are analyzed on a return-on-investment basis. At this point, an estimate of the future market *must* be made; usually this estimate is coupled with a market survey.

As was explained earlier in this section, the information acquired

---

[11] *Developing a Product Strategy.* See "Supplementary Opportunities for Technical Innovation," by W. Wade, pp. 125–130.

through a market survey must be examined with an experienced and skeptical eye. Many companies have been seriously misled by accepting survey results at face value. One incident, reported by a vice president of Westinghouse, concerns portable television receivers. When portable receivers were first being considered, two electronics manufacturers conducted surveys on the receivers' market potential and both received negative reports. One company abandoned the idea, the other went ahead. Today, of course, portable television sets are a major product.[12] The point of the story is that the wants of today (which are mostly what a market survey will reveal) may be quite different from the wants of *tomorrow*.

Another case is from the author's own experience and involves a market survey in which he participated. The subject of the survey was trading stamp dispensers. As a part of the survey, operating executives of large retail outlets, including oil companies and grocery chain stores, were interviewed. The results were strongly negative. Some of the interviewees were adamant in their assertions that they would not install dispensers and had seemingly excellent reasons for their position. Yet within a few years, trading stamp dispensers were in widespread use and were being used by the very chains that were so strongly opposed to them.

It should not be inferred from the foregoing that market surveys are useless and a waste of time. On the contrary, survey information has many times proved extremely useful when viewed in a careful and discriminating light. Almost invariably, unexpected—and sometimes startling—information will be turned up.

In its *coordinating* function (number 3), the new products department is expected to take an overall view of the company's operations and to provide a balance-wheel for any excessive enthusiasms generated by salesmen and by engineers.

The general criticism against engineers is that they are overenthusiastic about the technical improvements their ideas offer and insufficiently responsive to what the market wants and is willing to pay for.[13]

The criticism against most salesmen is that, while they automatically wax enthusiastic over *any* new idea (a generally desirable quality in a salesman), this enthusiasm blocks true objectivity.[14] Another point against

---

[12] *Developing a Product Strategy.* See "Gauging the Potential of a Product or Product Change," by C. J. Whittling, p. 134.

[13] J. W. Lorsch and P. R. Lawrence, "Organizing for Product Innovation," *Harvard Business Rev.,* vol. 43, January–February, 1965, pp. 109–122.

[14] *Developing a Product Strategy.* See "Competing in an Expanding Market," by M. E. Mengel, p. 154.

relying upon line salesmen for new product ideas is that they tend to think too much in terms of the sale they could have made last week if they had had such-and-such a feature and do not think broadly enough in terms of the future.

Many products fail because of insufficient field testing under actual market conditions. The customer can be relied upon to find all sorts of defects in the product that have somehow not shown up during in-plant testing. More efficiently conducted, field testing can show whether the wants of the market place have been correctly identified, *before* costly and nearly irrevocable steps have been taken toward mass production and distribution.

An example which illustrates the point just mentioned, concerns a special bottle-warmer that Westinghouse was planning to place on the market. The warmer employed an unusual principle (thermoelectrics), and included a timer that would cause the heating cycle to start at a predetermined time, so that the bottle would be warm when the baby's parent got up for the 2 A.M. feeding. Westinghouse undertook extensive tests, interviewed department story buyers and sales people, and conducted panel discussions of young mothers. Finally, after carrying out actual field tests in various areas at different price levels, Westinghouse shelved the product. From the field tests, it was found that the product could command only a price in the $8-to-$25 range, whereas the company planning staff had envisioned a luxury $30-to-$50 range.[15]

One of the fundamental things a new products department can do is develop functional specifications to guide the R & D department. Functional specifications should be written in a way that clearly identifies *what* a product must do, without limiting the technical means by which the desired function can be accomplished (this identification includes a definition of function, appearance, and price); with good functional specifications, everyone knows exactly what it is that R & D is trying to accomplish—including R & D itself. Such specifications are not formulated in a single step, however: developing specifications for a particular product is a matter of continuing evolution. As the project proceeds, understanding grows, concerning what is wanted and what can be done technically. The functional specifications, which are continually undergoing revision, form a record of what the new product is turning into. Booz, Allen, and Hamilton state that one of the most commonly heard complaints in new product development centers on poorly written specifications.[16]

---

[15] C. J. Whittling in *Developing a Product Strategy,* pp. 137–138.
[16] *Management of New Products,* 1960 ed.; p. 24.

Return on investment analysis

Before a project goes very far, someone must take a good hard look at the future and try to decide if the proposed product has any chance of producing a profit. In order to do this, two things are necessary: 1) somebody must devise a reasonably clear configuration of the proposed product, so that a production cost can be estimated; 2) somebody must predict the anticipated annual sales.

Table 6–5 shows a typical return-on-investment analysis for a consumer product that will sell for $300. For this product, it is estimated that a million dollars will be required for development and another million for plant expansion, tooling, and distribution start-up (including sales training costs, service training costs, and the expense of staffing new offices). Such a capital investment is by no means unusual; in fact, the usual tendency is to underestimate the amount of capital required.

In the analysis shown, it is assumed that the third year after introduction of the product represents what will be a steady-state condition and that the return of 27 percent per year will continue henceforth. At this rate, the company's entire investment would be recovered by the fifth year.

Table 6-5. Sample of a return-on-investment analysis for a consumer product

	First year	Second year	Third year
Initial Investment (R & D, plant expansion, tooling, and so forth)	$2,000,000	$2,000,000	$2,000,000
Number of units required for sales inventory	4000	8000	12,000
Dollars tied up in inventory, at factory value	($150 × 4000) = $600,000	($100 × 8000) = $800,000	($90 × 12,000) = $1,080,000
Total capital investment	$2,600,000	$2,800,000	$3,080,000
Annual sales (number of units)	3600	7200	12,000
Manufacturing cost, per unit	$150	$100	$90
Selling price, per unit	$300	$300	$300
Selling expense (at 37½ percent)	$112	$112	$112
Gen. and Admin. expense (at 10 percent)	$30	$30	$30
Net return, per unit	$8	$58	$68
Gross annual return	$29,000	$420,000	$820,000
Annual return on investment, percent	1	15	27

However, such an assumption might be naïve. For one thing, the competition cannot be expected to stand still during this five-year period, and there is a high likelihood that additional R & D investments will be required during the five years, to keep ahead of the competition. Viewed in this light, even a 27-percent annual return could be regarded as a borderline profit, and the company perhaps should look for other products that might afford greater returns and faster recovery of capital. Furthermore, if the sales estimates are optimistic, as often seems to be the case, or the manufacturing cost estimate turns out to be too low, the whole proposition could become quite unattractive.

For example, someone on the board of directors might worriedly reflect, "Suppose only half the projected sales quantities is achieved and, further, that the actual manufacturing cost exceeds the estimates by 25 percent? After all, that's exactly what happened to us last year on Project XYZ." With such a pessimistic slant, a calculation shows that the first year would result in a loss, with the return rising only to 8 percent in the third year. At this rate of return, it would take from ten to twelve years just to recover the investment. Perhaps the board would finally decide that the truth could be expected to lie somewhere between the two extremes, with a pay-out time of six or seven years after introduction. If this view were to prevail, the project probably would be abandoned.

New products by acquisition

Many companies have grown very fast by acquiring other companies through exchanges of stock. Sometimes such mergers have proved highly advantageous, and sometimes they have been disastrous. Booz, Allen, and Hamilton state that less than two thirds of the acquisitions covered by their surveys have proved to be satisfactory to the acquiring companies.[17]

The motive most commonly behind an acquisition is the desire to obtain a new product line. Sometimes the "product" is only some patents and a breadboard model, although the attractiveness of a proposed merger is greatly enhanced if a manufacturing and marketing capacity is also to be acquired.

The source of much unhappiness in corporate acquisitions is that realities do not always turn out to be so agreeable as the picture seemed to be during negotiations. Such a transaction is like that of the man who buys a box of apples, only to discover that all the good apples have been carefully placed on the top. Both these situations can be avoided by using

---

[17] *Management of New Products,* 1964 ed.; p. 15.

good business sense, and many corporations employ their new products departments to advantage in the careful and objective evaluation of potential acquisitions.

An interesting outline of some of the problems involved in creating new products has been provided by C. F. Rassweiler, vice-president of research and development for Johns-Manville Corporation. He says that a product in his field may take as long as seven or eight years, from research discovery to commercial success, and that the decision on a new product will prove to have been justified:

If it can be achieved technically in the laboratory.

If it can be reproduced on a factory scale.

If after four years of research the board of directors will approve the appropriation to build the plant.

If rejects and costs are reasonably low in factory production.

If consumers will buy the predicted volume of the product in six years.

If consumers will pay enough for the product to provide a satisfactory gross profit.

AND

If all this comes to pass before a competitor markets a similar product.[18]

6.6 The weapons industry

Defense is big business. Moreover, of the roughly $40 billion spent each year on defense, it has been estimated that $14 billion is spent for technically advanced weapons, that is, weapons that require substantial inputs of research and development. This makes the advanced weapons portion of the defense industry about equivalent in size to the automobile or the steel industry.[19]

Most of the considerations previously mentioned in this chapter also apply to the weapons industry, but are modified in form. An important difference, however, is that a major "product" of the industry is research and development. In fact, Peck and Scherer (see footnote 3, Chapter Two) declare that research and development has become the central line function of the weapons industry. Another difference in the weapons industry is that the major customer is the United States government,

---

[18] *Developing a Product Strategy.* See "A Basis for Product Strategy Planning," by C. S. Rassweiler, p. 74.

[19] M. J. Peck and F. M. Scherer, *The Weapons Acquisition Process: An Economic Analysis.* Cambridge, Mass.: Grad. School of Business Admin., Harvard Univ., 1962, pp. 99–102.

although some might say that the industry has numerous "customers" since procurement is carried out by many different government agencies.

Today, a major segment of the weapons industry is aerospace, an activity engaged in by many companies that once were airframe manufacturers. During the period immediately following World War II, most of these companies apparently took the attitude that research and development contracts were attractive, not as ends in themselves, but only as a "foot in the door" for later, and more profitable, production runs. Later, they must have changed their minds, because aerospace companies now compete vigorously for research and development contracts, as well as for production runs. It has been estimated that R & D accounted for 24 percent of the total aerospace sales in 1961 and that this percentage is increasing.[20]

Weapons concerns must, of course, produce profits for their stockholders. Some of the profits arise from standard risks assumed on production contracts, but a significant proportion comes from fees earned on cost-reimbursement contracts. The most commonly employed type of cost-reimbursement contract is the cost-plus-fixed fee contract (CPFF). These are typically used for R & D contracts, since, understandably, companies are generally unwilling to bid a fixed price to do something that may turn out to be impossible. In the cost-reimbursement type of contract, the company and the government agree upon the objectives to be reached and upon an estimated cost. A fee is then calculated as a percentage of the estimated cost (usually 6 percent). If the costs exceed the estimate (known as an "overrun"), the government may terminate the contract; if it chooses to continue, the company's additional costs are reimbursed, but the fee remains the same.

In CPFF contracts, there is no incentive for a company to *inflate* costs (as has sometimes been charged), since the company's fee thereby only decreases as a percentage of the cost. On the other hand, there is no real incentive for the company to keep costs down. In fact, some critics have even accused defense firms of deliberately bidding low, in order to obtain contracts; once the work has started, the cost estimates are revised upward. If realistic cost estimates had been publicized at the outset, claim the critics, many projects would never have been started.[21] However, there can be reasons for contract overruns other than deliberate underbidding or excessive optimism. Such causes might be revisions in specifications, or the

---

[20] H. O. Stekler, *The Structure and Performance of the Aerospace Industry* (Berkeley and Los Angeles: Univ. of Calif. Press, 1965), pp. 83–84.
[21] Peck and Scherer, pp. 412–416.

genuine necessity for an entire change in attack if the goal proves elusive. Whatever the reasons, contract overruns are prevalent in the weapons industry. Peck and Scherer estimate that development costs in this industry exceed original estimates by 220 percent, on the average, and have been known to exceed the original estimates by as much as 1400 percent.

There seems to be a widespread belief that there is little cost-consciousness in the defense industry, perhaps because the government is footing the bill. But national resources are not limitless, and there are strong indications that the federal government is taking positive steps to promote efficiency and cost reduction among its contractors. For example, the U.S. Defense Department has urged firms to adopt "value-engineering" techniques, to seek out lowest-cost alternatives. Any cost savings that might result from these adoptions would be shared by the firm and the government.[22] Further, there is a swing toward the use of "incentive-type" R & D contracts, in place of CPFF.[23] With an incentive-type contract, all costs are reimbursed as under CPFF, but the fee is reduced if overruns occur. Superior performance is rewarded with an increased fee. Thus, it can be seen that definite restraints urge defense companies in the direction of cost reduction. Not the least of these restraints is the knowledge that inferior past performances may work to the companies' disadvantage on future contracts.

The cost of entering a new area of weapons technology, particularly a phase of aerospace, can be enormous for a company. This becomes apparent when it is realized that a company cannot hope to gain a contract until it can demonstrate research and development competence in the contract subject-matter. Just to prepare a proposal on a complex system may cost up to a million dollars. Grumman is estimated to have spent $14 million of its own money on laboratory facilities and research before receiving the Lunar Excursion Module (LEM) contract in 1962. United Technology Corporation (UTC) is said to have spent more than $30 million to establish itself in the industry.[24]

Once established, a firm must continue to spend its own money on research and development so that it can compete in future programs. Winning a program competition is likely to depend more upon the quality of the new ideas contained in a proposal than upon the associated cost estimates, and a continuing internal R & D activity is necessary to generate these ideas. However, once a company has a contract, it can

---

[22] *Aviation Week and Space Technology,* vol. 77, Dec. 3, 1962, p. 117.
[23] Stekler, pp. 64–69.
[24] Stekler, pp. 72, 127–128, 147–148.

charge a portion of these internal R & D costs to the contract as a legitimate overhead item; this leeway is a distinct advantage to those companies already in the business.

Unquestionably, the defense industry is an important employer of engineers and scientists—perhaps the single most important such employer today. Peck and Scherer estimate that about one quarter of all American engineers and scientists are employed in the weapons industry, of which aerospace (including avionics) forms the major part.[25] Of those in aerospace, about 25 percent have been estimated to be electronic engineers (1959).[26]

A key man in the weapons industry is the "project manager." This term is widely used to designate the level of senior technical management. In addition to possessing the necessary management skills, project managers must have a high level of technical knowledge. They make most of the important decisions that control the performance and cost of the United States weapons systems.[27] As a result, the project managers are the real line-managers of weapons programs, in contrast to the situation in other industries where production or sales people occupy most of the key line-positions.

---

[25] Peck and Scherer, pp. 172–173.
[26] Stekler, pp. 99–100.
[27] Peck and Scherer, p. 179.

7 ▸ | Engineering management

In 1957, an English gentleman with the delightful name of C. Northcote Parkinson wrote a book called *Parkinson's Law*.[1] It has been rattling skeletons in administrative closets ever since. The book is more than funny: it is hilarious. But, as one reads, he experiences a chilling sense of recognition as it becomes apparent that Parkinson is very much in earnest.

Briefly stated, Parkinson's "law" is that *work expands to fill the time available for its completion*. This statement has serious implications for administrators. If there is insufficient work of a truly essential nature to occupy the attention of the work staff, then additional work will be generated to fill the void.

Parkinson concludes that administrations are bound to increase in size and that this increase is virtually independent of the actual work load. He cites some statistics to demonstrate his point, one example of which will suffice here. From 1914 to 1928, the British Navy declined by a third in officers and men and by two thirds in capital ships; during the same period, the Admiralty administration *increased* by nearly 80 percent.

Closer to home, an examination of American growth figures for the decade from 1947 to 1957 reveals that productivity increased at the rate of 3.3 percent per year, while the nonproductive work force increased at a much faster rate: 5.2 percent per year.[2]

---

[1] Copyright 1957 by C. Northcote Parkinson. Published by Houghton Mifflin, Boston.

[2] D. W. Dobler, "Implications of Parkinson's Law for Business Management," *Personnel J.*, vol. 42, January 1963, pp. 10–18. The productivity-growth rate given above is per *production* employee. An examination of productivity per *total* employee reveals a *decelerating* growth rate (from about 3.0 percent a year to 1.9 percent). However, it should be noted that the "nonproductive" work

The question may be asked: "How does this pertain to engineering?" Just this: as soon as a company has more than a very few engineers on its staff, the need will be felt to create an organizational structure. Among the functions defined in an organizational plan will be many that are administrative in nature. Clearly, the manner in which the administrative structure is created and operated will have a considerable effect upon the overall efficiency of the engineering group.

7.1 Organizing for product development

Some engineers prefer to have no organization whatever (or at least they think they do, until the time when they become distressed by the lack of certain essential services). Others, if left to their own devices, will spend so much time in developing a smoothly functioning administrative machine that they have little time left over for actual productive work. Obviously, what is wanted is just the right amount of administration to provide the necessary support for the engineering activities, and no more. Many astute observers of the American industrial scene believe that we generally tend to err more in the direction of too much organization than too little.[3]

Two basic points are to be considered in building an organizational structure: 1) What is the job or mission to be performed by the group? 2) Which individuals *really* must have what kinds of information? In most organizations, a careful investigation can bring to light some kinds of activities that are not truly relevant to the basic mission of the group and can be dispensed with. Almost any group spends a certain proportion of its time preparing forms and reports—presumably for the information of others—and it is in this area that an investigation is likely to reveal

---

force includes many specialists (such as engineers), whose efforts are essential to industry. "Nevertheless," says Dobler, "the coincidence of these two situations— the expansion of the nonproduction work force and productivity's decelerating growth rate—should be sufficient cause for the individual practitioner to take stock of his own operations."

[3] For example, see the following:

W. C. Lothrop's *Management Uses of Research and Development* (New York: Harper & Row, 1964). For seventeen years, Mr. Lothrop was a scientific consultant and senior vice-president for Arthur D. Little, Inc.

P. F. Drucker's "Twelve Fables of Research Management," *Harvard Business Rev.*, vol. 41, January–February, 1963, pp. 103–108. Mr. Drucker is a prominent management consultant.

P. Franken's "Research Inhibitions," *Internat'l Science and Technology*, May 1963, pp. 46–49.

activities that have no justifiable purpose. It has been been observed that the most difficult thing to eliminate is a form that has acquired routine usage. As a typical case, one author tells of an instance wherein a form, reporting the number of square feet of drawings that had been completed by the group had to be filled out each month. Who needed this knowledge? A company statistician who had once been caught short without that particular piece of information and was determined never to be caught again.[4]

If the two points of *function* and *who needs to know* are used as the guidelines in forming an organizational structure, then almost any scheme of organization can be made to work. It can readily be observed that identical forms of organization are, in some places, successes and, in other places, failures. Therefore, the specific form of organization itself must not be the "magic" ingredient. It is more likely that *people* will turn out to be the magic ingredient, if there is one.

If all the various forms of R & D organizations are sifted down to their basic essentials, three basic types will emerge: the *project* structure, the *functional* structure, and the *hybrid* structure.

The *project structure* (Fig. 7–1) corresponds in form to that of the decentralized corporation: each subgroup of the department is responsible for a complete project (or projects) and contains within itself all the functional competencies necessary to complete the projects. The major advantage of such a structure is that the boundaries of responsibility are crystal-clear; the major disadvantage is that functions are duplicated among groups.

The *functional structure* (Fig. 7–2) is highly centralized. A department is split into its functional specialties, and the functional subgroups operate on all projects passing through the department. One typical kind of functional grouping would separate the work into electrical design and mechanical design. Another kind would break the organization into aerodynamics, stress analysis, weights, materials, and test groups. Obviously, the kind of grouping will depend upon the branch of industry in which the company operates. The major advantage of the functional structure is that a greater technical competence can be achieved in the various engineering specialities than under the project structure. (It is more likely that the company will possess true expertise in material science, for example, if a group can focus all of its attention on this activity rather than be obliged to spread among many project groups.)

---

[4] V. Cronstedt, *Engineering Management and Administration* (New York: McGraw-Hill, 1961), p. 65.

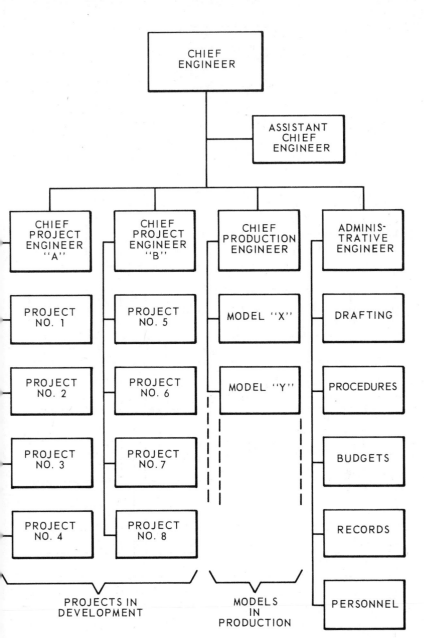

Fig. 7-1   Example of "project" organizational form.

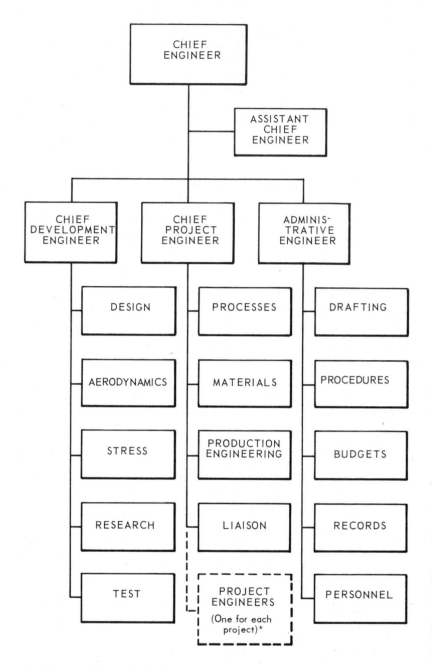

Fig. 7-2 Example of "functional" organizational form.

*If there are no project engineers (block in dotted outline), the organizational form is known as "functional." If there is a project engineer for each project, the organizational form is known as "hybrid."

The principal disadvantage of a functional structure is that it is difficult to pinpoint responsibility and certain important matters may get overlooked.

The *hybrid structure* combines the foregoing two forms and is characteristic of large companies. Functional groups exist, but each project is under the supervision of a project manager who shepherds his project through the various functional activities. Those who choose the hybrid structure generally do so in the hope that they will obtain the advantages of both the project form and the functional form. If they are successful in this aim, the hybrid form is the best of the three basic types. The danger is that, if the objective is not successfully attained, the result may be an achievement of the *disadvantages* of the other two forms—with none of the advantages.

There is yet another kind of functional structure, which is implicit in Figs. 7-1 and 7-2. These illustrations imply that each project goes first through a "development engineering" phase and, then, through a "production engineering" phase and that these phases are carried out by different groups of people. The "development" phase is presumed to end with the demonstration of a successful prototype. During the "production engineering" phase, redesign for production economy is supposed to be accomplished, provided the function is not tampered with. Often, the "development" phase is performed at a research and development laboratory physically isolated from any of the producing divisions, whereas the "production engineering" is carried out by an engineering department that is an integral part of a producing division.

Many companies work identically in the fashion just described and work successfully, too. However, it is reasonably safe to say that nearly all these companies experience severe organizational problems during the process of passing projects from one group to the other. There is, for example, the peculiar factor known as "NIH." NIH means "Not Invented Here," which is another way of saying that one engineering group is highly likely to distrust the work transmitted to it by another group and may do the whole job all over again. Alfred P. Sloan, Jr., for many years president of General Motors, tells of problems of this nature involving conflict between the research organization and the producing divisions.[5,6]

---

[5] A. P. Sloan, Jr., *My Years with General Motors* (Paperback ed.; New York: Macfadden, 1965), pp. 71–94. Orig. publ. by Doubleday, Garden City, N.Y., 1963.

[6] Others have commented on the same subject: For instance, C. W. Perelle, president of American Bosch Arma Corp., says, "The first and foremost difficulty of adding to the [product] portfolio by this approach [acquisition of other com-

At least a part of the problem is semantic and involves the phrases "completion of development work" and "demonstration of a successful prototype." To the development group, the term "development of a successful prototype" may refer to a loosely assembled collection of bench-top apparatus that demonstrates an idea. Much of the novel design work can properly be considered completed at this point, but a great deal of design remains to be done; most of it is lacking in true novelty, but it is essential to the profitability of the product that the remaining design be done well. Much of the conflict between "development" groups and "production engineering" groups stems from a development group's tendency to think that a project in such a state is mostly completed except for the shouting, whereas a production engineering group will probably believe that it is hardly begun.

Some improvement can be made by charging each group to exhibit greater forebearance, but it is likely that much more progress will result from an alteration of organizational concepts. Figure 7–3(a) presents a diagram of the "sequential-project flow" approach, which might be regarded as the classical image of the manner in which projects are conducted and includes a transfer of the project from a development group to a production engineering group. Each step is begun after the previous one has been completed. The major disadvantage of such a procedure is that it consumes a great deal of time, partly because of lack of communication among groups. As a result, there is a great compulsion, under modern-day competitive pressures, to achieve telescoping of projects, through overlapping of functions.

Such an overlapping is depicted in Fig. 7–3(b). Production planning begins even before the design is complete. In a limited way, some of the tooling may even be constructed before the design is finished, so that parts made from actual production tools can be tested in the engineering prototypes. However, it should be apparent that such a course of events entails a considerable amount of risk. The author knows of one case where the overlapping was carried too far and cost the company nearly a million dollars in scrapped tools, when the design turned out to be unsatisfactory and had to be changed.

There is an even more fundamental difference between the two

---

panies] is that our engineers cannot accept anyone else's engineering." R. C. Clark, Jr., Manager of Research and Development for the Western Company, says, "Oddly enough, researchers resist new ideas (not their own) more than any other group."—from *Developing a Product Strategy* (E. Marting, ed.; New York: Amer. Management Assoc., 1959), pp. 79, 88.

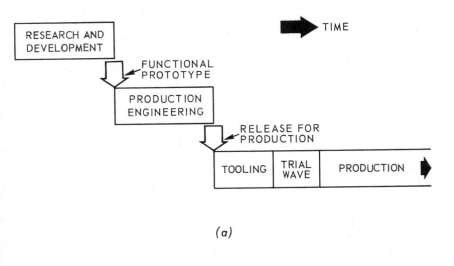

(a)

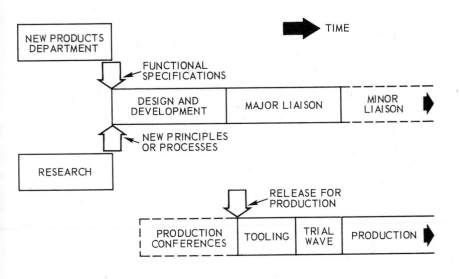

(b)

Fig. 7-3 Comparison of organizational approaches. (a) Sequential-project flow diagram. (b) Overlapping-project flow diagram.

approaches shown in Figs. 7–3(a) and 7–3(b): In Fig. 7–3(a), the project is transmitted to the other group in midstream, that is, in a semifinished stage. Fig 7–3(b), the project is never "transmitted"; the new products department transmits functional specifications to the design and development group, and the research department provides information on new principles or processes or both. The moment actual design work begins on a device that is ultimately destined for production, a "project" comes into existence. From then until the project is finally declared "complete," the project group maintains a strong degree of identity and continuity. However, the composition of the group undergoes considerable evolutionary change during its lifetime. During the early stages, the group is likely to be heavily staffed by theoretically oriented people and by those who are considered unusually creative. This make-up gradually shifts to include more production-oriented personnel. The main core of leadership of the group never undergoes any sudden drastic changes and, thus, most of the trouble caused by the NIH factor is avoided.

If a new product is essentially an improvement on the existing line—a new model, for example—then in most instances, the engineering would be done by an engineering department within a producing division. But if the product is completely new and different, there may be no existing expertise within any of the divisions: All the technical competence must be developed from scratch, and such work is frequently located away from the operating divisions. One of the reasons most frequently given for this physical isolation is that the development people must be protected from the demands of the production people, who will otherwise continually be calling upon them to put out "fires" (crises on the production line). However, there is an even more important factor: Development work within an operating division is likely to be primarily designed to support the daily operation and profit-making ability of the division. If a radically new, forward-looking project is located within a division (which is, by nature, deliberately profit-oriented), it may become a prime target for cost-cutting whenever profits get tight. For this reason, such projects are usually placed in the centralized laboratory, where they can be kept more under the longer-range eye of the corporate headquarters.[7]

One further aspect of an organization's structure, which seems to be considerably important, is whether it is relatively *closed* or relatively *open*. A *closed* system will typically exhibit a strong adherence to the usual organizational rules, with authority flowing from the top down

---

[7] See W. C. Lothrop, *Management Uses of Research and Development,* pp. 88.

along the lines of the organization chart and accountability for results flowing in the opposite direction. Great emphasis is placed upon productivity, upon enforcement of budgets and schedules, and upon going through proper channels. Even though such practices would seem only properly efficient and businesslike, it has been observed that some unexpected by-products can be high dependency (of individuals upon superiors), low autonomy, low opportunity for interaction, and low individual influence potential.[8]

In the *open* system, greater emphasis is placed upon the autonomy of individuals and less reliance is given to achieving results by means of administrative control. It might be said that the open system emphasizes subject-matter, while the closed system emphasizes the methods by which the subject-matter is to be handled. In a closed system, new jobs tend to be adapted to the organizational structure while, in an open system, the structure is adapted to the jobs.

L. B. Barnes of Harvard made a study in depth of two engineering groups, one of which had a relatively closed system (Dept "A") and the other, a relatively open system (Dept "B"). Barnes cautioned that conclusive results cannot be obtained by examining only two groups, but did observe that Dept "B" displayed higher individual satisfaction, less conflict, higher group performance, and greater individual opportunity, than did Dept "A."[9]

A recommendation in favor of an "open" system would seem to be equivalent to a vote for disorder, as opposed to order. Yet the implications of Barnes' study would seem to be that an excessively ordered environment may have an adverse effect upon productivity.

Lothrop has entitled these same two kinds of organization the *pyramid* and *the flat organization.* The pyramid, according to Lothrop, has the ultimate of control built-in. It satisfies ". . . status needs of the people on the top and dependency needs of the people on the bottom." He goes on to say that, although the pyramid organization does satisfy the human desire to be recognized, it also stereotypes individuals and is wasteful of talent. He strongly recommends the flat organization for product development, in which *people* are the focal point. Lothrop pictures the project leaders as a "group of peers," in which the director functions, not as a technical head, but as an administrator who provides the essential

---

[8] L. B. Barnes, *Organizational Systems and Engineering Groups.* Cambridge, Mass.: Grad. School of Business Admin., Harvard Univ., 1960, pp. 149–52.

[9] Barnes, p. 134.

services to the others. The word "flat" has been chosen because it indicates that a large number of people (perhaps as many as twenty) may report to a single head; in this way, the large amount of vertical structuring, which is a common feature of the more conventional pyramid, can be avoided.[10]

7.2 Manufacturing

If the work of the engineer is to reach the public, sooner or later, it must be manufactured. It might be supposed that the responsibility of the engineering department essentially ends with the release of engineering drawings to the manufacturing department, but this is far from the case. In fact, during the early phases of manufacturing, it may seem to the participants that *nothing* goes right and that the engineering department is constantly embroiled in putting down crises. Everything that worked so well in the prototype model seems to go wrong in the production model.

There is a good reason for this, of course. First, mistakes are bound to occur. They must be found and corrected, and this is why it is important to initiate production with a "trial wave" (See Figs. 7–3(a) and 7–3(b).) Second, statistical variations in production parts unavoidably take place, and this will produce a certain amount of malfunctioning. Third—and probably most important—the transition from engineering to manufacturing is a transition from a closely supervised, one-at-a-time kind of activity to a widely dispersed mass production effort. The tasks must be broken down into thousands of subtasks, performed by as many different individuals, that are coordinated only by organizational procedures and pieces of paper; many difficulties will occur before this complicated system is running smoothly.

When a crises arises on the production line, a frantic call is sent out for the engineers to come "put out the fire." Since everything is new and unfamiliar to the production people at this point, it becomes necessary to bring in the men who understand the product; and these are the men who designed it. In preparation for the start-up of manufacturing, a frequent practice is to assign a man to each project, in the very early phases, who knows his ultimate destiny is to become the "liaison engineer," that is, a man who really *knows* the product and can become the production line "crisis-stopper." During manufacturing start-up, this kind of arrangement helps to relieve the development people from

---

[10] Lothrop, p. 97.

demands that they drop their new projects and rush to put down crises. In any case, the early production period is likely to consume the attention of many engineers for a considerable time after start-up. Not until the occurrence of trouble has settled to a relatively low level, can the project be considered "complete."

Even after the subsidence of major crises, the engineering effort never entirely ceases on a product unless it is an extremely simple one. Tools wear and change, people are transferred, and new procedures are tried out. All of these may affect the product and probably will. Incomprehensible things like the following may occur, for example: A new tool is made to replace an old one, and in the process, it is discovered that the old tool was not producing parts that meet the dimensional specifications of the engineering drawing. Naturally, the new tool is made in correct accordance with the drawing, and then it is discovered that the new, "correct" parts don't function properly, whereas the old "incorrect" ones worked fine. Consternation ensues, and out goes the crisis-call to Engineering. Another "fire" must be put out.

On most mass production products, a perpetual cost-reduction program is under way throughout the product's effective life, and this requires the participation of the engineering department. The saving of a few cents on a part can add up to tremendous yearly savings. Elementary arithmetic will show that the saving of ten cents each on 100,000 parts a year will equal a man's salary, and 100,000 parts a year is not very much in terms of mass production. However, in comparing two processes, the current one and a proposed one, it should be realized that *everything* is known about the current process—especially all the bad things; on the other hand, the things that are known about the proposed project will be predominantly good. It is practically axiomatic that unforeseen things will turn up as any new process is put into effect, and that these will mostly be developments that will increase the cost. Hence, any cost-reduction proposal must not only excel in thoroughness, but it also must offer an unusually good prospect for payoff, so that it can absorb all the unexpected setbacks and still prove worthwhile.

7.3 Engineering administration

There are at least two ways to approach the subject of engineering administration. One is through detailed discussion of the forms, procedures, methods, and responsibility assignments that might be used by engineering organizations. However, these are likely to be of interest only to the man who is seeking an answer to a specific organizational problem.

Besides, since at least two entire books have been written on this subject,[11] no space will be given here to this aspect of the matter.

The other approach is to consider philosophical and policy matters affecting engineering administration. Since every engineer comes in contact, sooner or later, with these issues, they will be discussed here.

Budgets: a necessary evil

Any attempt to schedule creative activity would seem to be a patent absurdity. In a difficult and novel development project, it is impossible to state, with any certainty, just when the essential breakthroughs will come—or if they will come at all. Yet, this is precisely what development project schedules and budgets seem to be aimed at.

Many engineers fear budgets because they have learned, through experience, that administrative people tend to treat a budget as a firm commitment. Since this is held to be an unreasonable expectation for development projects, then the budgets should be dispensed with (or so the argument goes).

An intermediate point of view would call for an alteration in the budgeting concept that would recognize the validity of *both* of the following opposing ideas: 1) the scheduling of creative breakthroughs is impossible; 2) operating without schedules and budgets is possible, but intolerable.

Under this plan, it is assumed that a certain amount of faith exists, that the goal can be achieved without requiring a basic *scientific* breakthrough. This being the case, there also will exist some idea of the steps that will be necessary to reach the goal. From this knowledge of the necessary steps, some idea of the manpower and elapsed time can be estimated—imperfect though such estimates may be. These estimates then form the basis of a schedule, but it would be a mistake to consider such a schedule a firm commitment.

Even though these schedules are to be regarded as subject to periodic revision and up-dating, management will now have some rough idea of the extent of the proposed programs and can make financial plans to meet the costs. The basic point is this: the money to pay for research and

[11] V. Cronstedt's *Engineering Management and Administration* (New York: McGraw-Hill, 1961) and J. E. Thompson's *Engineering Organization and Methods* (New York: McGraw-Hill, 1947).

development is not automatically available when it is wanted. Such money must be consciously appropriated from some other purpose: from plant expansion, perhaps, or from dividends to the stockholders, or maybe from other development projects.

Schedule-making (which is a prerequisite step to budget-making) can be approached in at least three ways, and all three approaches should be simultaneously used. One (and the most obvious) is to subdivide the project into its different activity phases and, then, to estimate the man-hours required for each phase. Such a breakdown into phases may assume many forms: for example, a project may be divided into the phases of preliminary design, experimental prototype, test, detail design, production prototype, test, redesign, release, and trial wave. Sometimes a complicated system may be broken down into its subsystems and its sub-subsystems and schedule times may be estimated for these.

The second approach to scheduling is to assume a reasonable correlation between the number of parts in a unit and the time required to develop it. Obviously, this works only when the company has developed data of this nature for past projects and when the new project has sufficient similarity to former projects to make any sort of comparison valid.

The third approach is based on pure intuition and experience. The schedule-maker simply looks at the overall project, compares it in gross terms with other projects in his experience, and asks himself, "Now, how long do I *really* think this project will take, in view of the time required by other projects in the past?" The results of all three methods are then compared. If there are any gross discrepancies, it is probable that something important has been overlooked in one of the approaches. This realization will lead to revisions, and a better job of scheduling will be the consequence.

Once a schedule and its budget have been adopted, it becomes part of the official plan. A good schedule will contain numerous check points. If any check point is not met, it becomes necessary to prepare a new schedule to be considered by management for readoption. If schedules are prepared and revised in complete honesty and objectivity, they will form the best up-to-the-minute view of the future that is possible. This is an essential thing for higher management to have, in attempting to plot the company growth and development.

In large-scale programs, it becomes very difficult to coordinate the many activities that, together, constitute an entire project. Several methods have been developed in answer to this need: principal among them are **PERT** (Program Evaluation and Review Technique) and **CPM**

(Critical Path Method).[12] CPM was originally developed in the chemical and construction industries, whereas PERT had its beginnings in connection with the Polaris missile system project. Today, many government agencies are requiring that at least one of these methods be used for the scheduling of their contracts. No attempt will be made here to describe CPM or PERT in detail. However, the basic idea is that a network diagram is prepared that shows all the different activities and their interrelationships, especially those relationships that will cause any phase to be delayed if another is not completed on time. After this, the most critical chain of events will be worked out from the diagram; this sequence is the one that will limit the overall completion of the project. Special attention can then be given to this path, to see if any shortening can be achieved. During the execution of the project, if any phase fails to meet a check-point date, the entire network must be reanalyzed to see if this has caused a *different* sequence of activities to become the critical path. Then a new schedule may have to be prepared. In the case of an extremely large program, it may be necessary to use a computer for this analysis.

"Arm-waving," or the crash project

The author's personal introduction to the phenomenon known as the "crash project" came shortly after he had been employed in his first job. The project had really become hot, and his boss gave instructions that until the job was done, everyone was to bypass procedures and paperwork completely and to use "arm-waving," instead. What was arm-waving? It meant that, instead of stopping to make a drawing or even a sketch, one went directly to the shop and gave verbal instructions to make it "this big, this long, and this wide," indicating the desired dimensions by arm-motions.

The foregoing example is admittedly an extreme one, but crash projects are a fairly prominent feature on the American industrial scene, especially in the weapons industry. For one reason or another, top management may suddenly decide that a particular deadline must be met, regardless of cost, and a crash project is declared. Everything else suddenly finds itself in a lower priority, and everyone assigned to the crash project finds himself working long stretches of overtime. Jewkes, Sawers, and Stillerman have suggested that at least part of the explanation for

---

[12] For details of these methods, see J. J. Moder and C. R. Phillips' *Project Management with CPM and PERT* (New York: Reinhold, 1964).

huge development costs in the twentieth century may be found in this tendency of corporations to declare time to be of the essence in development projects—in spite of cost.[13]

An interesting personal view of crash projects has been provided by a senior engineer in an electronics company that manufactures semiconductors. A crash project had been declared, with the objective of developing a new transistor in the impossibly short time of only eight weeks. Wrote the engineer:

> In the end the project was successful—by late Friday afternoon of the eighth week! This leads to the inevitable conclusion that success could also have been achieved late Friday of the seventh week or the sixth, these goals being really no more ridiculous than the eight-week goal. We will pursue this avenue of thought no farther, but leave it instead to fester in the mind of the reader.[14]

The use of supporting personnel

During past periods of acute engineer shortages, questions concerning the proper utilization of engineers have regularly been raised. Are engineers being used at their highest potential? Are many of them required to perform tasks that could be given, instead, to technicians or to clerks?

Statistics show that the ratio of technicians to engineers is far from that which is considered optimum. A survey conducted in 1963 disclosed a ratio of only 0.38 technician per engineer,[15] whereas most people seem to believe that 2.0 technicians per engineer would be desirable and some even favor a ratio of 4 to 1.[16] Among the various segments of industry, Communications seems to be closest to the ideal, with 2.37 technicians per engineer.

What is a technician, and how may he be used efficiently? Broadly speaking, he is a technically trained person who works as a member of the engineering team in a support-capacity to the engineer, although he may possess certain skills which he has developed to a higher degree than

---

[13] Jewkes, Sawers, and Stillerman, *The Sources of Invention* (London: Macmillan; and New York: St. Martin's Press, 1958), pp. 202–210. Used by permission.

[14] From T. Moranian's *The Research and Development Engineer as Manager* (New York: Holt, Rinehart and Winston, 1963), p. 22.

[15] *Demand for Engineers, Physical Scientists, and Technicians—1964*. New York: Eng. Manpower Com., Engrs. Joint Council, 1964, p. 51.

[16] *Engineering Manpower, A Statement of Position*. New York: Engrg. Manpower Com., Engrs. Joint Council, 1963, p. 23.

has the engineer for whom he works. Such would be the case, for example, with the electronics technician who assembles experimental "breadboard" circuits, or with the mechanical draftsman who prepares crisp, workmanlike drawings from the engineer's sketches. The following list presents some kinds of activities in which engineering technicians engage:

Drafting	Surveying
Estimating	Technical Writing
Field Service	Testing
Inspection	Time Study
Installation	Tool Design
Maintenance[17]	

Formerly, technicians just "grew" on the job, but there has been a strong movement, during recent years, to systematize the education of technicians. The Engineers' Council for Professional Development (ECPD), which is the accrediting agency for professional engineering education, also accredits programs for technician training. The majority of these programs are two years long (some are three) and result in the award of a degree such as Associate in Engineering, or Associate in Science.

From the viewpoint of engineering management, all jobs that can be efficiently assigned to a technician, should be so assigned. This seems to be a simple enough imperative; yet it is often violated. Strangely, the utilization of technicians is sometimes resisted by the individual engineer. Some engineers gain personal satisfaction from working with their hands: wiring their own circuits, making their own drawings, or running machine tools in the experimental shop. From management's point of view, such practices are hardly justifiable because: 1) an engineer will seldom be as skilled as the technician who is a specialist in any of these fields, and 2) the engineer is being paid a salary higher than the technician's to do work that the technician could do better.

There are other—and more powerful—reasons why the technician-engineer ratio may be less than optimum. The main cause is simply that technicians are in even shorter supply than engineers. Furthermore, it looks as if this situation will continue unless there is a dramatic increase in technician enrollments. In recent years, this country has been producing less than one technician for every two engineers; this ratio is barely enough to maintain the status quo.[18]

---

[17] *Technician Career Opportunities in Engineering Technology.* New York: ECPD.

[18] From 1958 to 1962, there were about sixteen thousand graduates per year from technician-producing institutions, compared with about thirty-six thousand

Another reason for less-than-optimum technician–engineer ratios in some companies can be traced to layoff practices during periods of cost-cutting. When an engineer is laid off, a lot of know-how goes with him, and this know-how can be reacquired later on, only with much difficulty. Because there is a much smaller know-how investment in a technician, there is a natural tendency to let a high proportion of technicians go during a layoff and to keep the engineers. Naturally, the result of such a practice is that the remaining engineers must pick up the load formerly carried by technicians.

Many fine points of judgment are involved in deciding what should be handled by engineers and what should be handled by technicians. Often, technicians are capable of discharging some of the simpler phases of design and should be encouraged to do so, in the interests of efficiency. However, various responsible groups have expressed alarm over the tendency of many engineers to avoid design of a detail nature and, consequently, to allow responsibility for such work to be passed by default to technicians. In 1959, a committee appointed at the Massachusetts Institute of Technology to study engineering design, commented that many young engineers seem to believe any problems not requiring higher mathematics are beneath their dignity and, so, let them pass to technicians. "This attitude," said the committee, "often prevails in spite of the clear indication that the most important decisions in a design problem must often be made without assistance from higher mathematics."[19] The main inference to be drawn from the foregoing is that mature judgment is necessary to decide what should be left to technicians and what should not, and that mathematical content is not necessarily a good criterion.

The concern about detail work is not confined to the United States. The United Kingdom Atomic Energy Authority in 1963 commented, "There is a tendency for designs to be spoiled by lack of attention to detail and this often causes difficult and costly rectification work at site that could have been avoided by more rigorous thought at the design stage . . ." According to a British committee appointed to study such matters, one reason for this state of affairs is the unwillingness of qualified design engineers to work on detail design.[20]

---

engineering graduates per year—from *Engineering Manpower, A Statement of Position.*

[19] "Report on Engineering Design," *J. Engrg. Educ.,* vol. 51, April 1961, pp. 645–656.

[20] Dept. of Scientific and Industrial Research, Her Majesty's Stationery Office, *Engineering Design, Report of a Committee Appointed by the Council for Scientific and Industrial Research to Consider the Present Standing of Mechanical Engineering Design.* London: 1963, p. 16.

If there is a moral to be drawn from the preceding section, it is that engineers can profitably use technicians as assistants, but cannot abandon responsibility for a design matter to them, just because it happens to be of a detail nature. As the British committee on design said, "In design *everything* matters."

Dimensioning for the scrap pile

A subject for continual (and sometimes heated) debate, especially between engineering and manufacturing personnel, is the matter of *tolerances.*

The setting of tolerances is a very responsible matter and requires mature judgment: It is hardly something to be left to a drafting group, although some companies believe this is the correct thing to do.

Almost invariably, inexperienced engineers will set tolerances too tight. They do this partly because they lack knowledge of costs and partly because they sense that, in this direction, lies security. Some even exhibit an absurd tendency to specify all tolerances at ± 0.001 inches, simply because this is a convenient number.

Among manufacturing personnel, there is a tendency to believe that every tolerance is arrived at by Engineering through a comprehensive analytic process that will guarantee results if done correctly. This cannot be the case, of course. It is feasible and appropriate to analyze certain *critical* features of the design for their behavior under tolerance variations, but this is impossible for all the hundreds of thousands of dimensions involved in a complex product. Hence, most tolerances are established on the basis of judgment and experience. Again, the inexperienced (or the timid) will seek security in tight tolerances, but it is more advantageous to the company to find that magic condition wherein the tolerances are as loose as they possibly can be while they still permit the product to function properly. Tolerances that are tighter than necessary will only increase the number of parts which find their way to the scrap-pile. In fact, in some precision industries, it is taken for granted that extremely tight tolerances will be achieved only by virtue of a large amount of scrapped parts.

There is little agreement in the literature about the proper policy to follow in setting tolerances. Some authorities have advocated the deliberate setting of tolerances at a level less than the allowable amount (for instance, 75 percent of maximum), so that there will be something to "give" at a later time. Others are violently opposed to such a practice. There also is disagreement concerning tolerance accumulation. Some people believe that a tolerance analysis should be based upon obtaining proper function of the equipment, even when every tolerance accumulates to the maximum in the worst direction. Others believe tolerance-accumulation analysis should be based on the theory of probability.

The author believes it would be foolish for him to attempt to establish, for all time and for all places, which of these conflicting approaches is best. They have all been used and, apparently, have all worked. As a practical matter, however, the easiest policy to administer is the one that would require tolerances to be placed at their maximum permissible limit and that will result in properly functioning units even if all tolerances should simultaneously accumulate, to the limit, in the worst direction.

Although the preceding discussion relates primarily to mechanical products, the same considerations apply to electrical and electronic systems. In an electronic circuit, for example, the characteristics of each component will have allowable variations specified by the manufacturer, and the effect of these variations must be taken into account. Many circuits have worked admirably in the laboratory, but have failed in service, because the designer neglected to consider what would happen if all the resistors happened to vary to the limit in the wrong directions, or if the supply voltage dropped to 95 volts (as sometimes happens) instead of remaining at its nominal value of 115.

8 ▸ | Salaries and other rewards

8.1 The rising curves

It has been observed that *salary* almost never appears at the top of the list when engineers are asked to indicate those things that are important to them in the ideal job. Instead, it modestly shows up in third or fourth place. For example, in one survey, the leading desirable job characteristics were reported to be 1) opportunity for advancement, 2) creative, challenging work, 3) good salary, 4) recognition of achievement, and 5) the chance to keep up with new developments.[1]

Some have been tempted to believe that this means engineers have little interest in money. However, it is more likely that engineers simply have not experienced any need to worry about salaries, because they have been in a "seller's market" since 1950.

Although salary is well down the list, it will turn up in the Number 1 spot any time a man believes that his salary is not being handled in a fair manner. This usually means that he expects his employer to keep salaries in step with "what is going on outside." As a rule, he will not be seriously disturbed if he is subjected to outside offers that are moderately higher than his current salary, because he realizes that other employers are willing to offer a premium to entice a man to move. However, the premium cannot be *too* great if he is to remain unskeptical when his boss declares his employees are being treated fairly.

The widespread distribution of salary surveys makes the income of engineers among the best documented of subjects. Surveys are regularly

---

[1] *Career Satisfactions of Professional Engineers in Industry.* Washington, D.C.: The Professional Engrs. Conf. Board for Industry, p. 20; in cooperation with the Nat'l Soc. of Professional Engrs.

taken by all kinds of groups, including manufacturers' associations, regional organizations, engineering societies, and the United States government. Among the better-known surveys are those of the American Management Association (Executive Compensation Service), the National Society of Professional Engineers, and the Engineers Joint Council (Engineering Manpower Commission).

A major criticism of nearly all salary surveys taken in the past has been that they lumped all engineers together, regardless of their responsibility levels. Former engineers who had become company executives were still included in the surveys and acted as average-raisers. In 1964, the Engineering Manpower Commission, for the first time, divided its report so that the incomes of supervisors and nonsupervisors were separated. This innovation, plus the inclusion of nearly a quarter of a million engineers in the EMC survey, make it the most broadly useful one in existence. EMC's survey is concerned with only degree-holding engineers, and it has been estimated that nearly half the degree-holding engineers in America are included.

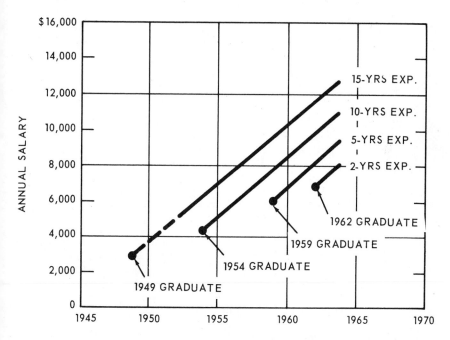

Fig. 8-1   Typical rates of salary increase for four hypothetical engineering graduates, based upon medians of salaries reported; actual dollars. Average rate of increase: $680 per year. (From *Professional Income of Engineers, 1964*. December 1964. Courtesy of Engrg. Manpower Com., Engrs. Joint Council, New York)

Figure 8-1 shows that the average *dollar* increase per year for a "median man" remained about constant for the fifteen-year period from 1949 through 1964. This calculation includes the effects of shortage, surplus, inflation, recession, merit, and growth of the profession. Obviously, there is no such creature as a "median man," but if there were, he would have experienced a salary growth rate of about 7 percent per year during this period.

Such a remarkable individual salary-growth rate has been possible only because of the unceasing upward movement of engineering salaries, plus the general inflationary trend. The inflationary influence is actually minor, however, as Fig. 8-2 shows. Despite inflation, the spendable median income of engineers increased by 40 percent from 1953 to 1964. It should be noted that the curves in Figure 8-2 show a distinct leveling-off tendency. It would seem reasonable to take this as a sign that acute shortages of engineers were abating during the early 1960s.

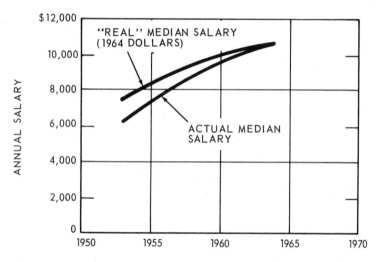

Fig. 8-2   Change in median salaries for engineers, from 1953 to 1964, adjusted for median experience of ten years; "real" salary curve represents adjustment for 16.2-percent increase in consumer price index (From *Professional Income of Engineers, 1964*. December 1964. Courtesy of Engrg. Manpower Com., Engrs. Joint Council, New York)

Figures 8-3 and 8-4 display the customary "maturity curves" obtained by plotting engineers' salaries against the years they have held their bachelor's degrees. The labels "10th, 25th, MEDIAN, 75th," and "90th" refer to percentile levels and mean that 10, 25, 50, 75, and 90 percent, respectively, of the persons in the survey are below the curves indicated.

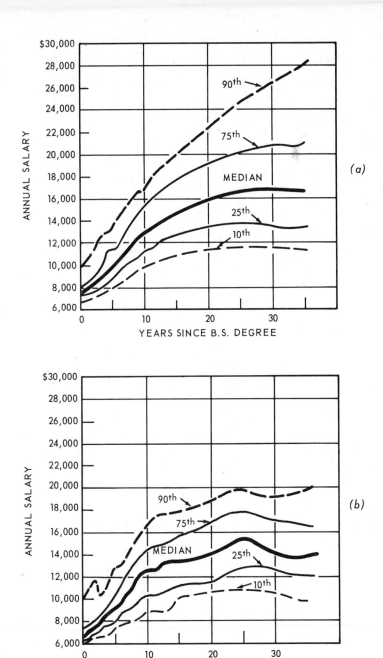

Fig. 8-3 Comparison between supervising engineers' salaries in government and industry. (*a*) Supervisors in industry. (*b*) Supervisors in government. (From *Professional Income of Engineers, 1964*. December 1964. Courtesy of Engrg. Manpower Com., Engrs. Joint Council, New York)

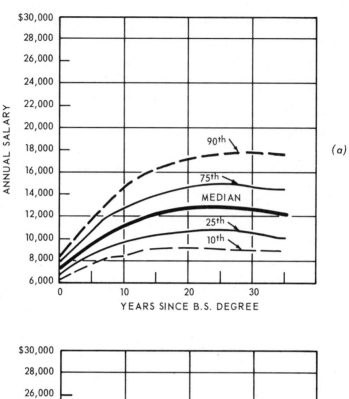

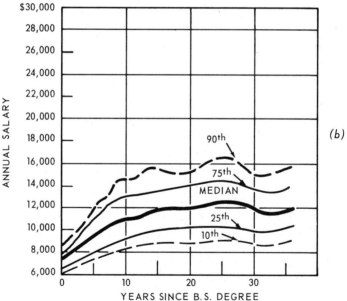

Fig. 8-4 Comparison between nonsupervising engineers' salaries in industry and government. (*a*) Nonsupervisors in industry. (*b*) Nonsupervisors in government. (From *Professional Income of Engineers, 1964*. December 1964. Courtesy of Engrg. Manpower Com., Engrs. Joint Council, New York)

Figures 8-5 and 8-6 show *median* maturity curves for eight different kinds of industries that are major employers of engineers. It probably will not surprise anyone that aerospace and electronics have been the highest-paying industries.

It almost seems presumptuous to add the following warning to all who would compare their own situations against percentile curves: a "median" curve means that, besides the 50 percent of the population above that curve, there are, necessarily, exactly 50 percent below it. It would be an unusual person who is willing to admit to himself that he is a below-median man; yet it is an inexorable result of mathematical definitions that precisely half of us are below median.

Starting salaries

For information concerning employment trends for college graduates, Dr. Frank S. Endicott, director of placement for Northwestern University, Evanston, Ill., has no peer.[2] Since 1947, Dr. Endicott has conducted regular surveys on employment trends. Figure 8-7 shows the movement in starting engineering salaries since 1947 (which has been unremittingly up). Since 1947, there has been a 150-percent increase in starting salaries, with only a 30-percent rise in the cost of living.

The observation has been made that starting salaries have moved upward faster than salaries for more experienced men: The name "compression" has been given to this phenomenon. However, Figs. 8-2 and 8-7 show the following: in the ten-year period from 1954 to 1964, starting salaries increased a total of about $3000, but the median salary level for ten-years experience rose by $3500. Thus, although, on a percentage basis, starting salaries rose a greater amount (since they started from a lower base); there was no "compression" on a dollar basis.

On the other hand, the starting salaries for men with advanced degrees show much more pronounced upward tendencies. For example: in 1965 through 1966, the average starting salary, nationwide, for newly graduated engineers with a bachelor's degree was $665 per month; for men with a master's degree, the average starting salary was $795 per month; and for men with the doctorate, it was $1113 per month.[3] In 1964, the "median" salary for men with ten years of experience (all degrees to-

---

[2] See F. S. Endicott's *Trends in Employment of College and University Graduates in Business and Industry, 1965*. Evanston, Ill.: Northwestern Univ.

[3] *A Study of 1965–66 Beginning Offers, Report No. 2, March, 1966*. Bethlehem, Pa.: The College Placement Council. (The averages given here are based upon approximately eight thousand cases.)

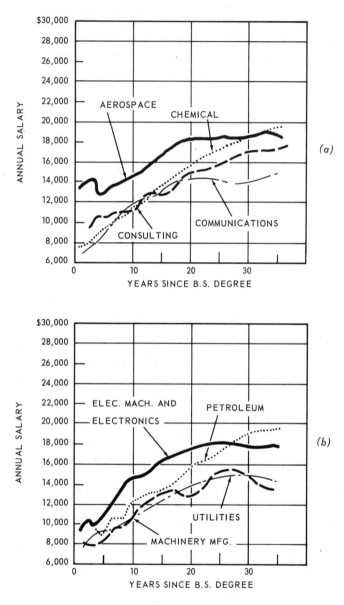

Fig. 8-5 Comparison of supervising engineers' salaries in eight different industries. (*a*) Median curves for supervisors in aerospace, chemical engineering, communications, and consultant engineering. (*b*) Median curves for supervisors in elec. machinery and electronics engineering, machinery-manufacturing, petroleum engineering, and utilities. (From *Professional Income of Engineers, 1964*. December 1964. Courtesy of Engrg. Manpower Com., Engrs. Joint Council, New York)

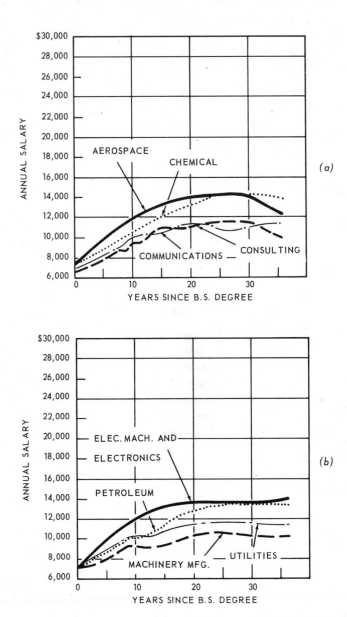

Fig. 8-6 Comparison of nonsupervising engineers' salaries in eight different industries. (*a*) Median curves for nonsupervisors in aerospace, chemical engineering, communications, and consultant
engineering. (*b*) Median curves for nonsupervisors in elec. machinery and electronics engineering, machinery-manufacturing,
petroleum engineering, and utilities. (From *Professional Income
of Engineers, 1964.* December 1964. Courtesy of Engrg. Manpower Com., Engrs. Joint Council, New York)

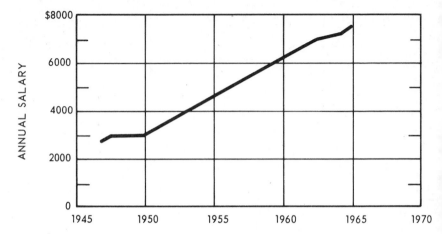

Fig. 8-7   Beginning salaries, from 1947 to 1965, for graduate engineers without experience (Courtesy of the F. S. Endicott Placement surveys, Northwestern Univ., Evanston, Ill.)

gether) was approximately $10,500. It would be expected that, by 1965–1966, this level would have moved upward, but it can readily be seen that the *starting* salary for men with master's degrees was not far behind that earned by men who had spent years in the field—and that the starting salaries for men with doctorates had leaped far beyond the "median" level.

Do bricklayers really earn more than engineers?

Many engineers believe that construction workers *are* paid more for their efforts and that the condition constitutes a gross injustice. They argue, with some logic, that a long and arduous college education should produce better financial results than this. But both the logic and their sense of injustice are wasted, because the premise is false.

It is easy to be misled. For example, a headline in *Engineering News-Record* declared, "Workers Average $4.25 an Hour." The article added that union scale wages for bricklayers (the highest-paid trade) had reached a nationwide average of $4.74 as of July 1, 1964.[4]

The engineer quickly multiplies (taking into consideration that an average month contains 173 hours, not 160) and concludes that the bricklayer makes $820 a month, or almost $10,000 per year. Since the engineer

---

[4] *Engrg. News-Record,* Aug. 20, 1964, p. 71.

generally doesn't earn $10,000 a year until he has been out of school seven or eight years, he decides that something is seriously wrong. The vital missing ingredient is steadiness of employment. The 1960 United States census reveals that less than a third of the nation's bricklayers enjoyed steady employment. Other building trades experience similar employment instability. The average annual earnings reported in 1960 were: carpenters, $4164; masons, $4793; plumbers, $5593; tool and die craftsmen, $6527; engineers, $8300; and new engineering graduates with no experience, $5900.[5]

8.2 Salary administration

Salary administration is a difficult, and sometimes frustrating, activity. Many employers expend considerable effort and expense in the attempt to analyze salary structures scientifically and to carry out carefully planned review systems. All this is done in a genuine attempt to establish a remuneration for each person that is commensurate with his contribution.

One of the more difficult matters handled by every salary program is determining the basis upon which a man is, or is not, to receive a raise. It is generally considered undesirable for a man to receive raises automatically as a function of length of service, except perhaps in the first year or so following employment. Instead, increases usually are granted on merit.

However, it is often difficult to decide exactly what is meant by "merit." One interesting salary program that handles this question in a straightforward manner is Union Carbide's.[6] This program calls for supervisors to make a forced choice, concerning each employee's standing among the categories *satisfactory, commendable,* and *outstanding.* (Presumably, if a man is classified *unsatisfactory,* he is terminated.) In 1964, a "satisfactory" man was given an increase of 3 percent, a "commendable" man received a 5- to 8-percent increase, and an "outstanding" man was raised by 12 percent or more. It was stated, "The satisfactory increase percentage is usually designed to correspond with the annual formula increase." (In 1964, the formula increase called for all salary ranges to rise by 3 percent.)

The truly outstanding man is no problem to handle under a salary administration program. Neither is the "commendable" man. Salary increases for both usually can be easily justified on a clear merit basis.

---

[5] U.S. Bureau of the Census, *U. S. Census of Population: 1960.* Washington, D.C.: vol. 1, pt. 1, 1964, p. 1-553.

[6] C. S. Dadakis, *Job Evaluation and Salary Administration for Engineers.* New York: Amer. Soc. of Mech. Engrs., ASME Paper No. 64-MD-24, 1964.

However, a glance at Figs. 8-3 and 8-4 reveals a distinct flattening in the salary curves of the "median man" after his twentieth year, when he is only halfway through his forty years or so of productive life. This means that, if it were not for the existence of upward-pushing forces such as inflation and continuously rising engineering salaries, our fictitious "median man" would reach a salary plateau halfway through his career and would never again get another increase. It is possible that inflation is a permanent fixture of our environment, but ever-rising engineering salaries are not. Generations of engineers who have come to accept salary growth as semiautomatic may find it difficult to adapt to a changed environment.

There appears to be a strong interest in a type of plan known as the "curve approach." It is a controversial one. One proponent frankly admits, "Many compensation managers damn it; many others have high praise for it."[7]

In such plans, three elements are allowed to influence salary growth: educational attainment, maturity factors, and job performance. The rationale for including maturity factors is that an increase in years of experience implies an increase in effectiveness and judgment and, further, that a man is entitled to salary growth as a reward for satisfactory performance. The third factor is included so that truly superior performance can be recognized by larger salary increases. One required step in the administration of these plans is that every employee be ranked on the basis of performance on a list, sometimes referred to as a "reverse layoff list." This list is then used to justify increases given for superior performance.

Proponents of the curve approach maintain it is more successful than other plans in achieving the basic objectives of all such programs, which are to reward outstanding performance and to establish equity of compensation among all employees, as far as this is possible. They also maintain that compensation plans based on the curve approach are simpler to administer.

In their efforts to build rational salary administration programs, companies that do not adopt the curve approach usually start from zero and attempt to build up a point value for each job, based upon its worth to the organization. Typical criteria would be the amount of knowledge or skill required, the degree of original thought and action necessary, and the extent of accountability and responsibility. These are used in a com-

---

[7] J. W. Blood, ed., *The Management of Scientific Talent*, New York: Amer. Management Assoc., 1963. See "The Curve Approach to the Compensation of Scientists," by E. A. Shaw, p. 147.

parative fashion against other jobs in the organization to establish a point-rating. They are also used to prepare job descriptions.[8]

Once a set of relative point values is obtained, it might be supposed that salary ranges, based upon these points, could immediately be established. However, the influence of the marketplace upon salaries for different kinds of jobs must be taken into account. This means that salary surveys must be consulted to ensure that rates will be competitive.

In salary administration, there may be a temptation to establish rate ranges *a little higher than the market,* to give a recruiting edge. Obviously, if all companies do this, the result is a bootstrapping operation; this effect alone would be enough to keep salary curves rising. Even if only a few companies do this and all the others merely aim at the median, a net upward force is still generated.

Once an overall rate range has been established, it is customarily broken down into five or six subranges. (See Appendix for a description of five levels recommended by the American Management Association, plus a sixth level for specialists.) These rate ranges generally overlap, for no clear-cut reason except that it is customary.

It is an unusual company that publishes its rate ranges for all to see. (A survey by Booz, Allen and Hamilton produced the remarkable information that 80 percent of the companies in the survey did not have written salary policies available to their technical personnel.[9]) Generally, a man is told his own range and, probably, he will be told what is necessary before he can advance into the next range. Information concerning salaries paid to specific individuals is almost universally considered confidential.

A basic ingredient of most salary programs is a provision for regular reviews of performance. If the results of surveys are to be believed, the manner in which many programs are carried out must be poor.[10] Some companies do a consistent job of handling performance reviews, but in many others, these activities are conducted sporadically, if at all. In some cases, if the man actually is to receive a raise, he is given a review by his supervisor, but if no raise is forthcoming, the matter of a review is ignored. Many times, the excuse is given that time is insufficient for periodic reviews, or supervisors may express doubt that higher management is really interested in having them take the time.

A desire on the part of an employee that he should have an opportunity,

---

[8] *The Management of Scientific Talent.* See "Compensating Scientific Personnel," by C. W. G. Van Horn, pp. 130–132.

[9] J. L. Wyatt, "Are Creative People 'Different'?" *The Management Rev.* vol. 48, July 1959, p. 21.

[10] J. W. Riegel, *Administration of Salaries and Intangible Rewards for Engineers and Scientists (Part 1).* Ann Arbor, Univ. of Mich., 1958 pp. 63–66.

every six or twelve months, to discuss his performance with his supervisor would not be unreasonable. Such a practice ought to be a positive requirement of any salary program. But the initiative must come from the supervisors. Many employees simply will not take the initiative themselves. Probably the greatest benefit that can be derived from a good salary administration plan is the secure knowledge of the employees that their performance and their salaries will be examined and discussed with them, on a regular basis, and that equity will be maintained.

Situations such as the following are nearly independent of any salary programs that may be in operation:

1) The rate at which an engineer just out of college advances in salary is almost independent of his performance. If he is judged sufficiently valuable to continue on the payroll at all, his increases in the first year or two will approach the point of being automatic. After his second year with the company, his individual performance will begin to show its influence, and the truly outstanding man can move ahead very fast. Even during the first five or ten years, a competent man can expect a more or less steady salary growth. After the tenth year, the salaries of many will begin to level out (see Figs. 8-3 through 8-6).

2) An individual's future salary history will be strongly influenced by the salary at which he was hired.[11] As a general rule, no matter what kinds of positions eventually become open to a man, each increase will be considered in the light of what he is currently making.

3) A curious feature of salary curves is visible from a study of Figs. 8-3 through 8-6. Most of the curves shown in these Figures turn *downward* at about the twenty-fifth year. This does not necessarily mean that men have been forced to take salary cuts as they grow older (although such a thing could happen to a man if he changed jobs late in his career). Instead, the "drooping" appearance of the salary curves probably means that the middle regions of the curves have been pushed up faster than the right-hand portions. This signifies that companies consider their younger men more valuable than their older engineers, which opens another question: "Why should companies feel this way?" To the author's knowledge, no study in depth has been focused on this phenomenon, but one factor seems obvious: these older men have probably allowed them-

---

[11] R. E. Walton, *The Impact of the Professional Engineering Union.* Cambridge, Mass.: Div. of Research, Grad. School of Business Admin., Harvard Univ., 1961, p. 64.

selves to become technically obsolescent. They have simply failed to keep up with their profession. Few more convincing arguments could be put forth, concerning the value of continuing education.

8.3 Rewards other than salary

It can hardly be questioned that there are other than monetary rewards in a job. Here are some comments from practicing professional engineers, about engineering as a career:

> The major thing is the creative aspect. There is a personal satisfaction in seeing a job completed.

> Mainly, there is the feeling of accomplishment, the challenge . . .

> . . . there is considerable variety in the work.[12]

J. W. Riegel found the following intangible rewards to be the most important to the engineers interviewed in his survey (salary was deliberately excluded):

(1) Challenge and variety in the work.
(2) Having ideas accepted and put to use.
(3) Treatment as a professional; status and personal freedom.
(4) Recognition of contributions by higher management.
(5) Association with able professionals.
(6) Opportunities to learn.[13]

Job security did not seem to rate very high on the lists—an understandable omission, in view of the sustained long-term demand for engineers. The same result was noted in the survey (cited earlier) by Opinion Research Corporation.

Other intangible rewards mentioned by survey participants are: being treated as part of management, having good clerical assistance available, and enjoying reasonably private working quarters. The preceding do not place very high in engineers' specifications of the ideal job. Yet, when the survey participants were asked what factors caused dissatisfaction because they were *lacking* in their own jobs, the factors just listed were at the top of the list.

An interesting type of reward is the bestowing of titles in lieu of raises. Even though this classic situation serves as the butt of countless jokes, it is unlikely that it often takes place for the implied reason. The giving of

---

[12] *Career Satisfactions of Professional Engineers in Industry*, p. 11.
[13] Riegel, *(Part 2)*, p. 6.

important-sounding titles is a form of intangible reward essentially independent of, and in addition to, the giving of raises. The justification usually offered is that an impressive title helps a man in dealing with outsiders. A more realistic reason is that it is another way of satisfying the need of an individual to show growth in his career. The only real danger in the practice is when it extends so far as to confer managerial-sounding titles upon positions that have no managerial content whatsoever.

Many a writer has lamented that an engineer-turned-manager is an engineer lost to engineering. Yet, it has also been pointed out that promotion into management has long been the only method of further advancement open to technical people. Some companies have attempted to alleviate this situation by offering dual promotional ladders: one ladder leads into the conventional management route; the other provides for salary levels equal to those of middle management, but for outstanding scientists or engineers who do not have administrative responsibilities.[14] That this approach has limitations is put into words by an engineer in one survey, who said, ". . . there are more steps available in the managerial direction, and they lead all the way up to the president of the company. Obviously, the technical steps available stop far short of that."[15] Nevertheless, programs of this type have done much to relieve former distress and anxiety. Many promotable engineers, who really don't want to be managers, are thereby given considerable extra salary potential.

---

[14] D. S. Beach, *Personnel: The Management of People at Work* (New York: Macmillan, 1965), p. 697.

[15] *Career Satisfactions of Professional Engineers in Industry*, p. 16.

9 ▸ | Design and development

9.1 The nature of design

In engineering education circles, an enormous amount of heat has been generated, over the word "design." Some educators are alarmed because, in recent years, courses with design content have been largely squeezed out of engineering curriculums by courses in theory and analysis. On the other side, some educators fear that courses labeled "design" are substantially equivalent to the much-despised activity of "handbook engineering" and, therefore, should be abolished.

Meanwhile, within the profession itself, engineers take it for granted that their natural function is *to design* equipment and structures and worry very little about what their activities are called. In truth, some of them may be inclined to call the things they do "research" or, perhaps, "development," but this is probably because these last two words have more prestige value than the term "design."

To avoid great semantic gaps between what the author means and what the reader thinks the author means, some definitions of the key words involved in this controversy will be introduced:

> design: Engineering design is the process of applying the various techniques and scientific principles for the purpose of defining a device, a process or a system in sufficient detail to permit its physical realization. . . . Design may be simple or enormously complex, easy or difficult, mathematical or non-mathematical; it may involve a trivial problem or one of great importance.—Massachusetts Institute of Technology, COMMITTEE ON ENGINEERING DESIGN.[1]

> development: . . . technical activity concerned with *nonroutine* problems which are encountered in translating research findings or other gen-

---

[1] From "Report on Engineering Design," *J. Engrg. Educ.*, vol. 51, April 1961, pp. 645–660.

eral scientific knowledge into products or processes. . . . The engineering activity required to advance the design of a product or a process to the point where it meets specific functional and economic requirements and can be turned over to manufacturing units.—NATIONAL SCIENCE FOUNDA-TION.[2,3]

applied research: (sometimes called "developmental research or "engineering research"): . . . Investigation directed to discovery of new scientific knowledge and which [has] specific commercial objectives with respect to either products or processes.—NATIONAL SCIENCE FOUNDATION.[3]

basic research: (sometimes called "fundamental research"): . . . original investigation for the advancement of scientific knowledge and which [does] not have specific commercial objectives.—NATIONAL SCIENCE FOUNDATION.[3]

Although these definitions have reasonably wide acceptance, they have not been universally accepted. If one does accept them, he can see that the term "development" is included within the meaning of "design," but describes the nonroutine end of the design spectrum. Furthermore, a difficult or novel design project is almost certain to involve applied research; consequently, some might say that "design" embraces applied research, too, although this would seem to be pushing the all-inclusiveness of the word too hard.

In the literature, design and research have often been regarded as opposing, and mutually hostile, functions. In the author's belief, not only is there no intrinsic antagonism between these two, but in fact, they are extremely important to each other. Research can be, and often is, performed as a completely closed function within itself, but the scientific knowledge subsequently made available cannot benefit the public without *design*. From the other side, some design projects can be carried out without any research at all, but it is unlikely that the results will represent a very large advance. For the kinds of novel and sophisticated engineering projects that represent the greatest challenge to the professional engineer, the two functions are not only merely compatible—they are complementary and essential to each other.

In a similar vein, the author does not believe there is any natural antagonism between the terms "design" and "analysis," although some writers have assumed so. In truth, analysis is an indispensable component of all but the simplest of design projects. Trouble does arise, however, when it is assumed that research and analysis are all that are worth talking

---

[2] Italics have been added by the author.

[3] From the U.S. Dept. of Commerce's *Instructions for Survey of Industrial Research and Development During 1964*. Washington, D.C.: 1965, p. 4. Source is the Nat'l Science Foundation, for whom the survey was made.

about, in a design/development project. Some other vital elements are *invention, economics,* and *human factors.*

"Invention" is a rather unfortunate word, because it has too many bobby-pin–safety-pin–mousetrap connotations for most people. As a result, the words *"creative synthesis"* are usually substituted, because they sound more dignified. But it is still the same old process: one must have a new idea before he can have a new product.

Much criticism has been directed at engineering educators, for their apparent failure to prepare their graduates for the design function. For example, an aerospace executive has said:

> . . . the over-emphasis on engineering science is producing people who are as hypnotized by analysis as were the handbook engineers hypnotized by gears, clutches, and bolts. The entire critical area of synthesis is being neglected in favor of an overwhelming emphasis on analysis.[4]

The MIT Committee on Engineering Design (see footnote 1, this chapter) encountered the following criticism, during its investigations:

> Recent engineering graduates were criticized for unwillingness and inability to consider a complete problem such as a design problem. Instead they showed a desire to seek a fully specified problem which could be answered by analytical methods. It was stated that engineers with advanced degrees were even more prone to avoid a complete problem. . . . In short, young engineers feel at home in solving problems which have numerical answers—the kind of problem used in school for teaching analytical techniques.[5]

No doubt, the blame for the conditions just expressed belong at the door of the educators, for at least two reasons: 1) because of the frequently held assumption, among educators, that the engineering student can be exposed to four years (or more) of highly structured problems that emphasize analytical techniques and, yet, experience little difficulty after graduation when he discovers that the problems he must henceforth deal with are almost totally unstructured; and 2) because of the recent efforts of

---

[4] W. J. Schimandle, "Science and Engineering in Space," *Seminar Proceedings: Mechanical Design of Spacecraft.* Jet Propulsion Lab., Calif. Inst. of Technology, Pasadena: 1962. Mr. Schimandle is chief, Spacecraft Development Section, for Jet Propulsion Lab., developers of the Ranger and Mariner spacecrafts.

[5] From "Report on Engineering Design." The MIT Committee interviewed leading engineers in the following fields: airplane design; machine tool design; design of bridges, tunnels, and airports; design of diesel engines and gas turbines; design of electrical machinery; operations research; design of electronics systems; design of nuclear submarines; design of chemical plants; design of communications systems.

educators to cram more and more material into a four-year curriculum. The last circumstance came about substantially as follows: World War II taught engineering faculties that the typical engineer was unable to cope with the problems of the day, because his background in science and mathematics was insufficient. After the war, educators set about the job of getting more science and math into the engineering curriculum, but were naturally reluctant to increase its length. As a result, much traditional material was squeezed out (and most of it rightly so). In general, the eliminated material was too specialized, too repetitious, or too elementary and belonged more to the realm of the technician than that of the engineer. However, in the process of thrusting all the desired science and math into the program, many portions of design courses involving creative synthesis (the "good" part of design) were squeezed out, along with those portions that were too specialized, repetitious, or elementary (the "bad" part).

9.2 The design process

The great interest in design has stimulated the publication of a number of books that emphasize the design *process,* as distinct from the design of technical hardware in itself.[6] Some of these focus on techniques of optimization and have, as one objective, the optimization of the entire process of design, as well as optimization of the components of the design. Analysis of the design process can become very complex and the author will not present much detail here. In fact, only five major phases in design will be identified:

1) Problem definition
2) Invention
3) Analysis
4) Decision
5) Implementation

---

[6] Some prominent ones are:

J. R. M. Alger and C. V. Hays' *Creative Synthesis in Design* (Englewood Cliffs, N.J.: Prentice-Hall, 1964).

M. Asimow's *Introduction to Design* (Englewood Cliffs, N.J.: Prentice-Hall, 1962).

E. V. Krick's *An Introduction to Engineering and Engineering Design* (New York: Wiley, 1965).

W. E. Wilson's *Concepts of Engineering System Design* (New York: McGraw-Hill, 1965).

Problem definition

Problem definition is one of the steps an inexperienced engineer is likely to skip entirely. Having been subjected to an intensive schooling during which his problems were almost always given to him in clearly defined form, he is uncertain of just what to do, when faced with a problem that is vague and largely unstructured. Since he is thoroughly familiar with *analysis,* he may be inclined to get into this phase as rapidly as possible and may start analyzing something before being completely sure he is analyzing the correct problem. Naturally, there is a real risk that he will wind up with an answer to a problem nobody is interested in. Therefore, the first task of the engineer is to *find out what the problem really is.*

Very often, the original statement of a problem is vague and may even be entirely misleading. Sometimes, merely accepting stated constraints at face value could be the wrong thing to do. For example, a problem statement from the chief engineer might be, "Design an electrical meter that will measure the torque in a rotating shaft without using slip-rings." The constraint involving slip-rings might conceivably have been issued because the chief engineer once tried to use slip-rings on something and found them objectionable for their electrical noise. The constraint, then, actually is against noise, rather than against slip-rings. The engineer working on this problem might discover that the use of improved slip-rings could give him an outstanding design, while limits are maintained on noise. In presenting his arguments to his boss, the engineer must, of course, be tactful in explaining why he failed to follow orders, but the basic point is that the original problem statement should be critically examined to see if it is saying the things that need to be said.

An important aspect of problem definition that is frequently overlooked is *human factors.* Matters of customer use and acceptance are paramount. (It has already been mentioned that two out of three "successful" R & D projects are commercial failures, mostly because of lack of market acceptance.)

Invention: the making of schemes

Engineering, by definition, is concerned with new things. This is precisely what invention is: the coming up with new ideas. A new idea may involve a combination of old components, but if a new and useful effect results from this combination, then invention has taken place. For the present, any questions of patentability[7] will be excluded from this discus-

---

[7] Patentability is extensively treated in chap. 10.

sion, and the author will focus upon the creative act of conceiving an idea for hardware that may solve a particular problem. This potential assemblage of hardware is what was referred to, in an earlier chapter, as a "scheme."

At this stage of affairs, one cannot be sure that the scheme in hand will actually solve the problem. However, the purpose of the next phase of design—analysis—is to shed some light upon the probability of success. Before analysis can begin, though, at least one scheme has to be generated; otherwise, there is nothing to analyze.

As an example of what is meant by a "scheme," suppose that a supervisor instructs an engineer to design an electric accelerometer. The instrument is intended to measure the acceleration of an automobile and is to be mounted on a dashboard for visual reading, although it must be possible also to use the output of the accelerometer to make a record on paper. Hopefully, the engineer will come up with many systems of hardware that, in principle at least, will perform the desired function, but for the purposes of this book, only two of his systems will be described. The engineer's two "schemes" are:

1) Mount a mass to be as free from friction as possible and provide a spring so that, as the automobile accelerates, the inertial resistance of the mass will cause the spring to be compressed. Connect the mass to an iron core mounted within a coil, so that displacement of the mass (and core) will change the inductance of the coil and, thus, give an electrical indication of acceleration.

2) Gear a d-c generator to the drive shaft of the automobile and hook it in series with a capacitor, so that the current in the circuit is proportional to the acceleration (a differentiating circuit).

Our engineer realizes that many questions of feasibility have still been left unsettled in both these schemes, but that is what the analysis phase is for—to answer such questions. The important thing is that he now has something physical and concrete to analyze.

One of the most important aspects of scheme-selection to be noted here, is that the engineer has actually posed a textbook type problem for himself. For either of the foregoing examples, he has described a physical structure and has then asked himself, "How does the current vary with car speed?" Nobody gave him the problem in this form. He had to pose the problem for himself, and this posing is one of the most important elements in the design process.[8]

---

[8] See D. W. Ver Planck and B. R. Teare, Jr.'s *Engineering Analysis, An Introduction to Professional Method* (New York: Wiley, 1954).

Analysis

It is primarily because of the analysis phase that engineers go to college. All of the other functions—problem definition, invention, decision, and implementation—can be carried out, to a very large extent, without the benefit of a college education. (This helps to account for the remarkable success in design achieved by many noncollege men in the past.) Even today, much design can be performed without recourse to the analysis step: the designer proceeds directly from invention to decision, on the strength of experience and intuition.

However, the basic rationale for engineering is that a *better* job of design can be done through the intelligent application of science and mathematics. In fact, some of today's more difficult design tasks can be accomplished only with the assistance of advanced mathematics and scientific know-how. It was once a popular expression that the engineer can do, for one dollar, what the untrained person requires two dollars to do. But an untrained person could not design a jet liner or a satellite even with an unlimited amount of dollars.

The basic analytical tools used by the engineer are mathematics and a collection of scientific "laws." Applying his knowledge of science, the engineer constructs for himself a mathematical model and then, by means of mathematical manipulation, extracts from this model the information he needs. The model should be reasonably representative of the physical system and, obviously, should be no more complex than is absolutely necessary to produce the required information. Herein lie two common errors of inexperienced engineers: 1) frequently, the model chosen only slightly represents the physical system, but has been chosen primarily because it is one the engineer knows how to analyze or because it is elegant; 2) far too often, the model is more complex than it has to be; a lengthy and involved analysis could be a complete waste, for example, if the purpose of the analysis is to produce order-of-magnitude figures for a comparison with competing schemes.

If the engineer possesses insufficient scientific information to construct a good mathematical model, he may have to initiate a research program to get the information he needs. Therefore, the analysis phase of design may include research. In fact, *all* of the first three phases of design may require research before a man can properly define a problem; test out a scheme and, thus, arrive at an invention; or obtain the scientific information necessary for the purposes of analysis.

The most useful thing about the analysis phase of design is its production of quantitative information that can be used as a basis for scheme selection, as opposed to the purely qualitative nature of the invention phase. Thus, it is necessary to get *numbers,* at this point, and to become specific about the hardware nature of components and their interconnection. Through mathematical analysis, the influential system parameters can be identified and optimum values selected. After this has been done, at least in a preliminary way, the decision phase can follow.

Decision

Even after mathematical analysis, individual judgment is necessary. For one thing, economic considerations enter the picture at this stage. The product must be produced at a low enough cost, and at sufficient volume, to recover all of the development expenses and produce a profit.

Selection of a particular scheme will depend upon which of the various schemes offered appears the most favorable, as a result of optimization. Optimization is finding the best combination of certain variables that will maximize a desired result. This desired result is known as a "criterion function." But in establishing the relative importance of various criterion functions, we are forced to resort to value judgments. Through the application of value judgments, the engineer can state how much the different aspects of the design are worth to him: that is, the appearance, the weight, the durability, the selling price, the serviceability, the quietness, the sensitivity, and so on. If all these can be placed together on a value scale, it is possible to pick out an optimum combination and to make a single selection from among the competing alternatives. Optimization is too extensive a subject to be treated here, beyond the general indication of its nature that the author has just given.[9]

Implementation

Before the design process may properly be considered complete, detailed manufacturing instructions must be prepared so that the device, structure, or system can be produced. Historically, the medium for such instructions is the working manufacturing drawing, although computer output data are beginning to figure, in the form of punched or magnetic tape.

However, even before working drawings (or tape) can be produced, much detail design, involving spatial considerations, strength, weight, economy of manufacture, and the like is necessary. This detail design is

---

[9] For more information on optimization, see M. Asinow's *Introduction to Design.*

customarily carried out on the layout board, and to many people, this is what the term "design" means. If one adds to this, the fact that many nonprofessionals who are given the job title of "designer," engage in this activity, it can be seen why so many professional engineers are emotionally biased against the word "design."

Although detail design is only one of the many phases of design it is an important phase and one that cannot be abandoned by the professional engineer. His responsibility for a design extends to the last detail, though he will have many technicians to assist him in the latter stages of this endeavor. One of the things to be hoped for in the future is that large numbers of qualified people will take advantage of the two-, three-, and even four-year educational programs that specifically aim at this phase of design.

There used to be a fear, on the part of many new engineering graduates, that they might get "stuck on the drawing board," but today, this is unlikely to happen in most companies. Engineers are paid high salaries because of the special analytic tools they possess, and it is wasteful to use them as draftsmen. Nevertheless, engineers (especially mechanical engineers) should realize that the drawing board can be a very useful tool to them, at times. For example, before it is possible to perform an analysis, it may be necessary to see just how big the parts may be, or what spatial constraints may exist on their interconnections. Usually, this can be established only by means of a layout on the drawing board; trying to accomplish it through a draftsman can often be inefficient (or even impossible) if the item is extremely complex, simply because of the inadequacy of human language as a communication means.

Iteration

Lest it be thought that a design project should be expected to proceed neatly down through all the phases directly in order, special mention must be made of *iteration*. What this elegant word means, is that the designer frequently may find it necessary to back up and do something all over again. New data may be uncovered, a new idea may be generated, mistakes may be found, or things simply may not work as expected. This last point, *things may not work as expected,* is especially important: Careful analysis must be followed by careful testing. Failures on the test bench may even require complete abandonment of a given scheme.

It has been aptly pointed out by A. J. Winter, that *iteration is* one of the special characteristics that distinguishes the design process from analysis or from research. In analysis, the *starting* point is known, and one works through the process until an end point is reached. In design, the *end* point is specified, and a starting point must be assumed. During the process of design, one attempts to work from the assumed starting point to the required end point. As errors in direction occur, backing-up periodically takes place, and this is "iteration."

9.3   Undermathematizing and overmathematizing

As has been previously mentioned, a primary reason for requiring engineers to have a college education is to provide them with the tools of analysis—and mathematics is the most powerful of these tools. Nevertheless, two types of engineering graduates with serious misconceptions about the role of mathematics in engineering regularly emerge from school. The first is the *under*mathematizer, who cannot wait to get out of school so that he can forget about calculus and differential equations. The other is the *over*mathematizer who is so deeply impressed by the power of mathematics in physical problems that he thinks mathematics *is* physics. The existence of the undermathematizer is easily accounted for: he has been talking to practicing engineers in industry who have assured him that calculus is useless—after all, *they* never use it. The creation of the overmathematizer is a more subtle process and comes about through basic misconceptions concerning the nature of mathematics.

Exactly what *is* mathematics? It is probably safe to say that most engineers have never asked themselves this question, nor have they ever thought that such a question could be relevant to their activities. Yet the question is highly relevant. The eminent engineer T. Von Karman once wrote, "Sometimes we have the feeling with mathematics that we have learned to start the mechanism of mathematical operations, but after the gears begin to work the machine gets out of hand and we do not know what it is doing or where it is going."[10]

It is not an idle exercise to inquire into the nature of mathematics. Far too often, the impression left upon the new graduate is that mathematics controls physical reality—that, moreover, it *is* reality. Without realizing it, such a graduate is adopting a view that is hundreds of years old and was most strongly focused in the philosophy of Immanuel Kant (1724–1804). Kant believed that all propositions could be divided into two types: *empirical* (those that depend upon perception by the senses) and *a priori* (those that have a fundamental validity of their own).[11] According to Kant,

---

[10] T. von Karman, "Some Remarks on Mathematics from the Engineer's Viewpoint," *Mech. Engrg.*, vol. 62, April 1940, pp. 308–310.

[11] J. F. Morse, ed., *Funk and Wagnalls Standard Reference Encyclopedia.* (New York: Standard Reference Works Publ. Co., 1963), p. 5341.

mathematics belongs to the latter category, wherein intuitional perception of space and time constitutes an *a priori* frame into which all physical experiences can be fitted.[12]

Two physicists, H. R. Lemon and Michael Ference, comment as follows on the grip that ideas like the foregoing still have upon students:

> Too often our technical students at the beginning of their career are left with the impression that phenomena follow and conform to certain 'laws' derivable from *a priori* grounds and of the utmost mystery as to origin. The fact that the laws themselves—at least the more fundamental ones—have no *a priori* basis but simply describe, generalize, and integrate a great range of interrelated experimental facts too frequently dawns upon the more mature physicist rather late in his own development.[13]

It has been shown that even great triumphs of reason, such as the development of Einstein's theories of relativity, had their genesis in experimental data. In the words of another physicist, George Gamow:

> . . . the abandonment of classical ideas of space and time and their unification in a single four-dimensional picture were dictated not by any purely esthetic desire on the part of Einstein . . . but by stubborn facts that emerged constantly from experimental research, and that just wouldn't fit into the classical picture . . .[14]

The fundamental point is that mathematics is an *invention* of man; its purpose is to systematize the processes of logic. If the human mind were equal to the task, it could solve problems without recourse to mathematics. For example, it is conceivable that almost any arithmetic problem could be solved entirely in one's head, but most people reach answers faster, and with greater accuracy, by employing certain manipulative rules. Great faith is placed in the validity of the results, but people tend to forget (if they ever knew) that arithmetical manipulations are based upon some very fundamental axioms, known as Peano's Axiom System.

At a more sophisticated level, a system of differential equations will represent a statement of the relationships among a number of physical variables. Once the equations are written down, the answer has already been fixed and is implicitly locked in the equations. We would be able to perceive the answer directly, if the human mind could hold all the variables and their relationships in view at once and could comprehend

---

[12] J. R. Newman, ed., *The World of Mathematics* (New York: Simon and Schuster, 1956). See "The Crisis in Intuition," by H. Hahn, p. 1956.

[13] H. B. Lemon and M. Ference, Jr., *Analytical Experimental Physics.* Chicago: The Univ. of Chicago Press (copyright 1943 by the Univ. of Chicago), p. v.

[14] G. Gamow, *One, Two, Three . . . Infinity* (Mentor paperback ed.; New York: New Amer. Library, 1960), p. 93. Orig. publ. by Macmillan, London; and The Viking Press, New York, 1947. Used by permission.

the simultaneous effect, upon all the dependent variables, caused by changes in the independent variables. The human mind cannot do this, of course, but the desired result can be achieved by the operations of mathematics. In mathematical operations, certain theorems whose validity has been thoroughly established are employed and, if these theorems are correctly applied, then we have confidence that the result correctly represents the solution that was embodied in the original equations. This leads to the final point: the solution can convey no more factual information than was implied by the original formulation of the problem. In other words, mathematics can only transform information into more useful forms; it cannot, of itself, create information.

Mathematics is said to be *analytic*: the truth of analytic statements is self-contained in the axioms with which they begin, in precise definitions and in the logic of the proofs attached to the theorems that are employed. Analytical statements convey no factual information. Factual information is conveyed only by *synthetic* statements, which come from actual experience. The following is a comment by one more mathematician, this time Richard von Mises:

> Occasionally one finds also mathematicians who are of the opinion that physics is reducible to mathematics; they hold, for instance, that electrodynamics has become a 'part of geometry' through the theory of relativity. Such utterances are logical misconceptions and go ill with the critical subtlety which the mathematician otherwise often exhibits.
>
> By the mere manipulation of signs [symbols] according to chosen rules one can indeed learn nothing about the external world. All the knowledge we gain through mathematics about reality depends upon the fact that the signs as well as the rules of transformation are in some wise made to correspond to certain observable phenomena.[15]

The overmathematizer is unduly impressed by the role of mathematics in engineering and believes he is not doing engineering work unless he is doing mathematics. As a result of his point of view, he is likely to overemphasize the analysis phase of design to the virtual exclusion of the other phases. But he is at least in a better position than the engineer who undermathematizes. The overmathematizer can broaden his effectiveness merely by opening his eyes to the existence and importance of the other phases in the design spectrum. The undermathematizer, on the other hand, quickly finds that he has permanently limited himself in the scope of the kinds of problems he can handle. There are simply too many en-

---

[15] R. von Mises, *Positivism, A Study in Human Understanding* (Cambridge Mass.: Harvard Univ. Press. Copyright 1951 by the President and Fellows of Harvard College).

gineering problems in today's world that are too complex for the naked human mind to handle, unassisted by the powerful logical formalism that mathematics can provide.

9.4 Industrial design

Normally, industrial design is considered to be outside the sphere of the professional engineer, although it may affect his activities in various important ways.

Industrial design should not be thought of as synonymous with *styling*, although it consisted almost entirely of styling when it began, a generation ago. In the 1930s, an industrial designer was often conceived of as a "wizard of gloss," who could make his clients' sales zoom simply by glamorizing their products. Today, however, most industrial designers have gone in for "total service": Not only do they wish to take in hand every aspect of the product that affects the customer—usefulness, safety, ease of handling, styling—but they also would like to plan the client's future product line for him, make over his corporate offices, and refashion the company's "image" through its packaging, trademarks, and letterheads. *Fortune* quotes the president of one corporation who was talking about the industrial designer his company had retained: "Mind you, I like the fellow. But I sometimes get the feeling that he isn't satisfied to be a designer—he wants to be my right hand and maybe even me."[16]

Some companies retain outside consultants to perform their industrial design, while others have developed complete in-house design establishments. General Motors is one of the latter and employs 1400 people on its styling staff. Styling is very important to GM, and they have even established the office of vice president of styling.[17]

Matters do not always flow smoothly between engineers and industrial designers, or between engineers and architects (who strongly resemble industrial designers in their viewpoint and in the kind of service they offer). Industrial designers and architects believe that engineers tend to overemphasize economy and technical function and that they give scant attention to relationships between function and appearance, or to esthetics. They could be right. Some of the products of engineers possess a natural beauty all their own; jet aircraft for example, or the Golden Gate

---

[16] S. Freedgood, "Odd Business, This Industrial Design," *Fortune,* February 1959, pp. 131–132.
[17] A. P. Sloan, Jr., *My Years With General Motors* (Paperback ed.; New York: Macfadden, 1965), p. 277. Orig. publ. by Doubleday, Garden City, N.Y., 1963.

Bridge, or cities lit up after dark (provided they are viewed from a sufficiently great distance). However, other products of engineers are natural horrors; power plants, for instance, and many freeways and bridges. In 1964, a storm of protest arose in Portland, Oregon, over the appearance of a bridge that had been designed by engineers of the Oregon Highway Department. It was charged that the bridge had a "mediocre Erector Set" character. The protests were so strong that the city government requested that five alternate designs be submitted on the next bridge to be built, for prior examination by the city's art and planning groups.[18]

In San Francisco, there have been rumblings over the design of the Bay Area Rapid Transit System (BART), the first completely new urban transportation system to be designed in the United States in a long time. The *San Francisco Chronicle* editorialized:

> The problem is that the architects are really in the employ of the engineers (instead of the other way around), and engineers are primarily interested in building structures, only secondarily concerned with esthetic design.[19]

Even though not all engineers will agree with the Chronicle's views, it is true that engineers must be concerned about esthetics. The public is becoming increasingly interested in beauty in man's environment, and is demonstrating a willingness to pay the price to achieve it. It is rare that a competent engineer is also competent in esthetics. As a result, engineers will find themselves permanently in partnership with industrial designers and architects.

9.5 Will computers replace engineers?

To the extent that engineers are used for routine tasks, they will probably be replaced by computers. Jobs requiring a great deal of calculating, or detail design tasks that can be systematized, are prime candidates for computerization. But no one has yet discovered how to make a computer be creative, although there is plenty of effort in that direction. Computers have already been used to compose music of a sort and, even, to write low-grade poems. It has been predicted that machines may eventually take over the task of hammering out Tin Pan Alley tunes.[20] However, "creativity" of this type is dependent upon the ability of the computer's de-

---

[18] *Engrg. News-Record,* Oct. 8, 1964, p. 56.
[19] *San Francisco Chronicle,* "This World" sec., April 18, 1965, p. 20 ff.
[20] G. Burck, "Will the Computer Outwit man?" *Fortune,* vol. 70, October 1964, p. 120 ff.

signers to specify the creative rules by which the machine operates. Some people believe creativity is the ability to make random connections that turn out to be meaningful. If their view is correct, then computers might eventually be able to perform functions of this type and, thus, be creative. Nevertheless, the building of a computer with as many random connection possibilities as the human brain has, still lies an unforeseeable distance in the future.

In 1957, some experts were predicting that, within ten years, a computer would discover an important new mathematical theorem, write music of value, and reduce theories of psychology to computer routines. As the ten-year period drew to a close, these things had not happened—to the author's knowledge—although it might be hasty to declare that they will never come to pass.

Surprising things have already been done with computers in engineering applications. Almost every engineer is today familiar with the computer's capabilities for numerical calculation and is aware that computers have opened the door to the solutions of many problems that formerly had been unapproachable. But engineers may not be so aware of the following kinds of developments:

1) Fairly standard programs are now available to perform kinematic analysis of linkages, cam layout and design, gear design (including power transmission capability), spring design, shaft design, moment of inertia calculation, and stress calculations.[21]

2) Computers are now used in the design of products, such as electric motors, that are assembled to customer specifications from standard components.[22]

3) A large variety of devices are now available to help automate the drafting function; these include machines that can "read" a drawing and automatically punch a paper tape which is then used to control a production machine. On some kinds of drawings, for instance on wiring diagrams, it is claimed that the use of a semiautomatic drafting system permits a speed advantage of as much as 30 to 1 over a human draftsman.[23]

---

[21] L. F. Knappe, "A Computer-Oriented System," *Mech Engrg.* vol. 87, May 1965, p. 35 ff.

[22] G. Burck, "The Boundless Age of the Computer," *Fortune,* March 1964, p. 110.

[23] R. P. Washburn, "Methods of Automating the Drafting Operation," ASME Paper 64-MD-8. presented at the ASME Design Engineering Conf., May 11–14, 1964.

4) The General Motors Corporation has been testing a system (called DAC-1, for **D**esign **A**ugmented by **C**omputers) that will not only automate large portions of the drafting function, but may also play an important part in styling. The designer sits in front of a graphic console and uses an electric "pencil" to "draw" an image on the face of the display tube. Upon command he can enlarge, modify, delete, or cause views to be rotated so that they are seen from different directions. When finished, he can direct the machine to produce a permanent copy of the result or to produce numerical control tapes if he wishes.[24]

5) Probably the most visionary attempt to computerize the design function is the CAD Project (**C**omputer-**A**ided **D**esign) at MIT. Not only do the designers of CAD have similar objectives to those of DAC, but they also envision other things, such as a) a tube display to show the actual operation of proposed linkages, which can then be modified as desired; b) graphical display of stress distributions in pin-joined trusses; c) electric circuit analysis (does it seem that we have finally come full circle, in using electric circuits to simulate the action of electric circuits?); and d) utilization of the computer to write its own programs.[25]

If computers replace engineers at routine jobs, this will be just one more step in the process that began with the Industrial Revolution. One thing that several generations of men should have observed by this time, is that the displacement of men at routine jobs has always been more than compensated for by the creation of new jobs. The lurking fear, of course, is that the computer will ". . . eventually become so intelligent and even creative that it will relegate man, or most men, to a humiliating and intolerably inferior role in the world."[26] The day when this may happen is not yet in view.

---

[24] "Design Augmented by Computers," *Search,* October 1964. Publ. by Research Labs., General Motors Corp., Warren, Mich.
[25] R. W. Mann, "The 'CAD' Project," *Mech. Engrg.,* vol. 87, May 1965, p. 41 ff.
[26] Burck, "Will the Computer Outwit Man?" p. 120.

10 ▸ | Patents

10.1 Do patents really stimulate progress?

The distinguished Judge Learned Hand is reported to have said, "I am very little certain about anything, but least of all about patents." Since the judge is one of the nation's outstanding authorities on patent law, it seems highly likely that there is more to the subject than appears at a first reading. He meant that there is scarcely any subject more complex than patents—or more controversial. In spite of this, most Americans reach adulthood with clearly developed, and usually favorable, attitudes toward patents.

Most informed observers agree that a large percentage of issued patents have no commercial value. One group of authors speculates the proportion may even be as high as 95 percent,[1] although the author feels this estimate extravagant. Another upsetting factor is that well over half of those patents which reach litigation are declared invalid.[2] A study of one five-year period showed that, in 89 percent of all patent cases brought to the courts of appeals and the United States Supreme Court, the judgments held the patents to be either invalid or not infringed.[3]

So why should we be concerned about patents at all? For one reason, close to 50,000 patents are issued each year in the United States, and even if only 10 percent of these have value, the total is still an impressive 5000 *valuable* new patents a year. Once a company begins to collect a strong

---

[1] J. Jewkes, D. Sawers, and R. Stillerman, *The Sources of Invention* (London: Macmillan and New York: St. Martin's Press, 1958, p. 106. Used by permission.
[2] J. C. Stedman, "The U. S. Patent System and Its Current Problems," *Tex. Law Rev.* vol. 42: 450, March 1964, p. 464.
[3] D. G. Cullen, "Patents in Litigation, 1941–45," *J. of the Patent Office Soc.* vol. XXVIII, December 1946, pp. 903–904.

patent position (especially if it includes some court-tested patents), other companies will tend to steer clear and look for greener pastures. For example, the Polaroid Corporation has established such an impregnable patent structure that it still has no competitors, as of this writing. Largely as a result of the sheltered position offered by its patents, Polaroid's annual sales increased by a factor of 14 in the 1950s, to approximately $100 million.[4]

Unfortunately, many patents have only marginal value, and some even skirt the borderline of trivia. The United States Supreme Court has spoken harshly of the ". . . list of incredible patents which the Patent Office has spawned"[5] and has struck hard at the patenting of gadgets. The court has said, "It is not enough that an article is new and useful. The Constitution never sanctioned the patenting of gadgets. Patents serve a higher end—the advancement of science." Some people, however, believe the Supreme Court has gone too far in its high number of patent invalidations. One of these is United States Supreme Court Justice Jackson, who said acidly, in a 1949 dissenting opinion, "It would not be difficult to cite many instances of patents that have been granted, improperly I think, and without adequate tests of invention by the Patent Office. But I doubt that the remedy for such Patent Office passion for granting patents is an equally strong passion in this Court for striking them down so that the only patent that is valid is one which this Court has not been able to get its hands on."[6]

It is almost impossible to find a restrained, dispassionate statement about patents. Those who defend the practice often take the position that America's great technological progress can be directly attributed to the influence of her patent system. They point, with alarm, to the anti-patent movement that has developed in the United States during the last thirty years.[7] Many supporters of the patent system declare that industrial firms will not undertake expensive development programs unless they can be sure the results can be protected by patents. Executives of some corporations have declared that they would be driven to cut their research and development expenditures drastically, if the patent system were to be

---

[4] D. L. Brown, "Protection Through Patents: The Polaroid Story," *J. of the Patent Office Soc.,* vol. XLII, July 1960, pp. 439–455.

[5] *Great Atlantic & Pacific Tea Co. v. Supermarket Equipment Corp.,* 340 U. S. 147–158 (1950).

[6] *Jungerson v. Ostby & Barton Co.,* 335 U. S. 560–572 (1949).

[7] R. Spencer, "Thinking Ahead: Threat to Our Patent System," *Harvard Business Rev.,* vol. 34, May–June 1956, p. 21 ff.

abandoned.[8] Yet, others have stated that their innovative activities would not change at all, if there suddenly were no patent system.[9]

Practically no one can be found among the critics of the patent system who recommends such an extreme course of action as its outright abolition. One possible exception in the past was Thomas Edison, who wrote with some bitterness during long drawn-out litigation over his electric light patents, "Say, I have lost all faith in patents, judges and everything else relating to patents. Don't care if the whole system was squelched."[10] Edison's bitterness is understandable. Although he ultimately won his electric light suit, the victory cost his company $2 million and is said to have made his adversary, Westinghouse, almost insolvent.

The occurrence of such calamitous litigation is, at the same time, one of the patent system's chief evils and one of its chief advantages. It is bad because of the social waste; advantageous, because it makes potential infringers wary of the patents held by others. A prospective litigant would be very foolish to set about breaking another man's patent through the means of costly court actions, unless he were virtually certain, in advance, of the outcome. Herein lies a partial explanation of the high percentage of patents held invalid by the courts: generally, only weak patents are brought to court, in the first place.

The cost of monopoly

"Monopoly" is a bad word in America, and rightly so. It implies outrageous profits and social irresponsibility. Even defenders of the system admit the patent is a form of monopoly, but they point out that it is a *limited* monopoly, given to the inventor in return for his making known something that did not exist before. They hold that the granting of a limited monopoly to an inventor is an incentive necessary to increase the flow of inventions and, thereby, benefit society.

Nevertheless, critics of the patent system generally base their criticisms on monopolistic grounds. Most often the critics are economists, some of

---

[8] F. Machlup, "Patents and Inventive Effort," *Science,* vol. 133, May 12, 1961, p. 1463. Dr. Machlup's article essentially declares that "the evidence is insufficient to prove or disprove the claim that patent protection promotes inventive effort."

[9] F. L. Vaughn, *The United States Patent System* (Norman: Univ. of Okla. Press, 1956), p. 12.

[10] From *Edison* by M. Josephson. Copyright 1959 by Matthew Josephson; New York: McGraw-Hill, p. 355. Used by permission.

whom hold that the provision of a financial incentive to the inventor may come at too high a cost to the rest of society. A dramatization of this point, attributable to the Princeton economist Fritz Machlup, follows:

Assume that twenty corporations are engaged in selling a particular product and that 100 million units are sold annually at $1 each. One firm patents an improvement on the product that results in a ten-cent saving on each unit. If all firms were free to use the improvement, the public would be able to acquire the product at ninety cents each; obviously this would benefit the public. However, free use is impossible, because of the patent. Instead, the product continues to sell for $1, and the innovating firm makes the extra profit, which represents its incentive. If the firm continues to corner one-twentieth of the total market for seventeen years (the life of the patent), it will realize $8,500,000 extra profit, which is presumably enough to cover its research costs and give a return, besides. But during the same period, the public has been required to forego the opportunity to purchase the 100 million units per year at a reduction of ten cents each: The total cost to society, in lost savings, is $170 million.[11]

Admittedly, the example is oversimplified and extreme. In actual practice, the other firms would also introduce innovations that, in time, would tend to drive the price down. In addition, there is no valid reason to believe the price would remain at 1 dollar, even in the absence of other innovations. The original firm would probably try to increase its share of the market by lowering its price, and this would force the other firms to do the same thing. Still, the example displays in a graphic manner a principal ground upon which many economists base their recommendations for revision of the patent system. Some believe the seventeen-year period is too long; they suggest that ten years, for example, might be sufficient to reap the rewards. Defenders of the system—usually patent lawyers and officers of companies with strong patent positions—lash back at such proposals as disastrous to the cause of innovation and social progress.

Of a somewhat less theoretical nature, is the fact that some firms have acquired incredibly large patent holdings: this has caused them to come under government scrutiny as being in restraint of trade. The American Telephone and Telegraph Company (AT & T) and International Business Machines Corporation (IBM) are two such firms. These (among others) have been required to open their patents to licensing at "reason-

---

[11] *The Role of Patents in Research—Part II*. Washington, D.C.: 1962, pp. 198–200. (*Proc.* of a symposium sponsored by the Nat'l Academy of Sciences, Nat'l Research Council.)

able" rates. In the case of AT & T, almost nine thousand patents were involved.[12]

To summarize, the criticisms of the American patent system are as follows:

1) The rewards to the innovator may be coupled with a disproportionate cost to society.

2) Too many patents of doubtful validity are issued; these impose costly burdens on the nation's judicial system and needlessly impede competition in the American economy.

3) Patent procedures are too slow; an average of three to four years is spent in issuing a patent, and the continuing backlog is about two-hundred thousand patents.[13]

4) The patent system has lost standing with many inventors, because of the illusory rewards it has held forth, which did not materialize.

The value of patents

In spite of all the criticisms leveled against the patent system, the net judgment of investigators appears to be that the system substantially fulfills the purposes for which it was intended: the stimulation of invention and dissemination of knowledge.

In a sincere effort to get to the heart of the subject, the National Academy of Sciences (NAS) in 1960 appointed a distinguished committee to examine "The Role of Patents in Research." The committee held a symposium, to which they invited some of the people best-informed on patent matters, in the United States; the purpose of the symposium was to give full play to all sides of the question.[14] The committee's conclusions were substantially as follows:

1) The patent system does stimulate research and development.

2) The sheltered competitive position offered by patents is especially beneficial to small companies in diminishing the advantages possessed by large companies because of their size.

---

[12] R. Spencer.

[13] As of Dec. 1, 1964, the total of pending applications was 208,209; the oldest application awaiting action had been filed in 1953—from the *Official Gazette,* Jan. 5, 1965, vol. 810, p. 7. (Publ. by the U. S. Patent Office, Washington, D.C.)

[14] The committee members quickly discovered that they were investigating, not the effects of the patent system on *research,* but its effects on *development* (in other words, on engineering). In fact, they decided that the patent system and research are scarcely relevant.

3) One of the greatest benefits of the patent system is its encouragement of the publication and dissemination of information. Knowing that it is protected by a patent application on file, a company is thereby made willing to release information concerning its developments. The alternative would be industrial secrecy, which would be deleterious to progress.[15]

Some other important advantages of the system (not emphasized in the NAS study) are the following *defensive* uses of patents.[16]

4-a) Sometimes patents are taken out, not so much to prevent others from entering the field, as to make sure the corporation's freedom in its own field is preserved.

4-b) A storehouse full of patents can be trading material that enables a company to cross-license with others and, in this way, obtain rights to adversely held patents.

During the NAS symposium, it was proposed that the American patent system be changed to:

1) Provide for "petty patents" (petit patents) with a life of three-to-five years for minor inventions, as is now done in some European countries.

2) Provide for compulsory licensing at "reasonable" royalties.

3) Provide for renewal fees which must be regularly paid in order to keep the patent alive.

4) Establish consistent standards of patentability which would be adhered to both by the Patent Office and by the courts.

5) Establish a consistent policy for ownership of patents arising out of government research and development (R & D) contracts. Currently, there are two principal policies: a) the "title policy," under which patent rights become the property of the United States government (used principally by NASA and the AEC);[17] b) the "license policy," under which the contractor gets the patent and the government gets a royalty-free license (used principally by the Department of Defense).[18]

---

[15] *The Role of Patents in Research—Part I*. Washington, D.C.: 1962. (The Committee Report of the NAS, Nat'l Research Council.)

[16] To borrow John Stedman's words, patents can be a means of defense ". . . to protect one *against* the patent system, rather than to make use of it."—from "The U. S. Patent System and Its Current Problems," by J. C. Stedman.

[17] NASA stands for National Aeronautics and Space Administration; AEC represents Atomic Energy Commission.

[18] L. E. Preston, "Thinking Ahead—Patent Rights Under Federal R. & D Contracts," *Harvard Business Rev.* vol. 41, September–October 1963, p. 6.

10.2 Getting a patent

What is invention?

Invention has been discussed, in general terms, in Section 2.1. The author will now discuss its effect upon patentability.

The mere conception of an idea is insufficient to constitute invention: The invention must be "reduced to practice." Ordinarily, this means that an actual working model of the invention has been constructed and has successfully functioned. (Very seldom does the Patent Office require that an actual working model be sent to Washington, to support the application.) However, the simple act of filing an application that discloses an operable patentable structure is called *constructive reduction to practice* and will usually be accepted by the Patent Office. The patentee should realize that, if such a patent later becomes involved in litigation, it will be vulnerable to attack; a patent based upon actual working models is much stronger.

As the author has mentioned before, "invention" is extremely difficult to define, and this very difficulty has led to the strife between the United States Supreme Court and the Patent Office. Dictionary definitions are useless; one can never be certain his invention is truly patentable until his patent has been judged valid by the Supreme Court. Nevertheless, some general rules for patentability are used by the Patent Office. These are listed briefly in this section. (It should be borne in mind that a treatment of this extent cannot hope to reveal all the complexities of patent matters. The purpose here is to impart an awareness to the engineer that the patent system is like an iceberg, with 90 percent of its substance hidden beneath the surface.)[19]

Besides the requirement that the invention be new, several rules of invention are commonly applied:

1) A device is not invention if it is obvious to one "skilled in the art." Naturally, a big source of contention is, that something which appears obvious to hindsight may not have been so obvious in advance. Some of the best inventions appear to be the simplest, in the light of the improvement in vision afforded by hindsight.

2) A combination of old elements is not invention if no new result is

---

[19] For a more detailed treatment, see R. A. Buckles' *Ideas, Inventions, and Patents* (New York: Wiley, 1957); or A. K. Berle and L. S. DeCamp's *Inventions and Their Management* (3d ed.; Scranton, Pa.: International Textbook, 1951).

forthcoming; such a combination is called an *aggregation*. However, if there *is* a new and unexpected result because of the combination, then the combination constitutes patentable invention. The vast majority of patents that are issued are actually combinations of old elements.

3) A mere substitution of obvious equivalents, or a substitution of materials, is not invention, unless some surprising result is thereby obtained. Also, a mere change in size does not constitute invention, unless there is a new result. A famous example is that of Edison's electric light. Others had built operable incandescent lamps before Edison, and it was claimed that the only difference in his lamp was a reduction in size of the carbon filament. However, Edison's patent was upheld, on the basis that it was this reduction in size which caused his lamp to be practical, all previous models having burned for only short periods of time before going out.[20]

A preponderance of evidence

From the engineer's personal viewpoint, one of the most important things he can do to protect his employer's interests is to keep complete, accurate records. For a variety of reasons, it may later be necessary to establish in court the earliest date upon which conception of an idea took place. Further, it may be necessary to prove that the engineer's organization exercised diligence in pursuing an idea. A patent may easily be lost, unless diligence can be proved. In such cases, the engineer's notebook almost invariably constitutes the legal evidence that must be produced in court.

Engineers frequently become restless under the procedures laid down for the keeping of notebooks. Such procedural exhortations will generally include the following:

1) Keep a bound, stitched notebook, so that future jurors may be convinced that sheets have not been removed or added. Number all pages.

---

[20] A highly interesting account is given by Matthew Josephson in "The Invention of the Electric Light" *Scientific American,* vol. 201, November 1959, pp. 99–114) and, also, in his book, *Edison.* Josephson points out that Edison's true genius has been obscured by too much emphasis upon his invention of the electric light. Edison's contribution was of even greater significance: he invented an entire system of electric lighting. Earlier systems required tremendous amounts of copper, since they used low voltages and high currents. Edison conceived the high-resistance, high-voltage (100 volts), low-current system and, then, proceeded to develop the generator and lamp that made the system practical.

2) Keep all records in an absolutely uniform manner. Use every page. Do not erase, but mark out with neat lines instead. Use ink or indelible pencil.

3) Date and sign every page, and have every page witnessed and signed.

Engineers generally regard this kind of thing (especially the last point) as red tape. However, lawyers know that faithful adherence to these procedures will add up to the preponderance of evidence needed to win cases.

Generally, notebooks will be regularly reviewed by a corporate patent department, in order to ferret out overlooked inventions. If an invention has been made, the engineer will be asked to prepare a disclosure. A disclosure describes the invention in meticulous detail and points out its advantages and its potentially patentable features. In addition to the disclosure's possible future use as legal evidence, it will form the foundation upon which any patent application will be based.

After a disclosure has been written, its contents should be described to someone competent in the field (not a man's co-inventor, nor his wife), and then signed by the competent person, as a witness, thus: "Described to and understood by me: *(signed)* *(dated)*." It is better to have two witnesses. The witness(es) should sign, or at least initial, every page. After signing, witnessing, and sometimes notarizing, some companies even go to the extent of inserting a copy of each disclosure into an envelope and mailing it to themselves, via registered mail. These copies are then retained, unopened, against the day they may be needed to prove the date of conception.

In addition to the date of conception, it may be necessary to prove the date upon which reduction to practice took place. Therefore, continuing records of the work must be maintained, especially photographic evidence of model construction and operation, properly signed and witnessed. Such records will also be useful in proving diligence. If any substantial gaps appear in the record, this may be sufficient to constitute **abandonment,** and the patent may go to a more diligent person even though he has a later conception date.

The application

Many complicated ins and outs are involved in dealing with the Patent Office. Patent attorneys will shudder at the streamlined picture outlined here. They well know the many pitfalls that await the uninitiated. Nevertheless, stripped to its essentials, the process is something like this:

1) The application must be submitted in precise compliance with

complex Patent Office instructions. The drawings must be executed in accordance with exacting standards; the claims must be specific and must describe structure, not function.

2) After a long wait, an "office action" by a Patent Office examiner will list any prior art considered relevant to the application and will indicate the potential allowability of the claims. It is not unusual for all claims to be rejected in the first office action.

3) New arguments are then submitted, possibly along with some revised claims. This is followed by more long waits and more office actions, while the applicant and his attorney converge on claims that will be allowable.

4) If some claims are finally allowed by the examiner, then the patent issues.

Throughout the procedure, certain fees must have been paid as prescribed by regulations, but these costs are minor. The big cost is attorney's fees. Of course, if the inventor is the employee of a company, these costs are paid by the employer.

Most people consider the long delay before a patent issues to be a defect of the system, but other people think the delay adds to the effectiveness of the protection: If a patentee begins to manufacture a product the same day he applies for a patent on it, he cannot legally exclude others from manufacturing the product until the patent issues. But the day it does issue, he can command competitors to cease manufacture thenceforth, at the sacrifice of any tooling or other investment the competing companies may have made. Moreover, the delay in issue extends the date of expiration farther into the future and, thus, increases the period during which profits may be made from the patent. During the period until issue, the potential patentee will probably mark his product "pat. pending"; this marking may serve to warn off prospective competitors even though it has no legal force whatsoever.

Some additional items that must be borne in mind by patent applicants are:

1) The true inventor(s) must be identified. Affixing any person's name (such as the inventor's superior, for example) who is not legally and truly the inventor or a co-inventor is illegal.

2) The invention cannot have been patented or publicly described before.

3) If the invention is placed on public use or sale or is described in a printed publication, the inventor must file his application within one year, or he will forfeit his rights to the patent.

4) Laws of nature, systems of logic, methods of doing business, mental processes, theories, and systems of mathematics are not patentable.

5) There are three basic kinds of patents:
   a) *utility patents,* which may be granted on processes, machines, manufactured articles, or compositions of matter and are good for seventeen years.
   b) *plant patents,* which protect the developers of such things as special kinds of roses.
   c) *design patents,* which cover external appearance features and may be taken out for three and one-half, seven, or twelve years at the applicant's option, the only difference being the size of the fee.
6) Patents are issued to individuals, not to corporations. However, the inventor may *assign* his patent to a corporation. In many cases, the assignment is simultaneous with the filing of the application.

Interference and infringement

An *interference* is a dispute concerning the identity of the true inventor when two or more applicants claim substantially the same subject-matter; it is carried out within the Patent Office. An *infringement* is the making, using, or selling of something covered by a valid patent held by another.

As with almost every matter connected with patents, an interference can be an incredibly complex affair. Only the barest outline will be given here.

An interference can be brought to light when an examiner discovers he has conflicting applications on hand, or it may be provoked by an inventor who discovers a patent has issued covering matter that he believes he himself had first invented. The time period within which action must be taken is one year following issue.

Upon declaration of an interference, all parties are required to set forth the facts. The first party that filed an application is called the senior party, and the burden of proof falls upon the junior party to show that he was really the first inventor. If he can prove he was the first to conceive the invention, even though he achieved reduction to practice later, he will win the patent—provided he can also prove he was diligent. Not only must he possess documentary evidence, but he also must be able to produce corroborating testimony that supports his case. Hence, the emphasis upon witnesses.

As regards *infringement,* it might be supposed that companies would naturally take meticulous care to avoid infringing others' patents. This is not necessarily the case. There might be many different reasons why companies would knowingly infringe others' patents.

For example, if a company had knowledge that led it to believe the adverse patent would be judged invalid if brought to court, it might go ahead and infringe. The company probably would do so in the hope that the shaky nature of the patent would also be apparent to its holder and would thereby discourage him from pressing it into court.

Another typical case is that of a small company that knowingly infringes a patent held by a large company. In this instance, the hope is that the large company will be so worried about its position with respect to the antitrust laws, that no action will be forthcoming. Or the hope may be that the small company's activities will be considered so inconsequential by the large company, that costly judicial proceedings are unwarranted. It should be apparent, however, that the act of infringement carries risk with it.

While such proceedings are probably contrary to what was contemplated by the framers of the American patent system, they nevertheless constitute some of the realities of the system. Unless the patent-holder takes specific steps to protect his rights, infringers will operate with impunity: The government will not initiate action against infringers; the patent-holder must do it himself.

10.3 Anatomy of a patent

Patents are very imposing-looking documents. Many run to scores of pages; some to hundreds. Characteristically, there will be page upon page of complicated drawings followed by pages of even more complicated text and, finally, at the end, the most complicated part of all: the claims. There is a natural tendency to assume that the entire structure disclosed is covered by the patent. Such is seldom the case, however; the only part of the patent that has any legal force is that which is specifically contained in the claims.

The drawings

First come the illustrations, with every part identified by a key numeral that will be referred to in the descriptive material. Shading, cross-hatching, and the use of line weights are all rigidly prescribed.

The specification

The specification is a description of the device, complete as to every detail, so that a competent workman could construct an operable model from this part of the document. The beginning of the specification generally presents a statement of the objectives plus a brief resumé showing how the invention achieves these objectives and how it is an improvement over the prior art. Much "art" is taught by the description, and from the viewpoint of the dissemination of knowledge, this is the most important part of the patent.

The claims

As the author has already mentioned, the claims form the only part of the patent that gives any legal protection to the inventor. Even though a patentable structure may be described in the specification, it can be seized upon by competing companies unless it has been described by at least one of the claims.

The claims are usually very upsetting to the newcomer to patents because, often, they all sound very much alike, extending on and on into tedium. There are excellent legal reasons for writing them this way, however, and the future value of the patent is going to depend upon the skill, knowledge, and ingenuity of the claims-writer. Even for a basic invention, much of the potential protection can be lost if the claims are poorly drawn.

Generally speaking, the first claim will describe the invention in the broadest possible way, and the succeeding ones will become progressively more specific. It should be borne in mind that, the more specific a claim is, the narrower it is and the probability increases that someone will be able to get around it. As just one example, if a claim were to use the words "a straight member," and if a curved one would do as well, then the use of a curved member would avoid the claim.

Since it is generally very difficult to get broadly phrased claims allowed by the Patent Office, the patent attorney safeguards his client's interests by phrasing the proposed claims in every possible way he can think of, from broad to specific. Thus, when claims are finally allowed, at least one of them will be as broad as is permitted.

Another factor in favor of multiple claims is as follows: if a patent has only one claim and that claim is ever invalidated in the future, the whole patent is gone. But if there are many claims, graded in their degree of specificity, it is possible that adverse judicial action may not invalidate all of them. In this way, some of the coverage would still be intact. Many patents have large numbers of claims (frequently as many as forty or fifty). The all-time record-holder was issued in 1915 to Gubelman and had 797 claims. It had been pending for twenty-six years.[21]

Even with reading a patent with care, it is virtually impossible to tell,

---

[21] A. K. Berle and L. S. de Camp, p. 61.

with any precision, just what coverage it really offers. It is necessary to review the prior art (previously issued patents) to discover exactly what significance the claims possess. It is also necessary to obtain a copy of the "file wrapper" of the patent, which contains the complete record of all the transactions between the inventor's attorney and the Patent Office. File wrappers are open to public inspection and are very revealing documents. They include all the amendments that had to be made to the original claims before any were finally allowed. The limitations on the issued claims will thus become apparent. It is often surprising to discover how exceedingly narrow the claims of an otherwise impressive-appearing patent may actually be. As a general rule, the longer a claim is, the more restricted it is likely to be.

In many instances, a patented invention will be an improvement upon an invention already patented by someone else. In such a case, the patentee will discover that he has an expensive piece of paper which is useless to him until the more basic patent expires, unless he can persuade the prior patentee to enter into a licensing agreement.

All of the foregoing barely scratches the surface of patent matters. The most that can be hoped for in such a brief account is that the engineer will be aware that most of the iceberg is, indeed, out of sight and will act accordingly, whenever the question of patents arises.

10.4 Invention agreements

It has become an almost universal practice to require technical personnel to sign an invention-assignment agreement as one of the conditions of employment. Such agreements may vary in length, but all generally amount to the following:

1) The employee agrees to disclose to his employer all inventions he may make that fall in his employer's line of business and to assign these inventions to his employer during his term of employment.
2) The employee agrees to perform all acts necessary in applying for patents and in executing assignments.
3) The employee agrees to maintain secrecy on all knowledge gained during the course of his employment.[22]

With regard to point 1), note that it makes no difference whether the invention is made on the employer's time or on the employee's. Technical

[22] F. H. Crews, "That Patent Agreement—Should You Sign?" *Patent Problems,* 1961, pp. 23–25. (Booklet publ. by *Product Engrg.* magazine, McGraw-Hill, New York.)

personnel are *expected* to make inventions; it is one of the things they are hired for. It would be ridiculous to permit a man to withhold an invention from his employer, just because his idea came in the middle of the night. If this were possible, who could ever prove that *all* ideas did not occur in the middle of the night?

For nontechnical personnel, the situation is usually a little different. If the employer's time or facilities were used in making the invention, then the employer would have a royalty-free "shop-right" to use it, with title remaining in the employee's hands. If everything were done on the employee's time and without the use of any equipment belonging to the employer, then generally, all rights would remain with the employee.

Returning to the case of the technical employee, the next question is, "What happens if the invention is *not* in the company's line of business?"

If the invention is remote from the company's present line and if all work was done without the use of anything belonging to the employer, then any resulting patent will belong to the employee. However, if the employee attempts to sell his invention, he may discover that the prospective purchaser will demand a release from the inventor's employer, showing that he has a right to offer the invention for sale. This could be a sore point, because the company has no obligation to grant releases unless the employment agreement says so. As a further point, if the employee has made any inventions *prior* to employment and he wishes to retain clear title to them, he should make sure that they are listed, described, and specifically exempted from his employment agreement.

Sometimes an employment agreement will include a clause that extends the terms of the agreement six months or a year beyond termination of a man's employment. Many attorneys consider such clauses to be of doubtful legality. Even so, the attempted enforcement of such a clause could result in considerable unpleasantness, cost, and inconvenience.

An agreement to maintain secrecy is of a different nature. In fact, an employee is legally bound to maintain secrecy about his employer's trade secrets, both during and after his term of employment, even though he has not signed any explicit agreement to that effect.[23]

10.5 Confidential disclosure

There are hidden legal hazards in accepting ideas from outsiders. If there is nothing to indicate otherwise, the law has often taken the position that such disclosures are given in confidence and that, therefore, the

---

[23] J. H. Munster, Jr., and J. C. Smith, "The Care and Feeding of Intellectual Property," *Science,* vol. 148, No. 3671, May 7, 1965, pp. 739–43.

ideas may not be used without permission and payment.[24] If a corporation does not take appropriate protective steps, it could even find itself in the irritating position of having to pay for an idea it had already developed for itself, if it accepts suggestions from outsiders. Worse yet, it might be made to pay for something that is already well known and in the public domain, if it permits a relationship to develop which makes it appear that the submitter was entitled to payment.

Large corporations sometimes almost feel besieged by outside suggestions. Once in a great while, a really useful suggestion may come along, but it is astounding how spurious and trivial most of the ideas are. During the NAS Symposium previously referred to (see footnotes 11 and 15, this chapter), a company executive of the Polaroid Corporation stated that only 3 out of 2000 unsolicited ideas that had been submitted to his corporation proved to have any value and that even those 3 did not amount to much.[25]

Unsolicited (and presumably confidential) disclosures may be made in a myriad of ways. They may casually come up in social conversations and can create just as much legal trouble as those that arrive through more formal routes. Engineers, especially, must be alert to this possibility, since presumably, an engineer is in a qualified capacity to recognize and to make use of a good idea. The best legal advice, of course, is to prevent the disclosure from being given, if this is possible.

Most commonly, unsolicited disclosures arrive in the mail and the corporation is unaware that it has a confidential disclosure on its hands, until the envelope has been opened and its contents examined. A widely used protective procedure is to stop reading and to re-enclose the material in its envelope as soon as its nature is recognized, and then send it to the company's legal department. The presumption is that the legal department is too far removed from the operational end of the business to be able to apply the idea. The material is retained by the legal department (so that the company will later he able to prove exactly what was submitted), and a form letter is sent to the submitter explaining, in a friendly fashion, that the company *is* interested in receiving ideas, but only if they are accompanied by a signed release. A release form is included, which usually stipulates, among other things, that no relation of confidence exists and that the parties agree to abide by only such rights as may properly arise from issued patents.[26]

---

[24] "Corporate Protective Devices in the Acquisition of Ideas," *Harvard Law Rev.* vol. 65, 1952, pp. 673–685.

[25] *The Role of Patents in Research—Part II*, p. 185. See also sec. 2.7.

[26] See C. G. Baumes' *Patent Counsel in Industry*, New York: Nat'l Industrial Conf. Board, 1964, for more detail.

It may appear that the submitter is being asked to throw himself upon the mercy of the corporation, and this is approximately the situation. However, the corporation is actually the more vulnerable of the two parties, and so must protect itself.[27]

----

[27] For some details of actual cases, see C. D. Tuska's *Inventors and Inventions* (New York: McGraw-Hill, 1957), pp. 159–168; and R. A. Buckles' *Ideas, Inventions, and Patents.*

11 ▸ | Engineering societies

11.1 Membership and participation

Two hundred twenty-one engineering societies, or related groups, are listed in the *Directory* of the Engineers Joint Council. In addition, there are another twenty-four engineering societies in Canada and approximately ten international bodies. Probably, no other profession is organized into such a number of societies.

The remarkable proliferation of engineering societies often leads engineers to ask if some degree of unity is not desirable and possible. Actually, several major bodies work toward attaining unified action in the engineering profession; prominent among these associations is the Engineers Joint Council, which carries out numerous programs for the benefit of the 550,000 members of its affiliated societies. Moreover, the National Academy of Engineering, the Engineers' Council for Professional Development, the United Engineering Trustees, and the National Society of Professional Engineers are all concerned with the engineering profession as a whole.

Purpose

Most American engineering societies exist for the basic purpose of disseminating information. As an example, some purposes of the American Society of Civil Engineers (ASCE), this country's oldest engineering society, are given here:

(1) To encourage and publicize discoveries and new techniques throughout the profession.
(2) To afford professional associations and develop professional consciousness among civil engineering students.
(3) To further research, design and construction procedures in specialized fields of civil engineering.

(4) To give special attention to the professional and economic aspects of the practice of engineering.

(5) To enhance the standing of engineers.

(6) To maintain and improve standards of engineering education.

(7) To bring engineers together for the exchange of information and ideas.[1]

Most of the principal engineering societies have objectives similar to those of the ASCE. To fulfill the purpose of disseminating and publicizing information, the societies publish technical journals and hold numerous technical meetings at the national, regional, and local level. For example, during 1965, the ASCE sponsored 9 national meetings, at which 556 papers were presented. The American Society of Mechanical Engineers (ASME) was even more active, sponsoring 22 national meetings during 1965, with nearly 1000 technical papers. National meetings of the major societies regularly attract 3000 or 4000 engineers, while our largest society, The Institute of Electrical and Electronics Engineers (IEEE), drew more than 59,000 attendees to its 1965 International Convention. In 1966, The IEEE was publishing no less than 31 different technical journals (referred to collectively, as the *IEEE Transactions*). Some major engineering societies actually bear a strong resemblance to big publishing houses and maintain large full-time staffs principally to handle these publishing activities, at the United Engineering Center in New York. As an example, the IEEE published a total of 116 different issues of its *Transactions* in 1965, plus 35 issues of three different monthlies.

Numerous personal advantages are derived from membership in a professional society, especially membership in one of the five major societies referred to as the *Founder Societies*. These Founder Societies are:

> American Society of Civil Engineers
> American Institute of Mining, Metallurgical,
>   and Petroleum Engineers
> American Society of Mechanical Engineers
> Institute of Electrical and Electronics Engineers
> American Institute of Chemical Engineers

The Founder Societies have been given this name because in 1904, they founded United Engineering Trustees, Inc. (of which more will be said later). They all require that a man meet high standards before he can become a member and they account for a combined membership of 333,000 engineers (including some duplicate memberships).

---

[1] Unless otherwise noted, information concerning the societies has been taken from publications of the societies themselves and is obtainable from them.

Some personal advantages of membership relate to the regular receipt of journals and periodicals and to attendance at society meetings at a reduced cost. More important, it has been observed that members of professional societies have higher average earnings than nonmembers, although this particular statistic can probably be attributed to the fact that, the more natural ability an engineer has, the more likely he is to join a society. The most important reason for joining one or more professional societies, however, is simply this: if the various societies had never existed, the progress of the engineering profession (and, therefore, of all civilization) would be far behind its present position; the societies cannot exist or function unless engineers belong to them and support them; it follows, then, that the fundamental reason for belonging to a society is *to participate* in the activities of the profession and in the producing of the social benefits that flow from these activities.

Membership

Membership grades differ somewhat among the societies, but not significantly so. The ASME grades of membership are reasonably typical and, therefore, are briefly described in the following paragraphs:

Student member. Belongs to a student chapter at a school with a curriculum approved by the Engineers' Council for Professional Development (ECPD).

Associate member. Must have graduated from an engineering school of recognized standing, or have eight years of acceptable experience. No entrance fee for graduate members of student chapters.

Member. Requires six years of practice if a man was graduated from an engineering school of recognized standing; otherwise, twelve years are required. He must have spent five years in a capacity where he was in responsible charge of work.

Fellow. Requires nomination by fellow members, for an engineer or engineering teacher of acknowledged attainments. Also requires twenty-five years of practice, and thirteen years in Member grade. This is an honorary grade.

Honorary member. Requires nomination by membership, and election by the Board of Direction. This grade is given to persons of distinctive engineering accomplishment.

Executive affiliate. Not necessarily an engineer, but in a position of policy-making authority relating to engineering; he must be a man who cooperates closely with engineers.

Affiliate. Capable and interested in rendering service to the field of engineering.

Entrance fees for the major societies are generally about $25, while yearly dues for the grade of Member are from $25 to $30. Fees and dues for Associate Members are usually somewhat less than this.

11.2 Unifying groups

Engineers Joint Council (EJC)

Twenty-three American engineering societies cooperate in supporting the EJC (see Table 11-1). This body acts as the representative of the engineering profession as a whole, in cases where such representation is appropriate. It helps develop public policy regarding the engineering profession, although its constitution prevents it from devoting any substantial portion of its activities to direct attempts at influencing legislation.

One of EJC's most important components is the Engineering Manpower Commission (EMC), a group that conducts many studies, including investigations on efficient engineering-manpower utilization; the future demand for engineers, scientists, and technicians; and the placement of engineering graduates. The EMC regularly conducts the most accurate of all engineering salary surveys (see Section 8.1). It has also aided in the interpretation of engineering through the public media and has provided personnel to testify before governmental, professional and industrial groups.

Engineers' Council for Professional Development (ECPD)

The ECPD is made up of nine participating bodies and one affiliate as follows:

> American Institute of Aeronautics and Astronautics (AIAA)
> American Institute of Chemical Engineers (AIChE)
> American Institute of Industrial Engineers (AIIE)
> American Institute of Mining, Metallurgical, and Petroleum
>   Engineers (AIME)
> American Society of Civil Engineers (ASCE)
> American Society for Engineering Education (ASEE)

Table 11-1. Societies affiliated with the Engineers Joint Council or the Engineers Council for Professional Development[a]

Name of society	Location	Members	Year founded
Constituent Societies of EJC			
American Society of Civil Engineers (ASCE)	UEC,[b] New York, N.Y. 10017	54,409	1852
American Institute of Mining, Metallurgical, and Petroleum Engineers (AIME)	UEC, New York, N.Y. 10017	38,500	1871
Constituent Societies of AIME: Society of Mining Engineers Society of Petroleum Engineers The Metallurgical Society			
American Society of Mechanical Engineers (ASME)	UEC, New York, N.Y. 10017	59,268	1880
American Water Works Association (AWWA)	New York, N.Y. 10016	16,500	1881
Institute of Electrical and Electronics Engineers (IEEE)	UEC, New York, N.Y. 10017	155,000	1884
American Society for Engineering Education (ASEE)	Washington, D.C. 20036	11,400	1893
American Society of Heating, Refrigerating, and Air-Conditioning Engineers (ASHRAE)	UEC, New York, 10017	18,000	1894
American Society of Agricultural Engineers (ASAE)	St. Joseph, Mich. 49085	6,200	1907
American Institute of Chemical Engineers (AIChE)	UEC, New York, N.Y. 10017	25,900	1908
American Society for Metals (ASM)	Metals Park, Ohio	35,000	1913
Society of American Military Engineers (SAME)	Washington, D.C. 20006	26,000	1919
American Institute of Industrial Engineers (AIIE)	UEC, New York, N.Y. 10017	13,200	1948
Associate Societies of EJC			
American Institute of Consulting Engineers (AICE)	UEC, New York, N.Y. 10017	375	1910

Society	Location	Membership	Year
National Institute of Ceramic Engineers (NICE) (Affiliate of the American Ceramic Society)	Columbus, Ohio 43214	1,200	1938
Society of Women Engineers (SWE)	UEC,[b] New York, N.Y. 10017	549	1952
Society of Fire Protection Engineers (SFPE)	Boston, Mass. 02110	1,290	1950
American Institute of Plant Engineers (AIPE)	Cincinnati, Ohio 45208	2,600	1954
American Association of Cost Engineers (AACE)	University of Alabama, 35486	1,200	1956
Affiliate Societies of EJC			
American Society for Testing and Materials (ASTM)	Philadelphia, Pa. 19103	12,000	1889
American Society of Tool and Manufacturing Engineers (ASTME)	Dearborn, Mich. 48128	40,000	1932
Instrument Society of America (ISA)	Pittsburgh, Pa.	16,000	1945
American Society for Quality Control (ASQC)	Milwaukee, Wis.	19,000	1946
Consulting Engineers Council (CEC)	Washington, D.C.	1,800	1956
Members of ECPD but not of EJC[c, d]			
American Institute of Aeronautics and Astronautics (AIAA)	New York, N.Y.	35,942	1931
National Council of State Boards of Engineering Examiners (NCSBEE)	Clemson, S.C.	—	1920
The Engineering Institute of Canada (EIC) (Affiliate)	Montreal, Que.	20,149	1887

[a] Information given in this table has been taken from the *1965 Register and Directory* (courtesy of the EJC, New York) or from publications of the individual societies.
[b] UEC stands for United Engineering Center.
[c] The list of members of the ECPD is taken from the *33rd Annual Report: 1964–1965.* Courtesy of the ECPD, New York.
[d] Additional members of the ECPD are the AIChE, AIIE, AIME, ASCE, ASEE, ASME, and IEEE.

American Society of Mechanical Engineers (ASME)
Institute of Electrical and Electronics Engineers (IEEE)
National Council of State Boards of Engineering Examiners
  (NCSBEE)
Engineering Institute of Canada (EIC) (affiliate)

(At the time of this writing, negotiations were under way to include the National Society of Professional Engineers (NSPE) as another affiliate.)[2]

The ECPD concerns itself principally with 1) the accreditation of engineering curriculums, 2) the professional development of young engineers, and 3) the formulation of the Canons of Ethics.

The most visible activity of the ECPD is its work in curriculum accreditation. In order to become accredited, an engineering school must have already produced a number of graduates and must undergo a careful inspection of its program by an accreditation review team, which is usually composed of engineering educators. Accreditation is granted by individual *curriculum,* and not for a school or a college as a whole. Furthermore, accreditation is granted for the *first* professional degree granted in a particular curriculum; this usually is the bachelor's degree, although accreditation has sometimes been granted for master's degree programs, where this was offered as the first professional degree. In 1965, 171 American institutions had one or more engineering curriculums approved by the ECPD.

Curriculums in engineering technology also are accredited by the ECPD, and in 1965, 34 American institutions had such accredited curriculums. Engineering technology curriculums are at least two years in duration, but in some cases, may be three, or even four, years long.

Another important activity of the ECPD is in the area of high school counseling. Each year, about 100,000 high school students are contacted by the ECPD guidance organization, which works in cooperation with the other engineering societies.

For a list of important societies not affiliated with either the EJC or the ECPD, see Table 11-2. For a list of engineering honoraries, see Table 11-3.

National Council of State Boards of Engineering Examiners (NCSBEE)

The NCSBEE's membership consists of all members of the state boards of registration of the fifty states, the District of Columbia, the Canal Zone, Guam, and Puerto Rico—fifty-four boards in all. The NCSBEE works

---

[2] *33rd Annual Report,* New York: ECPD, 1965, p. 21.

Table 11-2. Other large societies

Name of society	Location	Members	Year founded
American Chemical Society (ACS)[a]	Washington, D.C.	101,737	1876
National Society of Professional Engineers (NSPE)	Washington, D.C.	60,800	1934
Society of Automotive Engineers (SAE)[a]	New York, N.Y.	26,781	1905

[a] Data from *Directory of Engineering Societies and Related Organizations.* Courtesy of EJC, New York.

toward improving engineering-registration laws, especially with regard to establishing uniformity among the states and interboard recognition of engineer registration. The Council meets once each year and publishes a quarterly *Registration Bulletin,* in addition to the *Proceedings* of its annual meeting. Further information concerning the activities of the NCSBEE is given in Chapter Twelve.

National Society of Professional Engineers (NSPE)

The NSPE has, as its primary objective, ". . . the promotion of the profession of engineering as a social and an economic influence vital to the affairs of men and of the United States." As one means to this end, it has its headquarters in the national capital and takes a direct interest in legislation that affects the engineering profession. The NSPE was founded in 1934 and, as of 1965, was America's second largest engineering society, with approximately 61,000 members. The annual *Engineers' Week* constitutes one of the activities of the NSPE.

The NSPE has focused a great deal of its attention upon universal registration for all engineers and believes that only thus can unity be achieved. One requirement for membership is legal registration as a professional engineer. The NSPE has urged that each registered engineer employ the initials "PE" following his name (standing for "Professional Engineer").

Fifty-three different state societies (such as the Illinois Society of Professional Engineers and the California Society of Professional Engineers) are member state societies of NSPE. Membership in a state society automatically makes one a member of the NSPE.

United Engineering Trustees, Inc.

The engineering profession owns a magnificent twenty-story *United Engineering Center* on United Nations Plaza, in Manhattan. The center was built with the help of $5 million donated by industry and $4 million by individual members of the profession and, today, is debt-free. It was completed in 1961 and provides a home for twenty-three engineering societies and related organizations. The United Engineering Trustees, acting for the profession, is the titular owner of the *United Engineering Center*.

Other activities of the United Engineering Trustees are the

Engineering Societies Library—a free public engineering library containing 200,000 bound volumes, maps, and similar material relating to the profession.

Engineering Foundation—an endowed foundation for "the furtherance of research in science and engineering, and the advancement in any other manner of the profession of engineering and the good of mankind." The foundation has assisted in the stimulation of many research programs, over the years, and in the formation of the National Research Council (National Academy of Sciences), and the National Academy of Engineering.

National Academy of Engineering (NAE)

It could almost be said that the engineering profession became of age on December 11, 1964, with the announcement that a National Academy of Engineering had been formed. As *Saturday Review* commented: ". . . the half million or more engineers in the country had achieved a voice in public affairs on a prestigious level equal to that of the country's quarter million scientists."[3]

The National Academy of Engineering (NAE) was set up by the joint efforts of the EJC, the Engineering Foundation, and the National Academy of Sciences (NAS), under the original congressional charter granted to the National Academy of Sciences in 1863. The two academies are to be autonomous and parallel, but spokesmen from both groups have declared their intention to operate them on a closely coordinated and cooperative basis.

Election to the NAS is one of the highest honors an American scientist can receive, and the same is expected to be true of the NAE, for engineers. The anticipated total membership is only 300 engineers.

---

[3] From article by John Lear, science ed.; *Saturday Review,* vol. 48, Feb. 6, 1965, p. 51.

Table 11-3. Engineering honoraries[a]

Name	Location	Members	Year founded	Remarks
Tau Beta Pi	Univ. of Tennessee, Knoxville 37916	131,000	1885	national engineering honorary; top fifth eligible
Society of the Sigma Xi	New Haven, Conn. 96511	185,000	1886	recognition of noteworthy achievement in research
Eta Kappa Nu[b]	Okla. State Univ., Stillwater	33,000	1904	national electrical engineering honorary
Pi Tau Sigma	Univ. of Ill., Urbana	35,123	1915	national mechanical engineering honorary: top third eligible
Chi Epsilon	Austin, Tex. 78712	17,977	1922	national civil engineering honorary: top third eligible
Alpha Pi Mu[b]	Drexel Inst. of Technology, Philadelphia, Pa. 19104	3,465	1949	national industrial engineering honorary

[a] Unless otherwise noted, the information in this table is taken from publications of the individual societies.
[b] From *Directory of Engineering Societies and Related Organizations*, 1963, courtesy of EJC, New York.

203

The purpose of the Academy is not only to honor outstanding engineers, but also to provide a body of expert engineering knowledge that can contribute strong guidance for the nation's technological affairs. The purposes of the NAE briefly are as follows:

(1) To provide means for assessing the constantly changing needs of the nation.
(2) To explore means for promoting cooperation in engineering in the United States and abroad.
(3) To advise Congress and the executive branch of the government on matters of national import pertinent to engineering.
(4) To cooperate with the National Academy of Sciences on matters involving both science and engineering.
(5) To serve the nation, in other respects, in connection with significant problems in engineering and technology.
(6) To recognize outstanding contributions to the nation by leading engineers.

Mergers between societies

Engineers have been remarkably active in creating new societies, but there have also been some notable mergers in recent years:

In 1963, the American Institute of Electrical Engineers (AIEE) combined its membership of 58,000 engineers with that of the Institute of Radio Engineers or IRE (about 93,000), to create the Institute of Electrical and Electronics Engineers (IEEE). The AIEE had been founded in 1884, and the IRE in 1912.

Also in 1963, the Institute of Aerospace Sciences (IAS) and the American Rocket Society (ARS) merged to form the American Institute of Aeronautics and Astronautics (AIAA). The ARS was founded in 1930, and the IAS in 1932.

12 ▸ | Professional registration

Most people are surprised to discover that the first state to adopt a registration law (in 1907) was not a big industrial state, but Wyoming. That state's registration law was passed to protect the public from a flood of persons of doubtful qualifications, who were representing themselves as engineers during an era of great water-resources development.

Today, all fifty states and four territories have engineer-registration laws. Unfortunately, there are great differences among the requirements for registration in the various states. For example, most states require a man to pass a written examination before he can register, but as late as 1963, eleven states still permitted registration of graduates of ECPD-accredited (Engineers' Council for Professional Development) schools without examination, after they had completed a certain number of years of experience.[1] Lack of uniform qualifications between states has been, and still is, a major barrier to the effectiveness of registration. Nevertheless, the registration movement has grown steadily and reached a total of 213,453 registered engineers in 1963.[2]

12.1 The case for registration

The public case for registration

Protection of the public was the justification for the passage of our first registration law and is, today, still the only justification for having such laws, from the viewpoint of public policy. The case for registration has been most eloquently stated by a Utah court of law, as follows:

---

[1] *Proc. Forty-second Annual Meeting, 1963.* Clemson, S.C.: Nat'l Council of State Boards of Engrg. Examiners, pp. 71–72.

[2] *Proc. Forty-second Annual Meeting, 1963.*

It has been recognized since time immemorial that there are some professions and occupations which require special skill, learning, and experience with respect to which the public ordinarily does not have sufficient knowledge to determine the qualifications of the practitioner. The layman should be able to request such services with some degree of assurance that those holding themselves out to perform them are qualified to do so. For the purpose of protecting the health, safety, and welfare of its citizens, it is within the police power of the State to establish reasonable standards to be complied with as a prerequisite to engaging in such pursuits.[3]

In a 1963 decision, a Delaware court quoted the preceding passage, in applying it to engineering, saying, "Professional engineering is recognized as one such occupation."[4]

It is commonly taken for granted that state engineering-registration laws apply only to those engineers who offer their services directly to the public. In many states this is indeed the case, and the laws in those states contain clauses that specifically exempt engineer employees of manufacturing companies from registration. But some states do not have such exemption clauses in their laws; and engineers in those states, who assume they are exempt, might find themselves in an equivocal position.[5] The "Model Law," prepared by the National Council of State Boards of Engineering Examiners (NCSBEE) as a guide for state law-making bodies does not contain such an exemption.[6]

The ambiguity of the current situation is best demonstrated by a consideration of the scope of protection afforded the public by registration. It has been adroitly pointed out by A. W. Weber, that registration is almost universally required for the engineering of *static* items such as bridges, highways, and buildings, but almost never for *dynamic* items such as automobiles, locomotives, and airplanes. Weber points out that there is far more danger of death and destruction associated with the latter group, yet such items are designed substantially by nonregistered engineers.[7]

That registration laws do act as a powerful force in eliminating the incompetent from practice, is attested to by the inability of more than a

---

[3] *Clayton v. Bennett,* 298 P. 2d 531.

[4] *State of Delaware v. Frank N. Durham,* 191 A. 2d 646 (1963).

[5] M. F. Lunch, "Engineering Registration: The Legal Opinion," *Mech. Engrg.,* vol. 86, May 1964, p. 23 ff.

[6] *A Model Law.* Clemson, S.C.: NCSBEE, 1964.

[7] A. W. Weber, "Licensing: the Engineer's Dilemma," *Mech. Engrg.,* vol. 87, May 1965, p. 116.

third of those who took the Engineering Fundamentals (EIT) Examination, in 1963, to pass it.[8]

Engineers often look at the medical profession with envy, wishing their own profession possessed the same degree of public identity and esteem. Some have concluded that universal registration is the key to the doctors' prestige and they seek a similar course for engineers. It should be observed, however, that a fine line exists between legislation that protects the public and legislation that *protects the profession*. It is a nice exercise in semantics to distinguish between 1) moves that enhance public esteem for the engineering profession in order to increase the confidence in which the public may seek the service of engineers and 2) moves that enhance public esteem for the engineering profession in order to increase the financial position and personal prestige of engineers. The former motive has a proper place in public policy; the latter does not.

Some groups within the profession have taken the viewpoint that an unregistered engineer is simply not a member of the profession.[9] However, it has not yet been possible to equate registration with professionalism. Far too many eminent engineers are not registered, and far too many of those engineers who *are* registered, achieved that status by routes which required neither a written examination nor a college degree.

A resolution passed in 1964 by the NCSBEE may have a profound effect upon engineering registration in this country. The NCSBEE stated its belief that:

> Formal education for the professional engineer requires one academic year beyond the present normal baccalaureate engineering programs.
> . . . The additional year should be at the graduate level, and successful completion of the program should be recognized with a Master's degree in a specific field of engineering.
> . . . the degree beyond the baccalaureate, which is designated as a Master's degree, should be considered the Professional Degree for entrance into the ranks of the Engineering Profession, and NCSBEE and its member State Boards should make this a goal of future attainment.[10]

If the fifty states and various territories effectively implement the NCSBEE's recommendations, the level of scientific and mathematical knowledge typically possessed by a registered engineer will be higher in the future. This can be expected to have a favorable effect upon the public

---

[8] *Proc. Forty-second Annual Meeting, 1963,* p. 53. Of the 7397 persons who took the EIT (Engineer-in-Training) exam, 2619 failed.

[9] Weber, p. 117.

[10] *The Registration Bulletin.* Clemson, S.C.: NCSBEE, No. 100, Sept. 1964, p. 8.

welfare aspects of registration and could also enhance the significance of registration for the individual engineer. But legislative mills grind slowly, and there are many problems to be overcome. Therefore, it will probably take years, and perhaps decades, for such a program to reach full implementation.

The personal case for registration

In spite of the problems and inconsistencies in registration, there are compelling reasons why every young engineer should become registered as quickly as possible after graduation. Among these reasons are the following:

1) Registration will probably become more important in the future. (If one extrapolates the trends of the past into the future, this conclusion is inescapable.)

2) No one can foresee the future course of his own career: An individual may believe his career will lie exclusively in areas not requiring registration; but he could change his mind, or unexpected opportunities may arise for which registration is required, or activities currently unaffected by the law might become affected in the future.

3) A court of law generally will not recognize an individual as an engineer, unless he is registered; this could be frustrating, should the engineer want to testify as an expert witness for example.[11]

4) If a nonregistered person engages in practice required by law to be performed by registered engineers, then at the very least, he may find that the courts will not aid him in attempts to collect his fee. "A statute requiring physicians, lawyers, or engineers to be licensed makes a contract by such persons, if not licensed, void."[12]

5) Many companies believe it is desirable for members of their engineering management to be registered; hence, registration could be an aid in promotion.

6) As the passage of a written sixteen-hour examination becomes more universal as a requirement, registration will undoubtedly be increasingly regarded, by employers, as an indicator of technical competence in a man seeking to be hired.

---

[11] *Questions and Answers About Registration for Engineers in Industry.* Washington, D.C.: Nat'l Soc. of Professional Engrs., 1962.

[12] D. T. Canfield and J. H. Bowman, *Business, Legal and Ethical Phases of Engineering* (New York: McGraw-Hill, 1954), p. 199.

Product liability

Civil engineers are almost invariably required by law to be registered before they can practice, but most mechanical and electrical engineers are little touched by registration rules because they work for manufacturing companies. In such cases, the engineer is not offering his services directly to the public; a finished *product* is being offered—and by the company, not by the engineer.

Many serious legal questions are involved in product liability: If faulty design of a product causes injury to someone, who is liable—the engineer or his employer? As of 1966, court decisions seem to have held that the company offering the product is liable.[13] In one case, the faulty design of an aluminum lounge chair was held to be the cause of an injury that resulted in the loss of a finger; the manufacturer was held to be liable.[14] In another case, an infant was burned when a vaporizer near his crib caught fire. The vaporizer was not equipped with a cutoff and caught fire after the water boiled away. A $65,000 judgment against the manufacturer was affirmed, even though it had been shown that some other vaporizers on the market did not have cutoffs either.[15]

Engineers sometimes confuse matters of product *quality* and product *safety*. If only the quality of a product is involved, then any unfavorable public reaction will be directed against the manufacturer, not the engineer. However, if product safety is involved, the engineer has an ethical obligation to protect the public and, most likely, a legal one as well. In cases of the latter type, the Engineering Board of Ethical Review has declared that engineers have an obligation to notify the authorities if their recommendations concerning safety are disregarded.[16] For an engineer to take such drastic action, the issues obviously should be clear-cut (the particular example cited by the Board of Ethical Review involved concealment of test data from the client, which showed that the product had failed its final tests in ways that could endanger the public safety). Also, in a case like this, the engineer clearly has placed his job in jeopardy. Even if he lets his superiors know in advance (as recommended by the Board of Ethical Review) that he intends to notify the authorities, he

---

[13] D. W. Dodson, "Problems of Product Liability Claims," *Mech. Engrg.*, vol. 87, Jan. 1965, p. 34 ff.

[14] *Matthews v. Lawnlite Co., Fla.*, 88 So. 2d 299.

[15] *Lindroth v. Walgreen Co.*, 94 N.E. 2d 847 (1950).

[16] *Opinions of the Board of Ethical Review.* Washington, D.C.: Nat'l Soc. of Professional Engrs., vol. 1, 1965. See cases 61–9 and 61–10, pp. 41–43.

can hardly expect his future relationships with his employer to be without prejudice.

Corporate practice

A surprising way in which engineers employed by manufacturers could find themselves in conflict with state laws arises from what is called "corporate practice." Nearly half the states allow corporations to practice engineering, provided their principals or officers are registered.[17] This is usually presumed to apply to instances wherein corporations offer engineering services to the public. But suppose Corporation "A," primarily a manufacturing company, offers to design and construct an item for Corporation "B," which will then be used by Corporation "B" in something it is constructing—in a power plant, for example. It is possible that Corporation "B" might be construed as a member of the "public," and then Corporation "A" would be violating the law unless its principal engineers were registered. Even the practice of engineering for internal purposes of a corporation might be in question. Thirty states make provision, in their laws, for unregistered persons (presumably intended to include corporations) to practice engineering on their own property, provided public safety is not involved. Eighteen states definitely prohibit such practice, while the remainder make no provision one way or the other. In this connection, courts of law might have to decide the meaning of "public safety." If groups of visitors regularly are taken on tours through an industrial plant, is public safety involved? Are employees of a company to be considered members of the "public," and does their regular use of the corporation's premises involve public safety? State laws are continually undergoing amendment to answer questions like these.

One group of engineers clearly unaffected by registration laws are those who are totally concerned with research. The National Academy of Sciences (NAS) estimates that only about 5 percent of all engineers are so engaged, however.[18] By the definitions of Chapter One, engineers engaged principally in research would be called "engineering scientists," and no one has yet attempted to write a registration law for scientists.

---

[17] *Synopsis of State Engineering Registration Laws and Policies and Procedures of State Boards.* Clemson, S.C.: NCSBEE, 1961. This report is the basic source used in this chapter, for information on registration practices throughout the United States.

[18] *Toward Better Utilization of Scientific and Engineering Talent.* NAS, Washington, D.C.: 1964, p. 8.

Interstate practice

Most states provide for temporary permits for registered engineers from other states to practice engineering in their territories. In addition, nearly all of them provide for what is generally termed, "comity"[19] (literally, friendliness; consideration for others); this means that a state board may register, without examination, an engineer who is registered in another state, provided he attained registration in his own state on the basis of comparable qualifications.

A practice misunderstood by many people is that of registration with the National Bureau of Engineering Registration (NBER). This is often assumed to be equivalent to registration for all states, or to registration with the federal government. Such interpretations are incorrect. The federal government does not register anyone; this is a right reserved to the states. The NBER is one of the activities of the NCSBEE and was organized to facilitate interstate practice. Specifically, it is ". . . a fact-finding and certifying agency, acting as a clearing house for state registration-authorities and as a reliable source of verified information regarding the professional records of engineers."[20] About two thirds of the states will accept NBER certification without further verification.

12.2 Requirements for registration

The pattern of requirements for professional registration prevailing in about half the states is as follows:

> Graduation from an ECPD-accredited school, plus four years engineering experience acceptable to the board, plus a 16-hour written examination
> *(or)*
> Eight years of engineering experience acceptable to the board, plus a sixteen-hour written examination

A very few states have requirements higher than the preceding, while about one fourth of them have requirements that are substantially lower. The remainder have requirements approximately equivalent to the ones just listed. (For the complete requisites of each of the fifty states, see Table 12-1.)

The general pattern is for the sixteen-hour written examination to be divided into two equal parts; the first is frequently known as the "Funda-

---

[19] Another term frequently used—though incorrectly—is "reciprocity."
[20] *National Bureau of Engineering Registration, Certificate of Qualification.* Clemson, S.C.: NCSBEE, 1965.

Table 12-1. Tabulation of registration requirements

State	Minimum age for professional engineers	Qualifications for		Experience credit[a]		
		Professional engineer	Engineer-in-training	Teaching	Military	Contracting
Alabama	none	ECPD + 4 *or* 8 + 16-hour exam[b]	no provision	if resp chg	if engrg[c]	no
Alaska	21	ECPD + 4 + 16-hour exam *or* 8 + 16-hour exam	ECPD + 8-hour exam	yes	if proper field	if proper field
Arizona	25	ECPD + 4 + 16-hour exam *or* 8 + 16-hour exam	ECPD + 8-hour exam *or* 4 + 8-hour exam	up to 5 years	if engrg	very little
Arkansas	21	ECPD + 4 + 16-hour exam *or* 8 + 16-hour exam	ECPD + 8-hour exam *or* 4 + 8-hour exam	up to 1 year	if engrg	if engrg
California	25 (CE)	ECPD + 2 + 16-hour exam *or* 6 + 16-hour exam	8-hour exam	up to 1 year (no, in CE)	if engrg	if engrg
Canal Zone	25	degr + 4 + exam	degr + exam	yes	if engrg	generally not
Colorado	25	8 + 8-hour exam	degr + 8-hour exam *or* 4 + 8-hour exam	yes	if engrg	if engrg
Connecticut	none	ECPD + 4 + 16-hour exam *or* 10 + 16-hour exam	ECPD + 8-hour exam *or* 6 + 8-hour exam	yes	if satisfactory to board	if satisfactory to board
Delaware	35, with no degr	ECPD + 4 *or* 12 + 8-hour exam	8-hour exam	yes	under certain conditions	no

				if satisfactory to board	discretion of board	discretion of board / depends on work
Dist. Columbia	25	degr + 4 + 16-hour exam	degr + 8-hour exam / or 8 + 8-hour exam			
Florida	24	ECPD + 4 + 16-hour exam / or 10 + 16-hour exam	ECPD	yes	if engrg	depends on work
Georgia	25	ECPD + 4 + 16-hour exam / or 8 + 16-hour exam	ECPD + 8-hour exam / or 4 + 8-hour exam	yes	if engrg	no
Hawaii	none	ECPD + 3 + 12-hour exam / or 12 + 12-hour exam	none	yes	if engrg	if engrg
Idaho	21	ECPD + 4 + 12-hour exam / or 8 + 16-hour exam	none	yes, varies	if engrg	if engrg
Illinois	none	ECPD + 4 + 16-hour exam / or 16-hour exam	ECPD + 8-hour exam / or 4 + 8-hour exam	yes	if engrg	if engrg
Indiana	none	ECPD + 4 + 16-hour exam / or 8 + 16-hour exam	ECPD + 8-hour exam / or 4 + 8-hour exam	yes	if engrg	no
Iowa	none	ECPD + 4 + 16-hour exam / or 8 + 16-hour exam	ECPD + 8-hour exam	yes	if engrg	if applicable
Kansas	none	ECPD + 4 / or 8 + 16-hour exam[b]	ECPD + 8-hour exam / or 4 + 8-hour exam	yes	depends on experience	depends on experience

Source: *Synopsis of State Engineering Registration Laws and Policies and Procedures of State Boards.* Clemson, S.C.: Nat'l Council of State Boards of Engrg. Examiners, 1961.

[a] When "experience credit" refers to teaching, it is assumed that the experience represents full-time teaching of engineering subjects.

[b] Means graduation from an ECPD-accredited school plus four years of engineering experience acceptable to the Board of Registration; *or* eight years of experience acceptable to the Board plus a sixteen-hour examination.

[c] Implies the experience will be acceptable if it genuinely represents engineering experience.

Table 12-1. Tabulation of registration requirements —continued

| State | Minimum age for professional engineers | Qualifications for | | Experience credit[a] | | |
		Professional engineer	Engineer-in-training	Teaching	Military	Contracting
Kentucky	none	ECPD + 4, or 8 + 16-hour exam[b]	ECPD + 8-hour exam or 4 + 8-hour exam	yes	each case on merit	if engrg[c]
Louisiana	none	ECPD	none	yes	yes	yes
Maine	none	ECPD + 4 or 8 + 16-hour exam	ECPD or 8 (exam optional)	yes (+ 2 years outside)	only qualifying experience	only qualifying experience
Maryland	35	ECPD + 4 or 8 + 16-hour exam or 12 years experience	ECPD + 8-hour exam or 4 + 8-hour exam	yes	if engrg	if engrg
Massachusetts	35, with no degr	ECPD + 4 or 8 + 8-hour exam or 12 years experience	ECPD or 4 years experience	yes	yes, if equivalent	no
Michigan	21	ECPD + 4 + 16-hour exam or 8 + 16-hour exam	ECPD + 8-hour exam or 4 + 8-hour exam	up to 4 years	yes, if equivalent	no
Minnesota	25	ECPD + 4 + 16-hour exam or 8 + 16-hour exam	ECPD + 8-hour exam or 4 + 8-hour exam	yes	if engrg	depends on work
Mississippi	21	ECPD + 4 or 8 + 16-hour exam	degr + 8-hour exam or 4 + 8-hour exam	yes	if engrg	if engrg

State						
Missouri	25	degr + 4 + 16-hour exam or 8 + 16-hour exam	8-hour exam	yes	if engrg	no
Montana	none	ECPD + 4 + 16-hour exam or 8 + 16-hour exam	ECPD + 8-hour exam or 4 + 8-hour exam	yes	no	if engrg
Nebraska	25	ECPD + 4 + 16-hour exam or 8 + 16-hour exam	degr + 8-hour exam or 4 + 8-hour exam	yes	if engrg	if engrg
Nevada	21	ECPD + 4 + exam or 8 + exam	ECPD + exam or 4 + exam	yes	if engrg	if technical
New Hampshire	none	ECPD + 4 + 8-hour exam or 8 + exam or 12 + age 35	8-hour exam	yes	no	
New Jersey	25	ECPD + 4 + 13-hour exam or 8 + 13-hour exam	ECPD + 8-hour exam or 4 + 8-hour exam	yes	if engrg	no
New Mexico	none	ECPD + 4 + 16-hour exam or 8 + 16-hour exam	ECPD + 8-hour exam or 4 + 8-hour exam	yes	depends on experience	if engrg
New York	25	degr + 4 + 12-hour exam or 12 + 12-hour exam	degr + 8-hour exam or 8 + 8-hour exam	if supplemented by outside experience	if engrg	if engrg
North Carolina	21	ECPD + 4 + 16-hour exam or 8 + 16-hour exam	ECPD + 8-hour exam or 4 + 8-hour exam	yes	if engrg	up to 2 years

Source: *Synopsis of State Engineering Registration Laws and Policies and Procedures of State Boards.* Clemson, S.C.: Nat'l Council of State Boards of Engrg. Examiners, 1961.

[a] When "experience credit" refers to teaching, it is assumed that the experience represents full-time teaching of engineering subjects.

[b] Means graduation from an ECPD-accredited school plus four years of engineering experience acceptable to the Board of Registration; *or* eight years of experience acceptable to the Board plus a sixteen-hour examination.

[c] Implies the experience will be acceptable if it genuinely represents engineering experience.

Table 12-1. Tabulation of registration requirements —continued

State	Minimum age for professional engineers	Qualifications for		Experience credit[a]		
		Professional engineer	Engineer-in-training	Teaching	Military	Contracting
North Dakota	none	ECPD + 4 + 16-hour exam *or* 8 + 16-hour exam	ECPD + 8-hour exam *or* 4 + 8-hour exam	up to 3 years	if acceptable to board	if acceptable to board
Ohio	none	ECPD + 4 + 16-hour exam *or* 8 + 16-hour exam	ECPD + 16-hour exam *or* 4 + 16-hour exam	yes	if engrg	if engrg
Oklahoma	25	ECPD + 3 *or* 8 (exam optional)	ECPD + 8-hour exam *or* 4 + 8-hour exam	yes	if engrg	if engrg
Oregon	21	ECPD + 4 + 16-hour exam *or* 8 + 16-hour exam	ECPD + 8-hour exam *or* 4 + 8-hour exam	yes	if engrg[c]	no
Pennsylvania	25	ECPD + 4 + 8-hour exam *or* 12 + 16-hour exam	ECPD + 8-hour exam *or* 4 + 8-hour exam	up to 7 years	if engrg	no
Puerto Rico	none	ECPD + 4 + 16-hour exam	ECPD + 16-hour exam	yes	if engrg	no
Rhode Island	—	ECPD + 4 *or* 8 + 6-hour exam	degr + 8-hour exam	up to 2 years	if engrg	no
South Carolina	none	degr + 4 + 8-hour exam *or* 8 + 12-hour exam	degr + 8-hour exam *or* 4 + 8-hour exam	yes	if engrg	if engrg
South Dakota	21	ECPD + 4 + 16-hour exam *or* 8 + 16-hour exam	ECPD + 8-hour exam *or* 4 + 8-hour exam	up to 1 year	generally not	no

		8 years school and/or experience	degree			
Tennessee	none			yes, varies	if engrg	if proper kind
Texas	none	ECPD + 4 *or* 8 + 16-hour exam[b]	degr + 8-hour exam *or* 8 + 8-hour exam	yes	if engrg	if engrg
Utah	none	ECPD + 4 + 16-hour exam *or* 8 + 16-hour exam	ECPD + 8-hour exam	up to 2 years	discretion of board	no
Vermont	none	ECPD + 3 *or* 8 + 6-hour exam	none	yes	if engrg	no, unless exceptional
Virginia	21	ECPD + 4 + 16-hour exam *or* 10 + 16-hour exam	ECPD + 16-hour exam *or* 6 + 16-hour exam	yes, if approved	yes, if approved	yes, if approved
Washington	none	ECPD + 4 + 16-hour exam *or* 8 + 16-hour exam	ECPD + 8-hour exam *or* 4 + 8-hour exam	up to 2 years	if engrg	no
West Virginia	none	ECPD + 4 + 16-hour exam *or* 8 + 16-hour exam	ECPD + 8-hour exam *or* 6 + 8-hour exam	yes	if engrg	no
Wisconsin	none	ECPD + 4 + 16-hour exam *or* 8 + 16-hour exam	ECPD + 8-hour exam *or* 4 + 8-hour exam	yes, if ECPD	if engrg	if engrg
Wyoming	none	ECPD + 4 + 8-hour exam *or* 8 + 8-hour exam	ECPD + 8-hour exam *or* 4 + 8-hour exam	up to 2 years	if engrg	if engrg
MODEL LAW (recommended)	24	ECPD + 4 + 16-hour exam *or* 12 + 16-hour exam	ECPD + 8-hour exam *or* 8 + 8-hour exam	yes, if ECPD	if engrg	if engrg

Source: *Synopsis of State Engineering Registration Laws and Policies and Procedures of State Boards.* Clemson, S.C.: Nat'l Council of State Boards of Engrg. Examiners, 1961.

a When "experience credit" refers to teaching, it is assumed that the experience represents full-time teaching of engineering subjects.

b Means graduation from an ECPD-accredited school plus four years of engineering experience acceptable to the Board of Registration; *or* eight years of experience acceptable to the Board plus a sixteen-hour examination.

c Implies the experience will be acceptable if it genuinely represents engineering experience.

mentals Examination" (the EIT) and the second, as the "Professional Examination." Practices concerning open- or closed-book tests vary from state to state and may even vary within a given state, from year to year. New York and New Jersey have offered open-book examinations, while California has used a combination open- and closed-book examination.[21]

Nearly all the states have made provision for an EIT status and will allow persons to take the first eight-hour (EIT, or "Fundamentals") portion of the written examination immediately before, or immediately after, graduation. EIT status conveys no legal privileges and is offered primarily as a convenience to new graduates, so that they may take the examination in fundamentals at a time when the material is fresh in their minds. California has an unusual provision in its regulations, which grants four years of engineering experience credit to anyone who passes the EIT examination.[22] However, the California examination has had a failure rate higher than the national norm. In November 1963, 1035 out of 1848 men failed the California EIT examination.[23]

Questions often arise concerning experience that will be acceptable to state boards. In general, a board will accept *creative* engineering experience requiring the application of mathematics and the engineering sciences to the planning and design of engineering works. Types of experience that are generally *un*acceptable are: 1) teaching of nonengineering courses; 2) periods of summer employment taken prior to graduation; 3) assignments in the armed forces that are nonengineering in nature; 4) sales work (except those portions that may be of a creative engineering nature); and 5) construction or contracting, unless it involves actual engineering.[24] It may take an individual more time than the stated minimum number of years of experience, before he can collect a sufficient amount of experience of the kind acceptable to a given board.

Many states make provision for cases of "eminence," whereby highly competent engineers of many years of experience can become registered without having to meet all the stipulated requirements. However, these practices are highly variable and usually are at the "discretion of the Board"; hence, they will not be discussed in detail here.

---

[21] J. D. Constance, *How to Become a Professional Engineer* (New York: McGraw-Hill, 1958), p. 81.

[22] *Rules and Regulations of the Board of Registration for Civil and Professional Engineers.* Calif. Administrative Code, title 16, chap. 5, sec. 460.

[23] *Newsletter.* Calif. Board of Registration for Civil and Professional Engrs., April 1964.

[24] Constance, pp. 98, 127.

13 ▸ | Engineers' unions

Unionized engineers are a very small fraction of all engineers. Even at the peak of engineering union activity (about 1956–1958), less than 10 percent of the total engineering population was organized into unions.[1] By 1963, it was estimated that union representation had decreased to the point where it accounted for less than 5 percent of all engineers.[2] Yet, the existence of engineering unions has caused an impact upon the public's mind completely out of proportion to the unions' size. To much of the public, the image of an engineer going on strike is highly incompatible with the image of the engineer as a professional who administers to the public welfare.

There are many ramifications to engineering unionism, but the basic question, in most engineers' minds, appears to be the one of professionalism versus unionism. Since most engineers' unions have claimed that it is both possible and proper for an engineer to be simultaneously a professional and a union member, it behooves us to look briefly at the record.

13.1 The rise of engineering unionism

Although some engineering unions existed prior to World War II, most of them were organized between 1945 and 1947, in response to three potent forces:

---

[1] R. E. Walton, *The Impact of the Professional Engineering Union*. Cambridge, Mass.: Div. of Research, Grad. School of Business Admin., Harvard Univ., 1961, pp. 388–395.

[2] *Professional Responsibility vs. Collective Bargaining*. Washington, D.C.: Nat'l Soc. of Professional Engrs., November 1963.

1) Engineers shared the uncertainty of virtually all employees, about their continued security of employment.

2) Many engineers believed their pay had seriously lagged in comparison with that of production workers. Many attributed this to the activities of the unions working on behalf of production workers.[3]

3) Many groups of engineers organized themselves to prevent being swallowed up by regular labor unions. Several National Labor Relations Board (NLRB) decisions under the Wagner Act showed that professionals might be forced, against their wishes, into bargaining units containing nonprofessionals.[4]

At first, the major engineering societies actively urged engineers to form their own bargaining groups because they believed the engineering profession would be irreparably damaged by inclusion in traditional labor organizations. Many managements also encouraged this formation, believing that the interests of both engineers and management would be enhanced by it.

In 1947, the passage of the Taft-Hartley Act ensured that professionals would not be required to join heterogeneous labor organizations (those that lump professionals and nonprofessionals together) against their wishes. This bill eliminated one of the most important motivating forces toward unionization for engineers. Furthermore: since about 1950, engineers and scientists have experienced a steady demand for their services, which has caused their salaries to be driven upward and has effectively removed any doubts about job security. Since 1952, there have been no major instances of groups of engineers voting in favor of unionization, but there have been at least four major cases where engineering unions have been voted out of existence.

In organizing their unions, engineers have usually proclaimed, at the outset, that they intend to behave as professionals and to be led only *by* professionals. As will be seen, the failure of some of these groups to adhere to their initial declarations has been a factor leading to their ultimate rejection by the engineers they represented.

A 1959 survey among unorganized engineers and scientists in ten well-managed companies showed that engineers' principal fears concerning unionism are: 1) that salaries and promotions would not reflect individual contributions; 2) that professional productivity would be reduced; 3) that relations between professionals and management would be impaired; 4)

---

[3] Walton, pp. 18–22.

[4] H. N. Rude, "White-Collar Unions and the Law," *Personnel J.*, vol. 43, February 1964, p. 88 ff.

that the objectionable policies and practices of labor unions might be introduced. Fifty percent of the engineers surveyed were *strongly* against engineers' unions, while only 5 percent were strongly in favor. However, many of those men opposing unions stated that their attitudes were based on the belief a union was "not necessary"; the implication was that their attitudes might change under different economic conditions.[5]

13.2 The decline of engineers' unions

Apparently, engineering unions declined partly because of the favorable economic climate engineers have enjoyed since 1950, and partly because of engineers' disillusionment when they discovered they could not have unions and still retain their professional ideals. Apparently, many early joiners of unions held the belief that their union could succeed in remaining dignified and "professional" and would act mostly as a discussion unit bringing problems to the attention of management. Some engineers have stated they joined unions only so that they could have a say in the activities of the organization that represented them.[6]

However, the basic purpose of a union is to employ forceful means to get an employer to do something he would not do otherwise. In his study of engineering unions, Walton has divided the history of engineers' union activity into the following periods:[7]

1945–1947. In this phase, management and engineers collaborated in establishing engineers' "associations," in order to exclude other bargaining agents.

1947–1949. This phase brought one-way cooperation with management by the unions. Unions were ignored by management.

1949–1953. Beginnings of conflict occurred. Unions attempted to put teeth into their efforts at collective bargaining. Walton calls this period one of "containment-aggression."

1953–1958. For most unions, the pattern remained containment-aggression while a few entered a period of accommodation and cooperation. In some others, however, the pattern became one of outright conflict, marked by many strikes.

---

[5] J. W. Riegel, *Collective Bargaining as Viewed by Unorganized Engineers and Scientists.* Ann Arbor: Univ. of Mich., 1959, p. 43.

[6] J. Seidman and G. G. Cain, "Unionized Engineers and Chemists: A Case Study of a Professional Union." *J. of Business,* vol. 37, July 1964, p. 238 ff.

[7] Walton, pp. 33–36.

1957–1963. This phase took place after the publication of Walton's book, but it might be called one of union *decline*. Four major decertifications[8] of engineers' unions occurred during these years.

Once organized, many unionized engineers decided that if they wished to force their demands upon an employer, they had to be willing to employ unions' traditional ultimate weapon—the strike. A three-day strike occurred in 1950, one of the first strikes to be carried out by an engineering union. The strike was unsuccessful, but five other major strikes occurred in the 1950s, some of which were considered by their participants to have been successful. Some tactics in addition to strikes were proposed, but not carried out; these were: the refusal to submit engineering reports and the refusal to perform duties directly affecting production.[9] Such actions could hardly be considered professional.

The worst instance involving striking engineers known to the author lasted only six days, but featured engineers' marching on the picket line, snake-dancing, and egg throwing. Seven engineers were arrested and charged with disorderly conduct, plus assault and battery of a police officer.[10] The worst fears of the engineers in Riegel's study[5]—that engineers' unions might adopt some of the objectionable practices of labor unions—had been fully realized.

Some other tactics that have been employed by engineers' unions are: referring to engineers who refused to cooperate in strikes as "scabs" and giving them the "silent treatment"; twenty-four-hour telephone campaigns threatening and harrassing those who would not walk the picket-line; after a strike, withholding essential technical information from nonmembers and feeding it to union members instead.[11]

In their efforts to operate from positions of strength, engineers' unions several times have attempted to form (or join) national labor organizations. In 1952, nine engineer unions formed the Engineers and Scientists of America (ESA). In 1956, this organization reached its peak, but then decline set in as internal conflict developed over inclusion of nonprofes-

---

[8] The NLRB supervises elections by groups of employees, concerning whether they wish to be represented by a union, and if so, which union. If the vote is "yes," the NLRB "certifies" that the union selected by the group is its official bargaining agent. If the vote is "no union," this outcome is referred to as a "decertification."

[9] Walton, pp. 28–31.

[10] "The Engineering Union—Dinosaur in the Space Age," *Amer. Engr.,* July 1961.

[11] Walton, p. 344.

sionals.[12] In 1960, after several disaffiliations and decertifications, ESA went out of existence.[13]

During the year 1958–1959, some of the groups that had split off from the ESA tried to organize the Engineers and Scientists Guild (ESG). The ESG would have allowed technicians and other nonprofessionals to join unions consisting predominantly of professionals. Apparently this movement was not successful, but another attempt, made in 1963, resulted in the formation of the Council of Engineers and Scientists Organizations— West (CESO-W), which claimed to represent 20,000 engineers and scientists.[14]

Another prominent trend of engineers' unions has been in the direction of affiliation with regular labor unions, notably the International Union of Electrical Workers (IUE), the United Auto Workers (UAW), and the American Federation of Technical Engineers (AFTE), all of which are AFL-CIO affiliates. Reportedly, traditional blue-collar unions are searching hard for ways to attract white-collar workers, a trend that has been attributed to the decrease in factory employment of production people. One important motive causing engineering unions to seek affiliation with the AFL-CIO is that the labor unions, upon occasion, have refused to support engineers' strikes unless the engineering unions joined a regular labor organization.[15]

The first major engineering-union decertification came about partly from the attempts of the union to affiliate with the UAW, in 1957. In choosing between the UAW, the ESA, and "no union," nearly two thirds of the 1400 professionals involved voted for "no union."[16]

Two major decertifications of engineering unions took place in 1960. One involved nearly 7000 engineers, in which the union was rejected by a vote of 3 to 2.[17,18] In 1963, two more decertifications occurred.[19]

One can draw his own conclusions from these events, but it appears clear to the author that thousands of engineers have tried unions and

---

[12] "Engineer Union Fights for Life," *Fortune,* May 1960, p. 246 ff.
[13] *The Engineer in Industry in the 1960's.* Washington, D.C.: Nat'l Soc. of Professional Engrs., 1961, pp. 61–70.
[14] "Unions for Engineers are Showing New Vitality," *Engrg. News-Record,* Apr. 11, 1963, pp. 82–83.
[15] *The Engineer in Industry in the 1960's,* pp. 64, 72–81.
[16] *The Engineer in Industry in the 1960's,* p. 64.
[17] "Engineers Say No to Union," *Chem. and Engrg. News,* vol. 38, May 30, 1960, p. 27.
[18] *The Engineer in Industry in the 1960's,* pp. 81–85.
[19] *Professional Responsibility vs. Collective Bargaining,* p. 4.

have found them unsatisfactory for their professional objectives. During decertification proceedings, company representatives have tended to stress that the interests of engineers are best served by cooperation and respect between engineers and management rather than by the hostility and conflict that has marked much union activity—and engineers appear to have agreed.

13.3 Conflict: professionalism versus unionism

There is little doubt that unionism and professionalism are incompatible. Professionalism holds that the interests of society and of the client (or employer) are paramount. Unions are collective bargaining agents that sometimes place the economic interests of their members ahead of those of the client or employer. The author does not wish to imply any general condemnation of unions, but wishes merely to point out that the requirements of professionalism and of unionism may, by their very natures, be in direct opposition. The Engineers' Joint Council, the major voice of the engineering profession, declared in 1956, "To the engineer who feels that life provides an opportunity for constructive contribution to society, collective bargaining with its attendant potentiality for creating conflicting obligations is not acceptable."[20]

As was mentioned in Section 1.2, some traditional labor unions have tried hard to convince engineers that they are not professionals, but have common interests with factory workers. However, surveys among engineers show that engineers perceive their role as entirely different from that of factory workers. Engineers want to be treated as individuals, with rewards based upon their individual contributions. They tend to identify with management and have a strong sense of idealism and professional responsibility. The *intangible* rewards (creative challenge, and sense of accomplishment) are as important to most of them as are the tangible rewards.[21] In Riegel's words, the engineer ". . . does not view his work merely as a way to earn a livelihood. To him it is a distinctive mission to which he has dedicated himself."[22] All these things make engineers difficult prospects for unionism. It takes considerable ineptness on the part of a company management to drive engineers to the conclusion that their only salvation lies in a union.

---

[20] *An EJC Report: Raising Professional Standards and Improving Employment Conditions for Engineers.* New York: Engrs. Joint Council, 1956, p. 9.
[21] J. W. Riegel, *Administration of Salaries and Intangible Rewards for Engineers and Scientists.* Ann Arbor: Univ. of Mich., 1958.
[22] *Collective Bargaining as Viewed by Unorganized Engineers and Scientists,* p. 89.

Union organizers blame the engineering schools and the professional societies for the engineers' lack of taste for unions. "Engineers are poisoned at the source—in the engineering colleges," is a charge ascribed to an AFL-CIO staff man.[23] One union official blames engineers' wives: "You would be surprised how much trouble we had with wives who simply were against having their husbands in unions."[24]

Walton's study showed that engineers in unionized companies have mixed feelings about unions. He studied eleven of the thirteen engineering unions in the country that consist primarily of professionals; his conclusions were that the engineers in those organizations thought unionism was an uncomfortable solution, at best.[25]

Unions have had some favorable results, of course, particularly in companies that have tended to treat their engineers with indifference. Unions have caused many managements to formulate more consistent and objective personnel practices (although management people almost universally find it necessary to deny that unions have had any influence whatsoever, according to Walton). Unions have also tended to protect their members from capricious actions by poor supervisors. It could be argued, however, that the managements in such cases brought the unions upon themselves, by suffering the existence of poor supervision and poor personnel practices in their companies in the first place.

In two important areas—salaries and job security—the unions have experienced mostly frustration. In some cases, engineering unions have found that the pay raises they obtained after much painful negotiation have been matched, or even exceeded, in nonunionized companies.[26] Since between 90 and 95 percent of the country's engineers are nonunionized, this can be a scant source of comfort to the unions. The point is that companies have found it necessary to retain their salaries at competitive levels, regardless of union activity. In some instances, companies have even granted increases on their own volition, which has been a source of embarrassment and irritation for the unions. In one case, a company voluntarily introduced an educational assistance program for its engineers. The union actually complained that the company's action constituted an unfair labor practice, since it had not been subjected to the negotiation process.[27]

Some unions have made overtime a special issue and have been successful in obtaining time-and-a-half pay for overtime. This has tended to put

---

[23] *Fortune,* May 1960, p. 251.
[24] *Amer. Engr.,* July 1961.
[25] Walton, p. 375.
[26] Walton, p. 55.
[27] Walton, p. 90.

many engineers in a difficult position: they appear to want to be treated both different from, and the same as, production people. Time-and-a-half is guaranteed to production workers by federal acts, but engineers are specifically exempted from such provisions because they are professionals. Such exemption has made it possible to treat engineers separately from other employees and to give them more freedom (freedom from time clocks, for example, and time off for personal business). Virtually everyone expects that an engineer will upon occasion have to work overtime, without extra pay, when the fulfillment of his responsibilities requires it; what the unions have aimed their fire at is the supervisors' subtle pressuring of the men under them to give "free overtime." Such pressure occurs, for example, when it becomes evident to the work group that merit increases and promotions go primarily to those who work plenty of free overtime. No one, including the unions, has as yet been able to draw a clear line between "proper" overtime, which is important and necessary, and "improper" overtime, which is a condition for advancement. Insofar as the latter practice has been curbed by union pressure, the results would undoubtedly be considered salutary, by most people.

Two principal fears that have been expressed concerning engineering unions are that 1) seniority would be made to take precedence over ability and 2) engineers would be pigeon-holed into narrow job classifications. Neither fear actually materialized to the extent anticipated, but it could be argued that this failure at least partly results from the favorable engineering employment climate prevalent in the United States since 1950.

Generally, unions have sought to have seniority included as a factor in layoff situations, but only after ability has first been taken into account. The measurement of ability, however, is the perfect breeding-ground for contention. Walton claims that, in such circumstances, many supervisors have retreated from any attempts to measure ability by subjective standards and have tended to rest their judgment of "ability" on objective items such as degrees and years of experience. Furthermore, in a layoff, a company may find it needs certain special skills more than others and may wish this factor to outweigh seniority and ability both. The unions have attempted to regulate this by forcing companies to maintain periodically up-dated ability lists and special skill lists, with no clear-cut result except conflict and frustration.

The efforts just mentioned have tended to work in the direction of realizing a main fear of engineers concerning unionism: pigeon-holing in job classifications. A union cannot hope to enforce its demands concerning layoff priority, unless it can clearly establish the categories within which ability and seniority will operate. In some instances, such trends have led to jurisdictional disputes, including attempts to limit the amount of engineering work an engineering supervisor can engage in, and complaints by draftsmen and technicians that engineers are performing work which rightfully belongs to them.[28]

Some managements report that the division of loyalty between union and company has caused them to limit the amount of confidence they can place in their engineers. They state that they have been hesitant to ask unionized engineers to sit in on policy meetings or to inform such engineers of confidential matters, for fear that the knowledge the engineers gain will be used against management as a union weapon. They have also been reluctant to grant unionized engineers full authority in dealing with customers.[29]

Some engineers' unions have tended to limit their efforts to the stabilizing of personnel policies, the bringing of issues into the open, and the publication of accurate salary information. Thus, they have actually operated much like the "sounding board" approach, favored by the National Society of Professional Engineers, as an alternative to unionization. Sounding boards are intended to promote communication between engineering employees and top management; they serve as objective fact-finding bodies and are strictly nonbargaining in nature. The NSPE in 1961 listed seventeen existing sounding boards throughout America.[30]

The possibility that engineers will some day be forced to choose between professionalism and unionism remains a cause for concern. It should be remembered that many engineers have stated, in surveys, that they were opposed to unions because they were "not necessary." Riegel concluded from his studies that engineers might feel themselves compelled to form unions any time they were subjected to great job frustration, impersonal treatment, or believed they had suffered in salary.[31]

If engineers should ever choose to join unions on a wide scale, one important result might be that the mantle of professionalism would pass to other groups, perhaps with higher qualifications, because professionalism and unionism are surely incompatible. Upon disbandment of the ESA, the former president of that organization evidently agreed on this point: "You can't ride two horses," he said.[32]

---

[28] Walton, pp. 118, 181–242, 287–289.
[29] Walton, p. 294.
[30] *The Engineer in Industry in the 1960's,* p. 96.
[31] Riegel, *Collective Bargaining as Viewed by Unorganized Engineers and Scientists,* p. 41.
[32] "ESA Folding Up," *Chem. and Engrg. News,* vol. 38, Dec. 19, 1960, p. 32.

14 ▸ | Engineering education

14.1 Crossroads

Probably, more changes in engineering education have occurred from 1955 to 1965 than in any other decade since the late 1800s. In 1955, the much-praised and sometimes-maligned *Report on Evaluation of Engineering Education*[1] (often called by its familiar but unofficial title, the "Grinter Report") was published; this report proclaimed it was time for a major change in engineering education. Engineering, said the report, must be made more scientific—and more scientific it has become. Then, in 1965 appeared the "Preliminary Goals Report,"[2] which reaffirmed the findings of the "Grinter Report" and called for the next big change: it was time for more official recognition of the role of graduate study, especially the master's degree program, in preparing men for entry into the profession.

The 1955 report stirred up a hornet's nest when it was published, and the 1965 report did the same. Critics of the 1955 report declared that too much attention to science would deprive engineering of that which had made the profession great—its emphasis upon creative design—and would turn American engineering schools into second-class science departments. Critics of the 1965 Preliminary Goals Report worried that 1) a stampede to graduate school might be caused, perhaps resulting in a downgrading of the master's degree; or that 2) professional recognition might be denied to those who could not qualify for graduate school; or that 3) undesirable conformity might be imposed upon engineering education.[3]

---

[1] *Report on Evaluation of Engineering Education*. Washington, D.C.: Amer. Soc. for Engrg. Educ., 1955. L. E. Grinter was chairman of the committee that prepared the report.

[2] *Goals of Engineering Education—The Preliminary Report*. Washington, D.C.: Amer. Soc. for Engrg. Educ., 1965.

[3] "Goals of Engineering Education—Dissenting Opinions," *Mech. Engrg.*, vol. 88, January 1966, p. 40 ff.

In view of all the commotion, one would hardly want to claim that the engineering education picture is a static one. In fact, some find it so volatile that they almost despair of a solution. But, in the midst of the confusion, certain trends do appear:

First, engineering undeniably has become much more firmly based upon science and mathematics, and almost everyone would agree this is desirable.

Second, engineering education during the 1960s had *already* moved substantially into the graduate school, not because anyone decreed it should, but because individual engineers found it was necessary. By 1964, one third of all American graduates earning B.S. degrees in engineering were going on to master's degrees; the Preliminary Goals Report estimated that, by 1975, the proportion would be one half.

Third, in the author's opinion, there is a strong national trend toward maintaining and strengthening the creative-design content of engineering curriculums. It should be noted that the 1955 *Report on Evaluation of Engineering Education,* which is blamed by some for causing an overemphasis on science, actually sounded a strong note in favor of creative design. The 1955 report said, "Education toward the creative and practical phases of economic design, involving analysis, synthesis, development, and engineering research is the most distinctive feature of engineering curricula."

In support of the conclusion just stated by the author, the following items can be listed:

Item: Some of this country's best engineering schools have initiated or strengthened programs emphasizing design and creative synthesis. Among these schools are the University of California, the Carnegie Institute of Technology, Case Institute of Technology, Massachusetts Institute of Technology, Rensselaer Polytechnic Institute, and Stanford University.

Item: In 1965, the Commission on Engineering Education, composed of sixteen outstanding national leaders in engineering education and industry, was formed with financial support from the National Science Foundation. The commission was established to stimulate the creative element in engineering education. Among its projects have been 1) the involvement of students in authentic design situations; 2) the introduction of computer applications into engineering curriculums; 3) the improvement of laboratory instruction; and 4) presentation of fundamental engineering concepts that are distinct from the concepts of science proper.

Item: Some of the most respected and influential leaders in engineering education are strongly outspoken on the importance of creativity and creative design in engineering education; for instance:

. . . the advanced engineering student must be given the opportunity to practice engineering, not science. For this, he must be given the opportunity to learn and to practice design, to create something new, rather than to explore why and how something works that already exists.—E. A. WALKER, president, The Pennsylvania State University, State College, Pa.[4]

Engineering students are subjected increasingly to the stimulating experience of dealing with real engineering problems involving design, experimentation and creative effort at all stages of their college careers.— T. KEITH GLENNAN, president, Case Institute of Technology, Cleveland, Ohio.[5]

It is pertinent to emphasize . . . that *design* is the *central* and *characteristic activity* and that without this function, the engineering profession would lose its coherence and identity.—M. P. O'BRIEN, dean emeritus, College of Engineering, University of California, Berkeley.[6]

14.2 The trend to graduate study

Historically, the length of education for the practicing professional engineer has been four years and has been carried out as an undergraduate operation. This is in sharp distinction to education in most of the other professions, which begins *after* a bachelor's degree has been granted.

In the past, graduate education in engineering has carried essentially the same implications as graduate education in science; that is, it was generally assumed that the man was preparing for a career in research or teaching. Full preparation for research or teaching meant going all the way to the Ph.D., but the master's degree was considered to be a step in that direction, since normal *professional* preparation stopped at the bachelor's degree.

Since World War II, however, more and more engineers have been going on to graduate degrees, especially the master's degree. In 1964, about seventeen hundred doctor's degrees, eleven thousand master's degrees, and thirty-five thousand bachelor's degrees were awarded in engineering in the United States. Moreover, the ASEE Preliminary Goals Report predicts that, by 1976, these numbers will have increased to six thousand doctorates, forty thousand master's degrees, and seventy-five thousand bachelor's degrees annually. If the ASEE prediction comes true, more than half of this country's B.S. graduates will be going on for graduate study.

In addition to recommending increased emphasis upon the master's degree, the Preliminary Goals Report advised that universities continue

---

[4] From *J. Engrg. Educ.*, vol. 51, February 1961, p. 421.
[5] From *Exptl. Mechanics*, vol. 3, September 1963, p. 3A.
[6] From *J. Engrg. Educ.*, vol. 51, March 1961, p. 575.

to offer strong four-year bachelor's degree programs in engineering. Such programs would serve as excellent educational backgrounds for fields like management, sales engineering, operations, and contracting. The report pointed out that large numbers of men with the engineering B.S. degree enter these fields every year and that this trend is expected to continue. In fact, it has been asserted by some writers that engineering is actually more of a liberal education than the typical "liberal arts" curriculum, since engineering includes a large measure of humanities, as well as a great deal of science, whereas liberal arts curriculums seldom include much science and practically never include engineering.

Increased emphasis on the master's degree would be expected to generate a very large demand, on the part of past B.S. graduates, for part-time programs leading to the higher degree. Therefore, the Preliminary Goals Report recommended that engineering schools offer high-quality programs to meet this need and that employers adopt released-time policies to permit their engineers to take advantage of these programs.

Insofar as curricular content is concerned, the 1965 report reaffirmed the recommendations of the 1955 report and stated that engineering education should continue to be based strongly upon the physical sciences, the engineering sciences, and mathematics; the liberal education content should be strengthened and improved, and diversity and flexibility should be encouraged; *analysis, synthesis, and design* of systems should be given increased emphasis in engineering curriculums at all levels. The report stated that engineering educators ". . . must develop greatly improved programs which will stress creative design and development, give the student an appreciation of the importance of costs and an opportunity for experiencing the thrills of invention—the excitement of original and imaginative thought in his chosen field."

The report strongly urged *laboratory* experiences, because of the "feeling" for the actual physical situation laboratories can provide and because, by permitting evaluation of the performance of designs, such experiences may lead to the discovery of results not anticipated by theory. (A recent writer, in comparing European and American engineering education, has noted a trend in Europe toward emulating the American way of mixing theory and application. He declares, "The expanded emphasis on laboratory, thesis, and practical problems at the Diploma Engineer level [in Europe] suggests that we should consider with alarm the American trend to a Master of Science degree with no laboratory and no thesis."[7])

---

[7] H. R. Weed, "Trends in European Engineering Education," *J. Engrg. Educ.*, vol. 56, December 1965, p. 103.

In recommending the five-year master's degree program, the ASEE Preliminary Goals Report noted that several schools have offered five-year programs leading to the *bachelor's* degree in the past, but that such curriculums have, for the most part, disappeared. For example, in 1965, Cornell and Minnesota, two major engineering schools that had been prominent in the five-year bachelor's field, converted their five-year programs to yield master's degrees, instead.

Another special kind of graduate engineering program used by some schools leads to the degree of "Engineer." In past years, this degree has occasionally been awarded to practicing engineers who have completed five years of experience plus a thesis. According to the Preliminary Goals Report, the foregoing mode of handling the Engineer degree has essentially disappeared and has been replaced by another, which treats the Engineer degree in the same fashion as the master's and doctor's degrees, but places it in an intermediate position. In 1963–1964, about two hundred "Engineer" degrees were awarded across the nation, more than 80 percent of them by the Massachusetts Institute of Technology, Stanford, and Columbia.[8]

Students usually would like to know exactly what it takes to get into graduate school and soon discover that nowhere are any clear, hard, fast rules written down. It is generally assumed that a "B" average is necessary, but even this may turn out to be a flexible requirement, depending upon the school and the individual case. The ASEE's *A Report on the Education and Training of Professional Engineers in the United States*[9] offers about the clearest information known to the author:

> To qualify for admission to study leading to a master's degree, a strong postgraduate university may require an applicant to have a standing in the upper quarter of his class, if the undergraduate school is considered relatively weak. However, a graduate school of modest standards may admit a man from a strong undergraduate school if he stood in the upper three-quarters of his class. A master's degree usually requires a minimum of one academic year, although a year and a half or even two years may be required if the student must make up any deficiencies.
>
> Candidates for doctoral degrees have rarely ranked below the upper quarter of their undergraduate classes, and probably ranked in the upper five or ten percent. A minimum of three years beyond the bachelor's degree is required for a doctor's degree, although the time typically is longer—from four to six years. One of the reasons for the longer time is that doctoral candidates usually work part-time as teaching assistants or research assistants. The usual engineering doctoral degree is the Doctor of Philos-

---

[8] *Preliminary Goals Report,* p. 53.

[9] Publ. by the Engrgs.' Council for Professional Development, New York, 1962. The passage given here has been paraphrased from this publication.

ophy (Ph.D.), although some schools offer the Doctor of Engineering (D. Engr.), Doctor of Engineering Science (D. Engr. Sc.), or the Doctor of Science (Sc.D.).

Some schools require a thesis for the master's degree, and some do not, but a thesis is universally required for a doctor's degree. The doctoral thesis is expected to represent an original contribution to the literature, but the master's thesis more generally is expected to represent "a contribution to the training of the candidate, rather than a contribution to knowledge."[10]

14.3 The professor: researcher or teacher?

A few years ago, the term "publish or perish" was rarely heard outside academic circles; today, it is practically a household term. To students, the expression implies a neglect of teaching; to parents, an unhealthy preoccupation with academic snobbery. Educators themselves are sorely split over the issue. Some are quite frank in their support of research and publication, even to the exclusion of teaching values; on the opposite side, some would like to heave research overboard and concentrate on teaching. But most teachers occupy a middle ground; they vigorously support the value of research, but would like to see teaching carry more weight in the academic picture than it has in recent years.

Some students ask why research should have any position, at all, in universities. "Don't universities and colleges exist for the purpose of *teaching*?" they ask. The answer is that teaching is only one function that universities are expected to serve in our society. Universities serve three principal and co-equal functions: 1) the preservation of knowledge, 2) the dissemination of knowledge, and 3) the creation of new knowledge. The first function is carried out principally by the library, and the latter two— the teaching–research function—by the faculty.

If teachers concerned themselves only with teaching what they find in textbooks, who would write the textbooks of the future? Where would the advances in knowledge come from? A certain amount would come from industry, of course, but no one would seriously suggest that industry should be relied upon to serve as the basic knowledge-source of society. It is the role of the university to discharge this function.

Further, it is pointed out by educators that the man who performs *only* as a lecturer invites the danger of becoming dull and repetitious. Hence, engagement in research can actually improve a professor's competence as a teacher. "The professor who himself is at grips with some unsolved

---

[10] The quoted passage is from *Manual of Graduate Study in Engineering.* Washington, D.C.: ASEE, 1952, p. 19.

problem as a part of his professional activity, can and does usually bring to his students a spirit of inquiry, a stimulation to tackle new ideas, and an urge to question deeper into partially understood phenomena."[11]

Of course, the hazard in all this is that research may become over-emphasized. If the actions of administrative authorities lead faculty members to believe that research bears considerably more weight in advancement than does teaching, then there is a natural tendency for these professors to favor research, and teaching may suffer as a result.

The engineering professor faces an especially difficult task. First, he is usually expected to perform capably as a researcher in some branch of engineering science and to publish his results in acceptable journals. (This means he is expected to perform as a *scientist*—an *engineering* scientist.) Second, he generally must perform as a teacher of two distinct kinds of professionals, both of which are at the graduate level: he must teach 1) those who will become researchers themselves (and perhaps teachers as well) and 2) those who will do neither teaching nor research, but will become practicing professional engineers. The teaching of students of category 1) is a natural outcome of research activity and is thoroughly understood by all academic departments within a university —by physics and mathematics departments, for example. The teaching of students of category 2) is a function peculiar to professional schools, such as law, medicine, and engineering. The engineering professor must perform *all* these functions. Dean Burr of Rensselaer Polytechnic Institute has commented:

> In developing a truly professionally-oriented program, a faculty faces a paradox: the fact that college professors largely further their own professional development and reputation through research. The students inevitably tend to emulate their professors. Thus the very best students in most colleges are convinced that research is the height of sophistication in engineering.[12]

Thus, the choices facing engineering faculties are not only those of research versus teaching, but also those of what *kind* of teaching. In M. P. O'Brien's words, ". . . are the schools bent on preparing students for teaching and research in universities or for the practice of engineering? . . . research in the engineering sciences must be effectively served but,

---

[11] H. L. Hazen, "The ECPD Accreditation Program," *J. Engrg. Educ.*, vol. 45, October 1954, p. 106.

[12] A. A. Burr, "Problems of Developing a Professional-School Program in Engineering," *J. Engrg. Educ.*, vol. 55, June 1965, p. 289.

in the aggregate, the engineering schools will harm this country's ability to sustain and increase productivity if they do not develop engineer-designers of superior ability."[13]

14.4 Continuing education

Soon after an engineer has graduated, he usually begins to feel that his education was lacking in certain respects. A Purdue University study shows that the kind of lack that is sensed is fairly categorizable by age groups; thus:

> Those who have been out five years or less wish they had taken more courses of a practical nature.
> Those who have been out five to fifteen years wish they had taken more math and science.
> Those who have been out between fifteen and twenty-five years wish they had taken more courses in business and management.
> Those who have been out more than twenty-five years wish they had taken more humanities and fine arts.[14]

Whatever the stimulus, there is a tremendous demand today for continuing education for engineers. Part of the demand stems from the rapid changes in technology, a factor that has led to the popular but inaccurate cliché that "the half-life of an engineering education is ten years." The implication is that half of what an engineer learns in school today will be obsolete in ten years. This is nonsense, provided the man's education emphasized *fundamentals*. Fundamentals do not decay at that rate, although other things may. A man's own ability decays, unless kept alive by exercise; the demand for a certain special kind of skill may decay; the level of competence for the entire profession may move upward, and this may cause a given individual to experience relative "decay" if he doesn't keep up. In addition, a great deal of new scientific knowledge is continually being generated. As a result, the job of "keeping up" is a never-ending one, and engineers are coming more and more to accept the idea that a major portion of their time—throughout their entire careers—will be engaged in learning.

---

[13] M. P. O'Brien, "Professional Graduate Study in Engineering," *J. Engrg. Educ.*, vol. 51, March 1961, pp. 579–580. O'Brien is dean emeritus of the College of Engineering, Univ. of Calif., Berkeley, and serves as a consulting engineer in numerous capacities. See also footnote 3, chap. 1.

[14] G. M. Nordby, "Where is Engineering Education Today?" *Civ. Engrg.*, vol. 35, February 1965, p. 56.

Continuing education for engineers is predominately of three types:

1) Specific and detailed courses on the performing of certain professional functions, for instance, computer programming.
2) Courses in new technology, so that a man can cope with a declining demand for his current skills by learning some new ones. One example is the shift to integrated electronic circuits, as opposed to those made by assembling components.
3) General up-grading courses, which bring a man to a higher technical level.

Engineers who take courses in categories 1) and 2) generally do so because of specific needs in their jobs and, so, usually are unconcerned about receiving graduate credit. However, those who pursue work in the third category are usually anxious to have their studies lead to a master's degree. With the new emphasis on the master's degree caused by the Preliminary Goals Report, this last trend can be expected to intensify. For the next decade or two, we can expect to see tens of thousands of engineers engaged in part-time study leading to advanced degrees.

▸ Appendix

a. Some definitions

The following four definitions are reproduced by permission, from *Webster's Third New International Dictionary*, Copyright 1961, by G. & C. Merriam Co., Publishers of the Merriam-Webster Dictionaries.

engineering: The science by which the properties of matter and the sources of energy in nature are made useful to man in structures, machines and products.

research: Studious inquiry or examination; *esp:* critical and exhaustive investigation or experimentation having for its aim the discovery of new facts and their correct interpretation, the revision of accepted conclusions, theories or laws in the light of newly discovered facts, or the practical applications of such new or revised conclusions, theories, or laws.

science: Accumulated and accepted knowledge that has been systematized and formulated with reference to the discovery of general truths or the operation of general laws.

scientist: One learned in science and *esp.* natural science: a scientific investigator ("what distinguishes the scientist is his ability to state problems, to frame questions, so that the technicians can make the machines yield facts that are significant"—W. A. L. JOHNSON.)

The following definitions are from the Model Law, as prepared by the National Council of State Boards of Engineering Examiners. The Model Law serves merely as a guide to law-making bodies and has no legal effect unless written into law by a legislative body.

engineer: The term, "engineer," within the intent of this Act shall mean a person who, by reason of his special knowledge and use of the mathematical, physical, and engineering sciences and the principles and methods of engineering analysis and design, acquired by engineering education and experience, is qualified to practice engineering.

practice of engineering: The term, "practice of engineering," within the intent of this Act, shall mean any service or creative work, the adequate performance of which requires engineering education, training, and experience in the application of special knowledge of the mathematical, physical, and engineering sciences to such services or creative work as consultation, investigation, evaluation, planning and design of engineering works and systems, engineering teaching of advanced engineering subjects or courses related thereto, engineering surveys, and the inspection of construction for the purpose of assuring compliance with drawings and specifications; any of which embraces such service or work either public or private, in connection with any utilities, structures, buildings, machines, equipment, processes, work systems, or projects and including such architectural work as is incidental to the practice of engineering."

The following definition was prepared by the Engineers' Council for Professional Development (ECPD).[1]

engineering: Engineering is the profession in which a knowledge of the mathematical and natural sciences gained by study, experience and practice is applied with judgment to develop ways to utilize, economically, the materials and forces of nature for the benefit of mankind.

b. Profession and professional practitioners

The following material also was prepared by the ECPD.[2]

Attributes of a profession and its practitioners

Of a profession:

1. It must satisfy an indispensable and beneficial social need.
2. Its work must require the exercise of discretion and judgment and not be subject to standardization.
3. It is a type of activity conducted upon a high intellectual plane. (a) Its knowledge and skills are not common possessions of the general public; they are the results of tested research and experience and are acquired through a special discipline of education and practice. (b) Engineering requires a body of distinctive knowledge (science) and art (skill).
4. It must have group consciousness for the promotion of technical knowledge and professional ideals and for rendering social services.
5. It should have legal status and must require well-formulated standards of admission.

Professional practitioners:

1. They must have a service motive, sharing their advances in knowledge, guarding their professional integrity and ideals, and tendering gratuitous public service in addition to that engaged by clients.

---

[1] *Annual Report, 1963.* New York: ECPD, 1963, p. 3.
[2] *Annual Report, 1945.* New York: ECPD, 1945.

2. They must recognize their obligations to society and to other practitioners by living up to established and accepted codes of conduct.

3. They must assume relations of confidence and accept individual responsibility.

4. They should be members of professional groups and they should carry their part of the responsibility of advancing professional knowledge, ideals, and practice.

c. Canons of ethics

After several years of review, the ECPD, with the cooperation of the main engineering societies, approved a new set of Canons of Ethics in 1963.[3] Four principal things were accomplished by this revision: 1) The Canons were made more concise and explicit; 2) they were given improved meaning for the engineer employed in industry; 3) a set of *Fundamental Principles* was included, which would have a relationship to the engineering profession somewhat similar to that which the famous Oath of Hippocrates has to the medical profession; and 4) any possible conflict between the antitrust laws and the canon against competitive bidding (Canon 26) [4] was eliminated, by making it clear that engineering services involve creative intellectual effort and that competition should not be based on price alone.

Canons of ethics of engineers

Fundamental principles of professional engineering ethics

The Engineer, to uphold and advance the honor and dignity of the engineering profession and in keeping with high standards of ethical conduct:

I. Will be honest and impartial, and will serve with devotion his employer, his clients, and the public.

II. Will strive to increase the competence and prestige of the engineering profession.

III. Will use his knowledge and skill for the advancement of human welfare.

Relations with the public

1.1 The Engineer will have proper regard for the safety, health and welfare of the public in the performance of his professional duties.

1.2 He will endeavor to extend public knowledge and appreciation of engineering and its achievements, and will oppose any untrue, unsupported, or exaggerated statements regarding engineering.

---

[3] *Annual Report, 1963*, pp. 21–23.
[4] See sec. 1.3.

1.3 He will be dignified and modest in explaining his work and merit, will ever uphold the honor and dignity of his profession, and will refrain from self-laudatory advertising.

1.4 He will express an opinion on an engineering subject only when it is founded on adequate knowledge and honest conviction.

1.5 He will preface any ex parte statements, criticisms, or arguments that he may issue by clearly indicating on whose behalf they are made.

Relations with employers and clients

2.1 The Engineer will act in professional matters as a faithful agent or trustee for each employer or client.

2.2 He will act fairly and justly toward vendors and contractors, and will not accept from vendors or contractors, any commissions or allowances, directly or indirectly.

2.3 He will inform his employer or client if he is financially interested in any vendor or contractor, or in any invention, machine, or apparatus, which is involved in a project or work of his employer or client. He will not allow such interests to affect his decisions regarding engineering services which he may be called upon to perform.

2.4 He will indicate to his employer or client the adverse consequences to be expected if his engineering judgment is over-ruled.

2.5 He will undertake only those engineering assignments for which he is qualified. He will engage or advise his employer or client to engage specialists and will cooperate with them whenever his employer's or client's interests are served best by such an arrangement.

2.6 He will not disclose information concerning the business affairs or technical processes of any present or former employer or client without his consent.

2.7 He will not accept compensation—financial or otherwise—from more than one party for the same service, or for other services pertaining to the same work, without the consent of all interested parties.

2.8 The employed engineer will engage in supplementary employment or consulting practice only with the consent of his employer.

Relations with engineers

3.1 The Engineer will take care that credit for engineering is given to those to whom credit is properly due.

3.2 He will provide a prospective engineering employee with complete information on working conditions and proposed status of employment, and after employment will keep him informed of any changes in them.

3.3 He will uphold the principle of appropriate and adequate compensation for those engaged in engineering work, including those in subordinate capacities.

3.4 He will endeavor to provide opportunity for the professional development and advancement of engineers in his employ or under his supervision.

3.5 He will not injure maliciously the professional reputation, prospects, or practice of another engineer. However, if he has proof that another engineer has been unethical, illegal, or unfair in his practice, he should so advise the proper authority.

3.6 He will not compete unfairly with another engineer.

3.7 He will not invite or submit price proposals for professional services, which require creative intellectual effort, on a basis that constitutes competition on price alone. Due regard should be given to all professional aspects of the engagement.

3.8 He will cooperate in advancing the engineering profession by interchanging information and experience with other engineers and students, and by contributing to public communication media, to the efforts of engineering and scientific societies and schools.

d. Typical job classifications

The job classifications given in this section are those developed from many years of experience by the Executive Compensation Service of the American Management Association, New York. They are reproduced here with the Association's permission. The examples are for mechanical engineers, but the descriptions for other fields of engineering are similar.

The first three levels would generally be considered nonsupervisory and can be related to the curves in Chapter Eight by means of the experience requirement. Levels IV and V would be considered supervisory. Level VI might be considered supervisory in some companies, and not in others. Sometimes this type of position is specifically created for high-ranking engineers who do not have administrative responsibilities.

————

Mechanical engineer—level I
(junior engineer)

Definition of general field of engineering

This general field includes the generation, transmission and utilization of heat, gas and mechanical power; the design and production of tools, machinery and their products; the construction, installation and maintenance of facilities and equipment.

Typical titles of positions reported in this level

Junior Engineer	Engineering Trainee
Assistant Engineer	Junior Production Engineer
Junior Design Engineer	Associate Engineer

Normal qualifications

Education: B.S. Degree (Mechanical Engineering) or equivalent
Experience: 0–1 Year

Primary responsibility

Using established procedures, gathers and correlates basic data and performs detailed or routine engineering duties involving calculations and relatively simple tests. Works on the less complicated designs of specific parts or assemblies and the simpler phases of smaller projects, where little evaluation or ingenuity is normally required. Relieves supervising engineer of minor details.

Status and scope

This position is the entering professional engineering level. Work is performed under close supervision of senior or supervising engineer, following a predetermined schedule. In some companies this position is considered to be a training and development assignment.

Mechanical engineer—level II
(engineer)

Typical titles of positions reported in this level

Engineer
Engineer, Intermediate
Associate Engineer

Engineering Designer
Process Engineer
Product Development Engineer

Normal qualifications

Education: B.S. Degree (Mechanical Engineering) or equivalent
Experience: 1–3 Years

Primary responsibility

Under supervision of supervising engineer and using procedures standard to the company, designs specific parts or minor phases of a project and performs related engineering duties as directed. Translates technical guidance received from supervisor into usable data applicable to the particular engineering assignment; coordinates the activities of junior engineers or technicians occasionally assigned to specific projects; checks drawings for technical accuracy and issues work to drafting room. Work assignments may be varied and somewhat difficult in character, but usually involve limited responsibility. Some evaluation, originality, or ingenuity is required.

Status and scope

This position is one level above entering engineering classifications and usually reports to a senior or project engineer. Duties are performed under regular supervision of supervisor. Junior engineers or technicians may be occasionally assigned to assist the engineer on specific tasks.

Mechanical engineer—level III
(senior engineer)

Typical titles of positions reported in this level

Senior Engineer	Research Engineer
Senior Designer	Staff Engineer
Senior Test Engineer	Assistant Project Engineer

Normal qualifications

Education: B.S. Degree (Mechanical Engineering) or equivalent
Experience: 3–5 years

Primary responsibility

Under direction of project or senior project engineer, plans and performs engineering duties as assigned, including responsibility for the engineering of part of a major project or a project of lesser complexity and importance than those normally assigned to project or Level IV engineers. Conducts the development of each assignment; coordinates manpower assigned to each activity; coordinates the activities of his group with the various stages of the over-all program. Has some latitude for unreviewed action or decision. Assignments are broad in nature, usually requiring appreciable originality and ingenuity.

Status and scope

This position usually reports to a project engineer, section head or higher level engineering executive. Duties are performed with minimum direct supervision, and usually involve frequent conferences on planning, scheduling, progress, and difficulties. May supervise or be assisted by engineers, junior engineers or technicians assigned to a particular project or project phase.

Mechanical engineer—level IV
(project engineer)

Typical titles of positions reported in this level

Project Engineer	Design Supervisor
Machine Design Specialist	Plant Engineer
Senior Development Engineer	Supervising Engineer

Normal qualifications

Education: B.S. Degree (Mechanical Engineering) or equivalent
Experience: 5–8 years

Primary responsibility

Under general supervision, plans, conducts and supervises assignments normally involving several smaller or less important projects or one major project. Estimates manpower needs and schedules work to meet completion dates and technical specifications. Coordinates and supervises engineers and technicians assigned to projects; maintains liaison with manufacturing and sales divisions; reviews progress and evaluates results; makes changes in methods design or equipment where necessary. Generally operates with appreciable latitude for unreviewed action or decision.

Status and scope

This position usually reports to a senior project engineer or higher level engineering executive. Duties are performed following generally stated objectives for the projects or project phases, usually involving frequent conferences with higher level engineering executives. Regularly involves supervising engineers, junior engineers and technicians, and the submission of recommendations to supervision affecting the status of this group.

Mechanical engineer—level V
(senior project engineer)

Typical titles of positions reported in this level

Senior Project Engineer
Engineering Supervisor
Development Manager

Manager, Machine Design
Chief Product Engineer
Superintendent–Maintenance

Normal qualifications

Education: B.S. Degree (Mechanical Engineering) or equivalent
Experience: 9–15 years

Primary responsibility

Under administrative direction, plans, conducts and supervises assignments generally involving the larger and more important projects or more than one project of major magnitude and scope. Estimates manpower needs and schedules work to meet completion dates and technical specifications; coordinates and supervises engineers and technicians assigned to projects; works out proposals and cost estimates; evaluates progress and results and recommends major changes in procedures or objectives. Generally operates with considerable latitude for unreviewed action or decision.

Status and scope

This position reports in most instances to an engineering department head, laboratory director or to upper middle management or in some instances to management. It usually involves programming work of major projects or of a section or department, including administering personnel to achieve over-all objectives at minimum cost. Incumbents are usually required to act in liaison capacity with other departments, divisions and companies.

Mechanical engineer—level VI
(engineering specialist)

Typical titles of positions reported in this level

Engineering Specialist
Chief Development Engineer
Consulting Engineer

Chief Research Engineer
Director, Engineering Research

Normal qualifications

Education: Ph.D. Degree (Mechanical Engineering) or equivalent
Experience: 10 years

Primary responsibility

Plans, conducts and directs engineering research and development projects of major significance which are highly difficult and complex in nature, necessitating the expert application of advanced knowledge in a particular field of mechanical engineering or associated engineering and scientific fields. Originates and applies new and unique procedures and methods, and designs and develops special equipment. Supervises lower level engineers, scientists and technicians, reviews their progress and evaluates results of their work. Supplies technical advice and counsel to other professionals, and may represent the company or laboratory in outside discussions and technical forums. Generally operates with wide latitude for unreviewed action or decision.

Status and scope

This is usually a responsible position in the corporate or divisional engineering research and development organization, customarily reporting to a manager level or top engineering or research executive. Incumbents normally must have achieved recognized standing in their professional field. They usually receive little direct supervision, proceeding independently in directing projects to their completion.

Index